THE SCOTTISH COMPANION

Second Edition 1987

Carrick Publishing

The World O'er...

Jetstream 31 – designed, built and supported at Prestwick in Ayrshire – one of the world renowned civil aircraft produced in the U.K. by British Aerospace.

British Aerospace's facility at Prestwick, which employs over 2,000 staff, also produces components for the BAe 146 jetliner and has been chosen as the site for the Company's new residential Flying College.

British Aerospace plc. 11 Strand, London WC2N 5IT
Civil Aircraft Division – Prestwick.
Prestwick Airport, Ayrshire KA9 2RW.
Telephone: Prestwick (0292) 79888.

JETSTREAM 31

BRITISH AEROSPACE

...up where we belong

1986 IS INDUSTRY YEAR

The Best Bus Serves you best.

A Local Service

The Scottish Bus Group – the biggest and best bus around. Carrying around 300 million passengers a year. Locally: with essential daily services countrywide to work, school, shops and leisure activities.

A Nationwide Service

Or by Citylink. There are year-round services linking all major towns and cities. Not just in Scotland either; Scottish City Link takes you to most parts of the British Mainland too. With services to London (night and day), Manchester, Birmingham, Leeds, Newcastle, Liverpool and many more.

A Private Service

If you need the best bus for private use, choose a coach or a double-decker from the most extensive fleet around. For outings, day trips, parties. Available at competitive rates.

A Holiday Service

Take the best bus on holiday! For day or extended tours, we'll take you to a wide range of Scotland's loveliest tourist areas – the Borders, Galloway, Loch Lomond, the Grampians. Or take one of our luxury coaches down south to Bournemouth, Torquay or Brighton on holiday tours, which include hotel accommodation with full board.

It's clear whatever your needs, the Scottish Bus Group gets closer.

Published by Carrick Publishing,
28 Miller Road, Ayr KA7 2AY
0292 266679
Copyright Carrick Publishing 1987

ISBN 0 946724 14 8

R. 941. 0025

乙

Typeset by Communitype, Leicester
Printed in Great Britain by Antony Rowe Ltd., Chippenham

FOREWORD

by Fiona MacDonald, Editor The Scottish Companion

It is two years since the last edition of The Scottish Companion was published, and the need for a thoroughly revised edition has been long overdue. Again we aim to provide a comprehensive - dare we say, the only comprehensive - source of information about the public life of Scotland.

The foreword to the first edition stated: 'The Scottish Companion seeks to encourage the many different Scotlands to co-exist within its pages. It strives to be all-encompassing, as informative on the Scottish theatre as it is on the Scottish banks. Here, the reader will find learned societies jostling with major industries, tourist boards with judicial tribunals, further education colleges with regiments.' This remains the objective. Eleven hundred bodies - a healthy increase over the 1985 version - are listed. Many are here by virtue of their positions of importance in the life of Scotland; some - particularly in the case of sports governing bodies - are included as representative of a sphere of activity; and we also invited some organisations regional or local in scope, such as enterprise trusts and chambers of commerce. Generally, local branches of national bodies are not included.

There is an important change of emphasis. In the first edition, we listed a greater number of individual office-bearers and staff; on this occasion, the names are generally limited to principals, leaving more space for a description of objectives and functions. In this way, we hope that the book will be used as a source of greater knowledge and understanding about the bodies which help to shape and influence our lives, while remaining useful as a source of contacts. Organisations were encouraged to describe themselves in their own way; if some entries are unusually brief, others rather constitutional in style, this was not our choice.

In a typical entry, the name, address and telephone number of the organisation are given in bold, followed by the year of establishment, the names of principal office-bearers and a description of the organisation.

A common complaint about the first edition was that the arrangement of alphabetical entries, placing common prefixes at the end of the entry title, made organisations difficult to find. On this occasion, we have plumped for a straightforward A to Z sequence. A comprehensive index is provided in which all entries are classified under at least one subject heading.

Most entries have been compiled with the active co-operation of the organisations concerned, and we wish to place on record our thanks to all those who took the time and trouble to complete our questionnaire. As for the rest, some verified a basic entry compiled by our own staff, while others could not be traced or ignored our requests for information and were therefore reluctantly omitted.

UNIVERSITY OF GLASGOW

One of the largest universities in Britain, teaching and researching in over 130 subjects, Glasgow University is further developing its links with industry and with the community at large, and welcomes enquiries about its services to business, industry, the professions and the general public.

- Extra-Mural Courses, Training and Updating, University Certificate Courses
- Consultancies and Contract Research, Technology Licensing, Joint Ventures, Research Clubs and Science Park
- Purpose-built Kelvin Conference Centre Residential and Non-Residential Facilities

For further information contact:

University of Glasgow
Glasgow G12 8QQ

Telephone: 041-339 8855

Adult and Continuing Education	Ext. 4394
Industrial Liaison	Ext. 5199
Conference and Accommodation	Ext. 5385

PURE MALT

Glenfiddich
Scotch Whisky

1887 — 100 YEARS OF CRAFTSMANSHIP — 1987

WILLIAM GRANT & SONS AN INDEPENDENT
FAMILY COMPANY FOR 5 GENERATIONS

Celebrate 100 years of craftsmanship at the home of traditional whisky. The Glenfiddich Distillery.

In 1886 William Grant and his family built the famous Glenfiddich Distillery in Dufftown, Banffshire. On Christmas Day in 1887 the first drops of Glenfiddich ran from the stills. At this special time in the history of Glenfiddich we invite you to join us at the distillery to celebrate one hundred years of craftsmanship.

How to find us:
The Glenfiddich Distillery is in Dufftown, on the north side of Balvenie Castle.
Our 1987 opening hours are:
All year: (5th January to 18th December)
    Weekdays: 9.30am to 4.30pm
9th May – 11th October:
    Saturdays: 9.30am to 4.30pm
    Sundays: 12 noon to 4.30pm

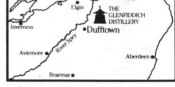

Evening tours are available on Thursdays until 7pm. Closed over Christmas and New Year holidays.
There is no need to get in touch with us beforehand, but for a large party it would be helpful if you could telephone Mike Don on Dufftown (0340) 20373. We look forward to welcoming you.

The Glenfiddich Distillery, owned and managed by
the Grant family for five generations

A

THE ABBEYFIELD SOCIETY FOR SCOTLAND LTD, Rosebery House, 9 Haymarket Terrace, Edinburgh EH12 5YA; T.-031-337 4392.
Founded: 1977.
Chairman: Mrs S. Robertson Cole, OBE; Vice-chairman: Mrs J. Morris, MBE; General Secretary: A.L. McNicoll; Honorary Treasurer: N.D.F. Reid.
Provides houses for elderly people through autonomous local Abbeyfield societies. Seventy-eight local societies have provided 116 houses in which, on average, eight elderly men and women live within the security and companionship of small households. The movement is administered mainly by volunteers.

THE ABERDEEN-ANGUS CATTLE SOCIETY, Pedigree House, 6 King's Place, Perth PH2 8AD; T.-0738 22477.
Founded: 1879.
Secretary: R. Anderson.
Represents pedigree breeders of Aberdeen-Angus cattle and keeps records of the cattle, aiming to promote and further the breed.

ABERDEEN ART GALLERY & MUSEUMS, Schoolhill, Aberdeen AB9 1FQ; T.-0224 646333.
Director: Ian McKenzie Smith.

ABERDEEN CHAMBER OF COMMERCE, 15 Union Terrace, Aberdeen AB9 1HF; T.-0224 641222.
Founded: 1877.
Chief Executive and Secretary: Derek G. Marnoch.
Represents 1,000 companies. Provides a range of services to members, including telex, fax, data base, certification, business bulletin, advice and information.

ABERDEEN COLLEGE OF COMMERCE, Holburn Street, Aberdeen AB9 2YT; T.-0224 572811.
Founded: 1959.
Principal: J.M. Ferguson; Senior Depute Principal: G.E. Eady; Second Depute Principal: W. Stephen; Registrar: H.A. Forrest.
College of further education with 6,500 students.

ABERDEEN COLLEGE OF EDUCA-TION, Hilton Place, Aberdeen AB9 1FA; T.-0224 42341.
Founded: 1958.
Chairman of Governing Body: W.B. Anderson; Principal: D.A. Adams; Vice Principal: Dr J.D. Taylor; Assistant Principal: J.A. Campbell; College Secretary: I.G. Coghill.
Primary function is to train teachers, both pre-service and in-service. Also trains youth and community workers.

ABERDEEN DISTRICT COUNCIL, CITY OF, Town House, Aberdeen AB9 1AQ; T.-0224 642121.
Founded: 1974.
Lord Provost: Henry E. Rae, JP; Town Clerk and Chief Executive: John M. Wilson; Director of Law and Administration: Jamus J.K. Smith; City Chamberlain: George G. Niven; Director of Planning and Building Control: Albert Allen; City Architect: Ian A. Ferguson; Director of Housing: Trevor Muir; Director of Cleansing: David S. Stephen; Director of Personnel and Management Services: Kevin Crook; Director of Art Gallery and Museums: Ian McKenzie Smith; Director of Leisure and Recreation: David Welch; Director of Development and Tourism: Gordon E. Henry; Director of Building and Works: Donald A. Macdonald; Director of Estates: Alexander J. MacColl.
Political composition of council: Labour 25, Liberal/SDP Alliance 20, Conservative 7.
Population of district: 214,082.

ABERDEEN AND DISTRICT MILK MARKETING BOARD, PO Box 117, Twin Spires, Bucksburn, Aberdeen AB9 8AH; T.-0224 696371.
Founded: 1934.
Chairman: Mr I. Marr; Vice-chairman: Mr W.J. Ferguson; Managing Director: Mr R.C. Naylor.
Concerned with the collection and distribution of milk and the manufacture and sale of dairy produce - butter, milk powder, cream and UHT products.

ABERDEEN ENTERPRISE TRUST, Willowbank House, Willowbank Road, Aberdeen; T.-0224 582599.
Director: John Freebairn.

ABERDEEN FISH CURERS AND MERCHANTS ASSOCIATION LTD, (AFCMA), South Esplanade West, Aberdeen AB9 2FJ; T.-897744.
Founded: 1944.
Chairman: Roger Still, MBE; Vice Chairman:

William Leiper; Chief Executive/Secretary: Robert H. Milne.
Trade association representing 160 fish merchants in Aberdeen. Operates a box factory, stores department, filling station, transport department, cafe and accountancy service. Represents members at all political levels.

ABERDEEN HARBOUR BOARD, Harbour Office, 16 Regent Quay, Aberdeen AB9 1SS.

Founded: 1960.
Chairman: J.W. Cradock; General Manager: J.R. Turner; Assistant General Manager and Secretary: J.R. Scott; Assistant General Manager and Harbour Engineer: R.B. Braithwaite; Harbour Master: Captain B. Atkinson.
Major Scottish port with extensive modern facilities for handling cargo of all types, an international passenger terminal, the largest fish market in Scotland and the largest and principal offshore support harbour in Europe.

ABERDEEN TECHNICAL COLLEGE, Gallowgate, Aberdeen AB9 1DN; T.-0224 640366.

Founded: 1960.
Principal: Andrew Bole; Depute Principal: Peter Watt; Second Depute Principal: Ian Jardine.
College of further education provided under the auspices of Grampian Regional Council. Courses offered for all modes of attendance are vocational in nature and are related to the many fields of employment in Grampian Region and further afield whether in the traditional industries or the oil related industry. Most students attend on a part-time (day or block release) basis at craft or technician level. All courses lead to nationally recognised qualifications.

ABERDEEN, UNIVERSITY OF, Regent Walk, Aberdeen AB9 1FX; T.-0224 480241.

Founded: 1495.
Chancellor: Sir Kenneth Alexander; Vice-chancellor and Principal: George P. McNicol; Rector: Hamish Watt, JP; Senior Vice-principal: Prof Philip N. Love, CBE; Vice-principals: Prof William Mordue, Prof Roy D. Weir; Dean of the Faculty of Arts and Social Sciences: Prof Peter H. Ramsey; Dean of the Faculty of Law: Prof Geoffrey D. MacCormack; Dean of the Faculty of Science: Prof George M. Dunnet; Dean of the Faculty of Divinity: Prof William Johnstone; Dean of the Faculty of Medicine: Prof Derek Ogston;

Secretary: William M. Bradley.
For 267 years, there were two separate universities in Aberdeen, each with its own statutory rights and degree-granting privileges. The first, King's College, was founded in Old Aberdeen under a papal bull in 1495. The second, Marischal College, was founded in New Aberdeen under a charter dated 1593. The two colleges remained rival institutions until 1860, when a royal ordinance united them. Today, there are five faculties within the University of Aberdeen: Arts and Social Sciences; Science; Divinity; Law; and Medicine. The university has around 5,500 students.

ABERDEEN, UNIVERSITY OF, DEPARTMENT OF ADULT EDUCATION AND EXTRA-MURAL STUDIES, Taylor Building, Aberdeen, AB9 2UB; T.-0224 480241, Ext. 6506.

Director: William D. Brooker; Tutor Organisers: Dr Cornelius Gillen (Aberdeen City), Donald Paterson (Grampian Region), Geoffrey Gill (Highland Region, South), Donald Omand (Highland Region, North and Islands).
Deploys outward to the general community the expertise available within the university, as far as practicable. Aim is to further and foster adult education throughout Grampian and Highland Regions, Orkney, Shetland and the Western Isles, by a programme of lectures, day and evening classes, short courses, conferences, residential schools and study tours. Offices in Aberdeen, Inverness and Thurso.

ADVISORY, CONCILIATION AND ARBITRATION SERVICE, (ACAS), Franborough House, 123/157 Bothwell Street, Glasgow G2 7JR; T.-041-204 2677.

Founded: 1974.
Director: Matt Cochran.
Independent, statutory organisation providing industrial relations services, free of charge, to both sides of industry and commerce. Its main functions are conciliation and the provision of arbitration facilities in industrial disputes; information, advice and practical assistance to companies on a wide range of industrial relations, personnel and manpower matters; and the settlement of complaints of alleged infringement of individuals' employment rights so as to try to avoid the need for an industrial tribunal hearing.

AGE CONCERN SCOTLAND, 33 Castle Street, Edinburgh EH2 3DN; T.-031-225 5000/1.
Founded: 1943.
Patron: Duchess of Buccleuch and Queensberry; Chairman: Dr Jack Kane, OBE; Vice-chairmen: Marjorie McInnes, OBE, Very Rev Dr R. Leonard Small, CBE; Law Agent: Brenda Rennie; Treasurer: Thomas R. Moffat; Director: Mary Marshall; Dumfries and Galloway Development Officer: Ann Ferguson, T.-046 12 2474 (9am - 1pm); Grampian Development Officer: Jan Robinson, T.-0224 480404; Strathclyde Project Administrative Officer: Charles Ferrier, T.-041-558 1511; Tayside Development Officer: Ian Borthwick, T.-0382 28945.
Formed as The Scottish Old People's Welfare Committee. Became known as Age Concern Scotland in 1974. Aim is to improve services for older people and campaign on their behalf. Supports a network of more than 200 local groups which provide practical services and acts as a centre of information and social advocacy on subjects related to the welfare of older people.

AGRICULTURAL TRAINING BOARD, 13 Marshall Place, Perth PH2 8AH; T.-0738 31481.
Founded: 1966.
Scottish Regional Training Adviser: I.K. Dewar; Senior Training Advisers: J. Kelly (South Scotland), M. Dean (North Scotland); Scottish Regional Administrative Officer: R.C. Chalmers.
Provides training on a national basis for people engaged in agriculture and horticulture. Training takes the form of short on-farm craft courses, supervisory and management skills courses, and financial management courses covering the whole range of enterprises. Most training is carried out through producer-orientated training groups, of which there are 130 in Scotland.

AIR TRAINING CORPS (SCOTLAND), RAF Turnhouse, Edinburgh EH12 OAQ; T.-031-334 0393.
Contact: The Commandant.

ALBINO FELLOWSHIP, 15 Goukscroft Park, Ayr KA7 4DS; T.-0292 42156.
Founded: 1979.
President: Dr W.O.G. Taylor; Secretary: James Wiseman; Treasurer: Alisdair Gordon.
Caring association for support of not only albinos themselves, but also of relatives, doctors, teachers, employers and many others concerned with their welfare.

ALLOA ENTERPRISE TRUST, (ACE), 70 Drysdale Street, Alloa FK10 1JA; T.-0259 217171.
Director: Tom Deeley.

ALZHEIMER'S DISEASE SOCIETY, (ADS), 40 Shandwick Place, Edinburgh EH2 4RT; T.-031-225 1453/ 9130.
Founded: 1979.
Scottish Co-ordinator: Annette Forster; Paisley Project Co-ordinator: Linda Lee; Kirkcaldy Project Co-ordinator: Jean Sullivan; Motherwell Project Co-ordinator: Moira Stratenberger; Group Worker and Scottish Administrator: Maitland Simpson.
Alzheimer's Disease is the most common form of dementia and it may affect anyone from the age of 40. Primary aim of ADS is to support the carers of dementia sufferers. This is done through a network of local support groups and projects where carers can get together to discuss problems and help each other, and telephone contacts. Thirteen support groups in Scotland: Aberdeen, Cupar, Dunfermline, Edinburgh, Glasgow, Inverness, Kirkcaldy, Paisley, Stirling, Bathgate, Dundee, Galashiels and Peebles.

ANCIENT MONUMENTS BOARD FOR SCOTLAND, 20 Brandon Street, Edinburgh EH3 5DX; T.-031-556 8400, Ext. 3076.
Founded: 1913.
Chairman: Magnus Magnusson; Secretary: J.C. Judson.
Advises the Secretary of State for Scotland on the exercise of his responsibilities under the Ancient Monuments and Archaeological Areas Act 1979 for the protection, preservation and presentation of ancient monuments in Scotland. Members are appointed by the Secretary of State. Produces an annual report each year, which is laid before Parliament and is on sale to the public.

AN COMUNN GAIDHEALACH, 109 Church Street, Inverness; T.-0463 231226.
Founded: 1891.
President: D.J. MacIver.
Exists for the promotion of Gaelic language, literature, music, the arts and Highland studies.

ANDREW CARNEGIE BIRTHPLACE MUSEUM, Moodie Street, Dunfermline, Fife KY12 7PL; T.-0383 724 302.
Founded: 1926.
Secretary and Treasurer: Fred Mann; Custodian: Derrick Barclay.
Exhibition devoted to the life and work of Andrew Carnegie.

ANGLERS' CO-OPERATIVE ASSOCIATION (SCOTLAND), 21 Heriot Row, Edinburgh EH3 6EN; T.-031-225 6511.
Secretary: Mr M.W. Thomson.

ANGUS DISTRICT COUNCIL, County Buildings, Forfar DD8 3LG; T.-Forfar 65101.
Founded: 1974.
Provost: Andrew Welsh; Chief Executive: W.S. McCulloch; Director of Finance: Harry C. Nicoll; Director of Housing: George Deans; Director of Planning: William Ferguson; Director of Environmental Health: Leslie Cameron; Director of Parks and Recreation: Michael Graham; Director of Libraries and Museums: Gavin Drummond.
Political composition of council: SNP 11, Scottish Conservative 8, Independent 2. Population of district: 94,288.

ANGUS TECHNICAL COLLEGE, Keptie Road, Arbroath DD11 3EA; T.-0241 72056.
Founded: 1956.
Principal: J.W. Wilson; Registrar: Mrs J.R. Sweeney; Assistant Principals: Mrs G. Black (Business Group), Mr M. Finn (Technology Group).
Further education college with 1,800 students.

ANIMAL BREEDING RESEARCH ORGANISATION, AFRC, West Mains Road, Edinburgh EH9 3JQ; T.-031-667 6901.
Founded: 1945.
Director: Dr R.B. Land; Secretary: J.A. Glen.
Concerned with biological research relevant to the improvement of farm livestock. While it is based on the science campus of the University of Edinburgh, it is made up of farms in Scotland and England and the Dryden Laboratory at Roslin, Midlothian.

ANIMAL DISEASES RESEARCH ASSOCIATION, Moredun Research Institute, 408 Gilmerton Road, Edinburgh EH17 7JH; T.-031-664 3262.
Founded: 1920.
President: J. Stobo; Vice President: G.B.R. Gray; Scientific Director: Dr I.D. Aitken; Secretary: M.J. Mackenzie.
Investigates into diseases affecting farm animals, particularly sheep.

ANNANDALE AND ESKDALE DISTRICT COUNCIL, District Council Chambers, Annan DG12 6AQ; T.-046 12 3311.
Founded: 1974.
Convener: Richard G. Greenhow; Chief Executive and Director of Administration: John A. Whitecross; Director of Finance: William J. Davidson; Director of Environmental Health: Thomas Finlayson; Director of Technical Services: Ian Smith.
Political composition of council: Independent 9, Liberal/SDP Alliance 4, Non-political/Non-party: 3. Population of district: 35,945.

ANNIESLAND COLLEGE, Hatfield Drive, Glasgow G12 0YE; T.-041-357 3969.
Founded: 1964.
Principal: William Morris; Depute Principal: Dr Ian MacIver; Registrar: Robert N. Irvine.
Further education college with over 8,000 students.

ARBROATH VENTURE, 115 High Street, Arbroath DD1 1DP; T.-0241 70563.
Director: Bill Chalmers.
Local enterprise trust.

ARDROSSAN SALTCOATS STEVENSTON ENTERPRISE TRUST, (ASSET), 21 Green Street, Saltcoats KA21 5HQ; T.-0294 602515.
Founded: 1981.
Chairman: Douglas Campbell Muirhead, OBE; Chief Executive: Kenneth D. Fraser; Project Officers: George Weir, William Gilmour (Business Development), Ernie Muir (Property), Alastair J. Muir (Tourism and Grants), Stewart McArthur, Jack Hunter (Loans).
Enterprise trust providing business development assistance, training, finance, property and marketing for small and medium sized companies in, or considering locating in, Ardrossan, Saltcoats and Stevenston. Over the past five years, it has dealt with several thousand enquiries and

helped over 250 businesses establish or expand, creating over 1,500 jobs.

ARGYLL AND BUTE DISTRICT COUNCIL, Kilmory, Lochgilphead PA31 8RT; T.-0546 2127.
Founded: 1974.
Chairman: Douglas C. Currie; Chief Executive: Michael A.J. Gossip; Director of Administration: J.A. McLellan; Director of Finance: G.M. Stewart; Director of Architectural Services: T.A. Paterson; Director of Planning: Michael Oliver; Director of Housing: R.J. Couper; Director of Environmental Health: John Smart; Director of Tourism, Leisure and Recreation: J.E. Moran.
Political composition of council: Independent 22, Conservative 3, SNP 1. Population of district: 65,873.

ARGYLL AND CLYDE HEALTH BOARD, (ACHB), Gilmour House, Gilmour Street, Paisley PA1 1DU; T.-041-887 0131.
Founded: 1974.
Chairman: Mr J.D. Ryan; General Manager: Mr I.C. Smith; Secretary: Mr A.K. Skirving; Treasurer: K.W. Brewer; Chief Administrative Medical Officer: Dr A.A. Reid; Chief Area Nursing Officer: Miss M.A. Somerville.
Health board serving a population of 447,951.

THE ARGYLL AND SUTHERLAND HIGHLANDERS, REGIMENTAL HEADQUARTERS, The Castle, Stirling FK8 1EH; T.-Stirling 75165.
Founded: 1881.
Colonel of the Regiment: Lt Gen C.P.R. Palmer, CBE; Regimental Secretary: Lt Col (Ret) G.P. Wood, MC; Assistant Regimental Secretary: Captain (Ret) D.S.R. McCheyne.
Deals with all matters concerning the Argyll and Sutherland Highlanders, including recruitment, welfare and the regimental museum and magazine.

ARK HOUSING ASSOCIATION, 8 Balcarres Street, Edinburgh EH10 5JB; T.-031-447 9027.
Chairman: Rev Peter Bowes; Director/ Secretary: Mrs Ruth Middleton; Treasurer: Gordon Watson.
Objective is to provide housing for people in need, particularly those with a mental handicap. Seeks to achieve this by the construction and management of various forms of housing throughout east and central Scotland. Community houses offer permanent accommodation for 10 mentally handicapped people with resident and non-resident staff support. Satellite and mainstream housing provide more independent living. Over 30 further developments offering various types of accommodation for those with a mental handicap are in the pipeline.

ARMY CADET FORCE ASSOCIATION (SCOTLAND), Army Headquarters Scotland, PO Box 85, Edinburgh EH1 2YX; T.-031-336 1761.
Secretary: Major Robert MacLean.

ARMY HEADQUARTERS, SCOTLAND, Craigie Hall, near Edinburgh; T.-031-336 1761.
General Officer Commanding the Army in Scotland: Lt Gen Sir Norman Arthur, KCB.

ARTHUR BELL & SON plc, Cherrybank, Perth PH2 0NG; T.-0738 21111.
Founded: 1825.
Chairman: Mr V.J. Steel; Deputy Chairman: Mr S.C. Dowling; Vice Chairman: Mr D.A.H. Harley; Managing Director: Mr R.W.A. Hermans; Production and Development Director: Mr G.G. Gardner; Sales Director: Mr R.E. Weeks; Director: Mr W.L. Young.
Owns four Highland malt whisky distilleries: Inchgower, Dufftown-Glenlivet, Blair Athol and Pittyvaich Glenlivet; a lowland malt distillery: Bladnoch; and modern blending and bottling facilities at East Mains, Broxburn and Dunfermline. Bell's, which is part of the Guinness Group, is closely involved with the local community and actively contributes to providing sport for youth.

ASSOCIATED SCOTTISH LIFE OFFICES, (ASLO), 23 St Andrew Square, Edinburgh EH2 1AQ; T.-031-556 7171.
Founded: 1841.
Chairman: C.M. Cavaye; Deputy Chairman: G.D. Gwilt; Secretary: W.W. Mair.
Exists for the advancement of the business of life assurance, with special reference to the interests of Scottish offices, by: promoting uniformity of practice among the offices in matters of general administration; watching over all legislative measures bearing upon life assurance with a view to joint action in regard to them; and affording opportunities for consultation and co-operation on all matters affecting the common interests of the offices.

THE ASSOCIATION FOR CHILDREN WITH HEART DISORDERS (SCOTLAND), (ACWHD), Dalreoch Ardross, Alness, Ross and Cromarty IV17 0YQ; T.-0349 884440.

Founded: 1981.
Chairman: Wilma Houston; Treasurer: Derek Wilson; Secretary: Jill Cassidy; Glasgow Representative: Marie Docharty.
Supports families of children with congenital heart defects. Active in fundraising for much needed specialised medical equipment and research. Membership is not limited to parents of 'heart children'. Anyone with a few hours to spare and a willing pair of hands is welcome. Seven area branches throughout Scotland. Membership: over 250 families.

ASSOCIATION OF DIRECTORS OF EDUCATION IN SCOTLAND, (ADES), Education Offices, 40 Torphichen Street, Edinburgh EH3 8JJ; T.-031-229 9166.

Founded: 1920.
President: I. Collie; Vice President: M. More; General Secretary: W.D.C. Semple; Treasurer: J. MacLean; Assistant Secretaries: J. Dobie, J.M. MacGregor.
Represents the interests of Directors of Education in Scotland and their directorate staff. Through its governing body, the council, it provides a forum for the exchange of professional news and information. Provides professional advice to COSLA, the SJNC, SED and various other national bodies. The council has a system of committees which facilitates the provision of advice on a range of important professional issues.

ASSOCIATION OF DIRECTORS OF RECREATION LEISURE AND TOURISM, Carberry House, Leven KY8 4JS; T.-Leven 27890.

Secretary: Mr A. Sneddon.

ASSOCIATION OF LECTURERS IN COLLEGES OF EDUCATION IN SCOTLAND, c/o David Crouch, National Secretary, Craigie College of Education, Beech Grove, Ayr KA8 0SR; T.-0292 260321.

Chairman: Ian McPherson (Dundee College of Education); Treasurer: Robert Cooper (Aberdeen College of Education).
Professional body.

ASSOCIATION FOR THE PROTECTION OF RURAL SCOTLAND, 14A Napier Road, Edinburgh EH10 5AY; T.-031-229 1898.

Founded: 1926.
President: Sir Ilay Campbell of Succoth, Bt; Chairman: Donald A. Reid; Vice Chairman: P. Playfair-Hannay; Director: Robert L. Smith, OBE, JP.
Central organisation to protect rural Scotland. Its objectives are: to stimulate and guide public opinion for the protection of the Scottish countryside; to act as a centre for giving advice and information on matters affecting the general welfare of rural areas, including towns and villages; and to encourage appropriate development in the countryside.

ASSOCIATION OF SCOTTISH CHAMBERS OF COMMERCE, 30 George Square, Glasgow G2 1EQ; T.-041-204 2121.

Chairman: Dr Derek Pringle; Secretary: Ewan Marwick.
Consists of most chambers of commerce in Scotland. Has over 6,000 member firms through affiliation by their local chambers to the association. Has a number of national publications, including the *National Directory of Scottish Chambers of Commerce*, published annually. The three major chambers (Glasgow, Edinburgh and Aberdeen) participate jointly in the Fraser of Allander Institute quarterly economic survey. The association makes representations directly to government and other bodies on a wide range of issues of particular importance and relevance to Scottish business.

ASSOCIATION FOR SCOTTISH LITERARY STUDIES, Department of English, University of Aberdeen, Old Aberdeen AB9 2UB; T.-0224 40241.

Founded: 1970.
President: Thomas Crawford; Secretary: Dr David S. Robb; Treasurer: Dr David S. Hewitt; General Editor: Dr Douglas S. Mack; Journal Editor: Kenneth Buthlay; Reviews Editors: Dr J.H. Alexander, Dr Cairns Craig; Editors, *New Writing Scotland*: Carl MacDougall, Edwin Morgan.
Promotes the languages and literature of Scotland through conferences and publications. Each year, there is a conference devoted to a major figure, period or topic from the Renaissance to the present day. For the year's subscription, each member receives an annual volume (a new edition of an out of print work of Scottish literature), the *Scottish Literary Journal*, and a

newsletter.

ASSOCIATION OF SCOTTISH LOCAL HEALTH COUNCILS, 21 Torphichen Street, Edinburgh; T.-031-229 2344.

Secretary: Linda Headland.
Aims are to: support local health councils in the performance of their duties by providing a forum for the exchange of views and discussion of matters of National Health Service concern; express and publicise these views at national level; provide information to local health councils, and organise educational conferences in any area covered by local health councils' work. The association also aims to promote the development of public participation in health matters.

ASSOCIATION OF UNIVERSITY TEACHERS (SCOTLAND), (AUT(S)), c/o Department of Botany, University of Glasgow, Glasgow G12 8QQ; T.-041-339 8855/4448/5080.

Chairman: Prof W.V. Wallace; Vice-chairman: J.S. Berridge; Honorary Secretary: B.W. Ribbons; Honorary Treasurer: Dr R.P. Doig; Immediate Past Chairman: A. Young. Represents the academic and academic-related staffs in the universities of Scotland. Deals with specifically Scottish aspects of the advancement of university education and research, the regulation of relations between university teachers and their employers, the promotion of common action by university teachers, and the safeguarding of the interests of the members. Consists of eight associations, one in each Scottish university. Membership: 4,200.

THE ASTRONOMICAL SOCIETY OF EDINBURGH, (ASE), City Observatory, Calton Hill, Edinburgh EH7 5AA; T.-031-556 4365.

Founded: 1924.
President: Ronald Veitch; Vice Presidents: Neil M. Bone, James Shepherd; Secretary: Iain Neil, T.-031-667 6138 (evenings); Treasurer: A. John Rostron; Observatory Director: James Shepherd.
Objective is to promote popular interest in the science of astronomy, principally in Edinburgh and the surrounding area. Activities include: monthly lecture meetings, junior astronomers' club, summer exhibition, use of telescopes and society's library, participation in observing programmes. Publishes monthly bulletins

and occasional journal. Membership: around 150.

THE AUTOMOBILE ASSOCIATION, (AA), Fanum House, Erskine Harbour, Erskine PA8 6AT; T.-041-812 0144.

Founded: 1905.
Director, Scotland and Northern Ireland: H.E.H. Murphy; Regional Manager, Road Services: P.C. Smith; Regional Manager, Membership Services: J. Mason; Regional Manager, Administration: B. Thorne; Regional Sales Manager, Insurance: Vic Hartley; Regional Sales Manager Travel: Bob Govan. World's largest motoring organisation, providing a comprehensive service to members.

AVIEMORE AND SPEY VALLEY TOURIST ORGANISATION, Tourist Information Centre, Main Road, Aviemore PH22 1PP; T.-0479 810363.

Founded: 1969.
Chairman: Major W. Dunlop; Area Tourist Officer and Secretary: M.W. Lowson. Exists for the promotion of tourism in the area.

AYR CHAMBER OF COMMERCE, 12 Alloway Place, Ayr KA7 2AG; T.-0292 264696.

Founded: 1949.
President: Kenneth J. Dickie; Secretary and Treasurer: John W. Laughland.
Promotes commercial and manufacturing interests in Ayr and South Ayrshire.

AYR COLLEGE, Dam Park, Ayr KA8 0EU; T.-0292 265184.

Principal: Robert McKinney; Depute Principal: Andrew McCallum; Registrar: John Gibson.
Further education college offering wide range of courses up to HND level, including National Certificate, City and Guilds, and SCE examining bodies. Wide range of disciplines offered. Day, part day, block release and full-time attendance.

AYR LOCALITY ENTERPRISE RESOURCE TRUST, (ALERT), 88 Green Street, Ayr KA8 8BG; T.-0292 264181.

Founded: 1983.
Chairman: W.J. Barr; Chief Executive: D.M. Troup; Secretary: W.J.M. Mowat; Treasurer: R. Morrison.
Aims to mobilise resources in an effort to

return Kyle and Carrick to its former prosperity. Full business advisory service given to clients for new business start-ups and for all existing businesses as required. Services are free and confidential. Based on a 50/50 funding split between private and public sectors. Has assisted approximately 200 new business start-ups which, in turn, have created around 400 new jobs.

AYRSHIRE ARCHAEOLOGICAL AND NATURAL HISTORY SOCIETY, (AANHS), 1 Portmark Avenue, Ayr KA7 4DD; T.-0292 42077.
Founded: 1947.
President: Mrs Sheena Andrew; Honorary Secretary: George E. Sleight; Honorary Treasurer: Ian L. Herd.
Special interests are the antiquities, history and natural history of Ayrshire. Winter lectures are held and excursions to places of archaeological or historic interest take place during the summer months. The society's *Ayrshire Collections* are published at regular intervals and are free to members.

AYRSHIRE AND ARRAN HEALTH BOARD, (AAHB), Board Headquarters, 1A Hunters Avenue, Ayr KA8 9DW; T.-0292 281821.
General Manager: Mr J.M. Eckford; Chief Administrative Medical Officer: Dr J.P. Wall; Chief Area Nursing Officer: Mr C.R. Mackie; Operational Manager (Administration): Mr F.H. Brown; Treasurer: Mr N.R. Lammie; Chairman: Mr W.S. Fyfe.
Serves a population of 376,242.

AYRSHIRE AND BURNS COUNTRY TOURIST BOARD, 39 Sandgate, Ayr KA7 1BG; T.-0292 284196.
Founded: 1982.
Chairman: Cllr Mrs Elizabeth Mitchell; Vice-chairman: George Giles; Tourist Officer: Jack Wild.
Exists to further tourism in the area by attending trade fairs and exhibitions in Britain, Europe and North America. Holds trade evenings locally to encourage traders to become members. Over 82,000 enquiries in main office in 1986. Produces visitors' guide, gazetteer and other leaflets. Membership: 412.

AYRSHIRE CATTLE SOCIETY OF GREAT BRITAIN AND IRELAND, (ACS), PO Box 8, 1 Racecourse Road, Ayr KA7 2DE; T.-0292 267123.

Founded: 1877.
Patron: The Queen; Honorary President: Sir Henry C. Plumb; President: Andrew Dunlop; President-elect: John MacKellar; General Secretary: Stuart Thomson.
Promotes the Ayrshire dairy cow and provides a number of services including: computerised pedigree registrations, progeny test selection, type classification, sire analyses, breeding information, field officer advice, conferences, nationwide breeders club activities and the marketing of bull semen and cattle for its 1,200 members.

AYRSHIRE VALLEYS TOURIST BOARD, 62 Bank Street, Kilmarnock KA1 1ER; T.-0563 39090.
Founded: 1982.
Tourist Officer: James Wilson.
Promotes the areas covered by Cumnock and Doon Valley District Council and Kilmarnock and Loudoun District Council.

B

BADENOCH AND STRATHSPEY DISTRICT COUNCIL, The Courthouse, 36 High Street, Kingussie, Inverness-shire PH21 1JA; T.-054 02 555.
Founded: 1974.
Chairman: Mr J.A. McCook; Chief Executive: Mr H.G. McCulloch; Director of Finance: Mr T.M. Robertson; Director of Environmental Health, Technical Services and Housing: Mr W.G. Walters.
Political composition of council: Non-party or Independent 10, SNP 1. Population of district: 10,000.

BANFF AND BUCHAN COLLEGE OF FURTHER EDUCATION, Argyll Road, Fraserburgh AB4 5RF; T.-0346 25777/8/9.
Founded: 1966.
Principal: James M. Crawford; Depute Principal: Alexander Gordon; Registrar: Mrs Margaret A. Green.
Has 1,950 students.

BANFF AND BUCHAN DISTRICT COUNCIL, St Leonard's, Sandyhill Road, Banff AB4 1BH; T.-Banff 2521.
Founded: 1974.
Convener: Norman Cowie; Director, Administration and Legal Services Department: Ronald W. Jackson; Director, Finance

Department: Daniel Urquhart; Director, Planning and Development Department: Peter Suttie; Director, Environmental Health Department: Douglas H. Miller; Director, Technical Services Department: Edward Blackwood; Director, Housing and Property Department: Brian J. Watson; Director, Leisure and Recreation Department: Gilbert K. Carling.
Political composition of council: Non-party 6, Independent 6, SNP 4, Conservative 1, Liberal/SDP Alliance 1. Population of district: 83,216.

BANFF AND BUCHAN TOURIST BOARD, Collie Lodge, Banff AB4 1AU; T.-Banff 2789/2419.
Tourism Manager: David M.H. Du Boulay.
Promotes and develops tourism in the area.

BANKING INSURANCE & FINANCE UNION, (BIFU), 7 Buchanan Street, Glasgow G1 3HL; T.-041-221 6475.
Founded: 1919.
Deputy General Secretary (Scotland): D.M. Paterson; Assistant Secretary: E. Sweeney; Chairman, Scottish Area Council: M. Airth.
Largest finance industry trade union in Europe with 160,000 members in all major banks, insurance companies, finance houses and building societies. Over 22,000 members working in Scotland and a further 8,000 working for Scottish banks in England. The union is affiliated to the STUC and its senior official sits on the General Council. Established in 1919 as the Scottish Bankers Association and merged with its English counterpart in 1945 to form the National Union of Bank Employees. Renamed BIFU in 1979.

BANK OF SCOTLAND, The Mound, Edinburgh EH1 1YZ; T.-031-442 7777.
Founded: 1695.
Governor: Sir Thomas N. Risk; Deputy Governor: The Rt Hon Lord Balfour of Burleigh; Treasurer and General Manager: D. Bruce Pattullo; Joint General Managers: Head Office: Thomas Bennie, A.T. Gibson; Management Services: J.R. Browning; Glasgow: R.L. Cromar; London: A.S.R. Davidson; Edinburgh: G.G. Masterton; International: P.A. Burt; Secretary: H.K. Young.
Major British clearing bank based in Scotland. More than 500 branches in Scotland and offices in the major commercial centres of England. Member of the Committee of London & Scottish Bankers. Issues its own bank notes. Offers a full range of clearing bank services for personal and business customers and numbers a merchant bank and a finance house among its subsidiaries. Innovative services include Home and Office Banking - bringing access to customers' accounts into the home and office. Overseas, there are branches in New York and Hong Kong, several representative offices in the USA and a joint venture office in Moscow.

BAPTIST UNION OF SCOTLAND, 14 Aytoun Road, Glasgow G41 5RT; T.-041-423 6169.
Founded: 1869.
Honorary President: Jack Spiers; Honorary Vice President: Rev V. Bundock; General Secretary: Rev P.H. Barber.
A fellowship of 166 churches with a total membership of 14,600. Has departments for mission, church life and publications, and publishes a monthly magazine, *The Scottish Baptist.* Its annual assembly takes place in October.

BARMULLOCH COLLEGE, 186 Rye Road, Glasgow G21 3JY; T.-041-558 9071.
Founded: 1964.
Principal: Daniel Martin Brown; Chairman, College Council: Robert W. Wait.
Community college providing vocational and non-vocational day and evening courses in a wide range of subjects. Provision is made in local communities where travel, cost or other difficulties prevent those interested from coming to college.

BARONY AGRICULTURAL COLLEGE, Parkgate, Dumfries DG1 3NE; T.-038 786 251.
Founded: 1952.
Principal: D. Rose.
Further education college with 240 students studying land based industries.

THE BARRAS ET, 244 Gallowgate, Glasgow G4 0DF; T.-041-552 7258.
Chief Executive: Martin Gauldwell.
Local enterprise trust.

BATHGATE AREA SUPPORT FOR ENTERPRISE LTD, (BASE), 19 North Bridge Street, Bathgate EH48 4PJ; T.-634024.
Founded: 1983.
Chairman: Mr K. Evans; Director: M.J. Fass; Business Services Manager: Mr R. Mairs.
Locally constituted development company responsible for a wide range of activities

related to the economic regeneration of the Bathgate area of West Lothian. Wide range of grants, loans, business improvement schemes and business training are available. Assists start-up and existing firms, large and small. Sponsored by the Scottish Development Agency, Lothian Regional Council, West Lothian District Council and Leyland Vehicles Ltd.

BBC RADIO HIGHLAND, Broadcasting House, 7 Culduthel Road, Inverness IV2 4AD; T.-0463 221711.
Founded: 1976.
Manager: Allan Campbell; Senior Producer: Craig Anderson; Acting Senior Producer, Gaelic: Hugh Dan Maclennan.
A regional VHF station, broadcasting to the Highlands, the Western Isles, and parts of Grampian and Argyll, producing news and current affairs and magazine programmes in English and Gaelic. Broadcasts over the the largest regional radio area of any station in Britain. Contributes in both languages to Radio Scotland and to network programmes.

BBC RADIO NAN EILEAN, Rosebank, Church Street, Stornoway, Lewis; T.-0851 5000.
Radio station for the Western Isles.

BBC RADIO ORKNEY, Castle Street, Kirkwall, Orkney; T.-0856 3939.
Founded: 1977.
Senior Producer: Howie Firth.
Broadcasts twice daily with local news, information, interviews, features and music, as well as programmes for local schools. Amongst its community activities, it operates an Orkney Sound Archive, and assists with the organisation of the Orkney Traditional Folk Festival.

BBC RADIO SHETLAND, Brentham House, Harbour Street, Lerwick ZE1 0LR; T.-0595 4751.
Senior Producer: John Fergusson.
Community radio station broadcasting every weekday evening from 5.30pm until 6pm (news and current affairs) and 6.15pm until 7.30pm (local cultural and topical subjects and local music programmes).

BBC RADIO SOLWAY, Elmbank, Lovers Walk, Dumfries; T.-0387 68008.
Founded: 1983.
Senior Producer: Iain J. McConnell.

Provides local BBC radio coverage to Dumfries and Galloway on VHF and medium wave. Broadcasts: 7.30am - 8am and 12pm - 12.30pm, Monday to Thursday, and 1pm - 2pm on Friday. Sport, what's on and general information. News and current affairs in morning programme, features at lunchtime.

BBC RADIO TWEED, Municipal Buildings, High Street, Selkirk TD7 4BU; T.-0750 21884.
Founded: 1983.
Senior Producer/Presenter: Stephen Haigh.
Community radio station broadcasting programmes of local interest throughout the area of Borders Region, and supplying local information, news, reports, and programmes to Radio Scotland.

BBC SCOTLAND, Broadcasting House, Queen Margaret Drive, Glasgow G12 8DG; T.-041-330 2345.
Controller, Scotland: Patrick Chalmers; Head of Radio, Scotland: Stan Taylor; Head of Television: James Hunter; Head of Production Resources and Engineering, Scotland: Donald Brodie; Head of Administration, Scotland: Stephen Ansell; Head of Finance, Scotland: Bryan Mitchell; Secretary and Head of Information, Scotland: John McCormick; Head of Drama, Television, Scotland: Bill Bryden; Managing Editor, News and Current Affairs, Television: George Sinclair; Head of Educational Broadcasting, Scotland: James Boyle; Head of Religious Broadcasting, Scotland, Ian Mackenzie; Head of Music, Scotland: Martin Dalby; Head of Sports, Scotland, Malcolm Kellard; Head of Gaelic, Scotland: Neil Fraser.

BBC SCOTTISH SYMPHONY ORCHESTRA, (SSO), BBC, Queen Margaret Drive, Glasgow G12 8DG; T.-041-330 2353.
Founded: 1935.
Manager: Patrick Garvey.
Oldest full-time symphony orchestra in Scotland. Size is that of the late classical period which gives it access to many of the smaller halls in Scotland. This allows the orchestra to be seen and heard throughout the country whilst taking the names of those venues over the air to millions of listeners. For Scotland, the ambassadorial role extends further afield with tours and television appearances taking place world-wide.

BEARSDEN AND MILNGAVIE DISTRICT COUNCIL, Municipal

Buildings, Boclair, Bearsden, Glasgow G61 2TG; T.-041-942 2262.
Founded: 1974.
Provost: R.W. Robinson; Chief Executive: Ian C. Laurie; Director of Technical Services: W.W. Dudgeon; Director of Finance: J.M. Hornby.
Political composition of council: Conservative 6, Liberal/SDP Alliance 2, Independent 1, Labour 1. Population of district: 40,000.

BEEF SHORTHORN CATTLE SOCIETY, Pedigree House, 6 King's Place, Perth PH2 8AD; T.-Perth 23471.
President: J.H. Dewhurst; Vice President: W. Anderson; Secretary: Barbara M. McDonald.
Breed society to further and promote the breeding and marketing of beef shorthorn cattle.

BELL COLLEGE OF TECHNOLOGY, Almada Street, Hamilton ML3 0JB; T.-283100.
Founded: 1972.
Principal: D. Baker; Depute-principal: B.H. Laidlaw; Assistant Principal: R.A. Rennie.
College of higher education offering courses in a wide range of disciplines. Has approximately 1,500 students attending full-time courses in addition to day release and evening students. Specialist short courses are offered on various topics where a demand exists.

BELL & SON plc, ARTHUR. See Arthur Bell & Son plc.

BERWICKSHIRE DISTRICT COUNCIL, District Council Offices, 8 Newton Street, Duns TD11 3DT; T.-0361 82600.
Founded: 1974.
Chairman: J. Evans; Chief Executive: R.A. Christie; Director of Finance: D.W. Dewar; Director of Environmental Services: N.C. Rhind.
Political composition of council: Conservative 8, Independent 3, SDP/Liberal Alliance 1. Population of district: 18,602.

BERWICKSHIRE NATURALISTS' CLUB, c/o Doughtys, WS, Ayton, Berwickshire TD14 5QH; T.-08907 81209.
Founded: 1831.
President: L.H. Cleat; Field Secretaries: Mr and Mrs D. Mackenzie Robertson; Corresponding Secretary and Treasurer: Miss

Sheila G. Stoddart.
Object is to investigate the natural history and antiquities of Berwickshire and its vicinage. Membership is by invitation only and is limited to 400.

BLACKFACE SHEEP BREEDERS' ASSOCIATION, (BSBA), 26 York Place, Perth PH2 8EH; T.-0738 23780.
Chairman: Keith Brooke; Vice Chairman: Peter Fisken; Secretary: Miss Audrey Fenton.
Exists to promote the breed. 1,200 members.

THE BLACK WATCH, REGIMENTAL HEADQUARTERS, Balhousie Castle, Hay Street, Perth PH1 5HR; T.-Perth 21281, Ext. 30.
Regimental Secretary: Col (Ret) The Hon W.D. Arbuthnott, MBE.
Headquarters and regimental museum.

BLACKWOOD HOUSING ASSOCIATION LTD, MARGARET. See Margaret Blackwood Housing Association Ltd.

THE BLACKWOOD TRUST, 17A Grange Road, Edinburgh EH9 1UQ; T.-031-667 7222.
Founded: 1972.
Honorary Treasurer: John Galloway George.
Small trust with the object of providing grants to disabled people in Scotland for special needs.

BLAIR CASTLE, Blair Atholl, Pitlochry PH18 5TX; T.-079 681 207.
Built: 1269.
Owner: His Grace the Duke of Atholl; Administrator: Brian H. Nodes; Assistant Administrator: Mrs Edna Mackay.
Scotland's most visited privately owned historic house. Opened in 1936. Thirty-two rooms on view, with collections of furniture, portraits, arms and armour, lace and embroidery, Jacobite relics, Masonic regalia. Set in extensive parkland, the castle is the home of the 10th Duke of Atholl, who still has the unique distinction of having the only private army in Europe (the Atholl Highlanders). Open to visitors during Easter week, Sundays and Mondays in April, and every day from the third Sunday in April until the second Sunday in October.

BOARD OF INLAND REVENUE, 80

Lauriston Place, Edinburgh EH3 9SL; T.-031-229 9344.
Controller, Scotland: W.S. Linkie.

BOOK TRUST SCOTLAND, 15A Lynedoch Street, Glasgow G3 6EF; T.-041-332 0391.
Chief Executive: Mary Baxter, MBE.
Aims to promote the role of books in the enrichment of life; to make books and reading more accessible to people of all ages, races and culture; to protect and further the interests of readers. Engages in activities designed to advance these aims. Book information, particularly Scottish and children's, available. Meet the Author and other in-house events held. Children's reference library. Annual exhibition, *Scottish Writing Today*. Occasional conferences and seminars. Administers the Kathleen Fidler Award.

THE BORDER COUNTRY LIFE MUSEUM, Thirlestane Castle, Lauder, Berwickshire TD2 6RU; T.-05782 430.
Founded: 1981.
Occupies the south wing of Thirlestane Castle. Provides an exhibition of the material culture of the Scottish Borders. Collects artefacts associated with the people who have lived and worked in the countryside through the ages.

BORDERLINE THEATRE COMPANY, North Harbour Street, Ayr KA8 8AA; T.-0292 281010.
Founded: 1974.
Chairman: Jim Wyper; Artistic Director: Morag Fullarton; Administrator: Edward Jackson.
Professional touring theatre company which has commissioned many new works, including plays by Billy Connolly, John Byrne, Alex Norton, Tom McGrath and Liz Lochhead. At least half of the company's work in any one year is devised and performed for young people. Tours extensively throughout Scotland, taking popular theatre to a wide range of audiences.

BORDERS COLLEGE OF FURTHER EDUCATION, Thorniedean, Melrose Road, Galashiels, Selkirkshire TD1 2AF; T.-0896 57755.
Founded: 1984.
Principal: R.C. Pearson; Depute Principal: A.C. Brown; Registrar: N. Govan.
Has 3,000 full- and part-time students,

around half of which are 16-19 year olds and the rest adults mostly in work. There is a range of courses for nationally recognised qualifications or specialised vocational skills, particularly in areas of new technology.

BORDERS HEALTH BOARD, (BHB), Huntlyburn, Melrose, Roxburghshire TD6 9BP; T.-Melrose 2662.
Founded: 1974.
Chairman: Mr J. Gibb; Vice-chairman: Mr A.C. Purves; General Manager: Mr D.A. Peters; Chief Area Nursing Officer: Mr T. Austin; Chief Area Medical Officer: Dr I. McDonald; Treasurer: Mr J.S. Wilson.
Responsible for the provision of a health service in Ettrick and Lauderdale, Tweeddale, Berwickshire and Roxburghshire. The area's population of 101,700 is served by an acute hospital of 225 beds, a psychiatric hospital of 321 beds, 14 cottage hospitals and 12 health centres. A new district general hospital of 416 beds to replace the present acute hospital should be completed and commissioned by late 1987.

BORDERS REGIONAL COUNCIL, Regional Headquarters, Newtown St Boswells, Melrose TD6 0SA; T.-0835 23301.
Founded: 1974.
Convener: T. Hunter; Chief Executive: Kenneth J. Clark; Director of Finance: P. Jeary; Director of Education: J. McLean; Director of Planning and Development: D.P. Douglas; Director of Property Services: D.A.S. Henry; Director of Roads and Transportation: R.I. Hill; Director of Social Work: D.A. Macdonald; Director of Water and Drainage Services: R.W. Fraser.
Political composition of council: Independent 11, Conservative 6, Non-political 3, Liberal/SDP Alliance 2, SNP 1. Population of region: 101,705.

BOTANICAL SOCIETY OF EDINBURGH, (BSE), c/o Royal Botanic Garden, Inverleith Row, Edinburgh EH3 5LR; T.-031-552 7171.
Founded: 1836.
President: Prof J. Raven; Secretary: Dr Ian Edwards; Treasurer: A. McKenzie; Cryptogamic Secretary: A. Bennell; Alpine Secretary: R. McBeath; Membership Secretary: Miss J. Muscott.
Scotland's national botanical society, with membership and activities extending throughout Scotland. Branches in Edin-

burgh, Aberdeen, Glasgow, Dundee, Inverness, Stirling and St. Andrews. There are active cryptogamic (non-flowering plants) and alpine sections. Activities include lectures, field meetings, surveys (for example, botany of the Lothians) and conferences. Publishes *BSE News* and *Transactions of the BSE*.

BOUNDARY COMMISSION FOR SCOTLAND, Room 226, St Andrew's House, Edinburgh EH1 3DE; T.-031 244 2196.

Founded: 1945.
Chairman: Rt Hon Bernard Weatherill, MP; Deputy Chairman: The Hon Lord Davidson; Secretary: A. Simmen.
Reviews Parliamentary constituencies and European Assembly constituencies in Scotland.

THE BOYS' BRIGADE, (BB), Scottish Headquarters, Carronvale House, Carronvale Road, Larbert FK5 3LH; T.-0324 562008.

Founded: 1883.
Brigade President: Rt Hon Viscount Thurso of Ulbster, JP; Vice President and Chairman of Executive: Col C.H.K. Corsar, OBE, TD, JP; Treasurer: L. Boyle, CBE; Secretary for Scotland: Alexander C. McLaren.
Works for the advancement of Christ's Kingdom among boys and the promotion of habits of obedience, reverence, discipline, self-respect, and all that tends towards a true Christian manliness. Membership (aged 6 to 18) totals 150,000 in the United Kingdom, of whom more than one third are located in Scotland.

BOYS' CLUBS OF SCOTLAND, 53 George Street, Edinburgh EH2 2HT; T.-031-226 7255.

Founded: 1938.
Chairman: David A. Blaikie; Vice Chairman: William Reid; Chief Adviser and Secretary: Les Beaton; Field Officer: Neil Conn.
Aim is to promote the spiritual, mental, physical and social well-being of boys and young men in Scotland. Services to member clubs include comprehensive insurance cover, sporting competitions, development training, outdoor pursuits, international exchanges, video library and use of video equipment, anti-drug abuse material for leaders, use of camping equipment, advice and support.

BRITISH AEROSPACE PLC, (BAe),

Civil Aircraft Division - Prestwick, Prestwick Airport KA9 2RW; T.-0292 79888.

Divisional Director and General Manager: G.J. Curran.
British Aerospace Civil Aircraft Division at Prestwick employs 2,100 people and is the largest engineering employer in Ayrshire. The factory is responsible for the design, development, production and support of the Jetstream 31 twin turboprop 18/19 seat airliner. The Prestwick factory is also responsible for producing engine pylons for the BAe 146 four jet airlines.

BRITISH COAL, SCOTTISH AREA, Green Park, Greenend, Liberton, Edinburgh EH17 7PZ; T.-031-664 1461.

Founded: 1947 (as National Coal Board).
Director: G. McAlpine; Marketing Director: D. Hunter.
Carries out deep mined and open cast coal mining.

THE BRITISH COUNCIL, 3-4 Bruntsfield Crescent, Edinburgh EH10 4HD; T.-031-447 4716; 6 Belmont Crescent, Glasgow G12 8ES; T.-041-339 8651.

Founded: 1934.
Chairman, Scottish Advisory Committee: Lewis Robertson; Representative for Scotland: Norman Bissett (Edinburgh); Regional Director: Arthur Sanderson (Glasgow).
Exists to promote a wider knowledge of Britain and the English language abroad and to develop closer relations with other countries through educational, technological and cultural exchange. The offices in Scotland each year administer a large number of overseas students, principally at postgraduate level, in Scottish universities and colleges, and organise programmes of official visits by foreign professionals, particularly in education, technology and the arts. Support is also given for outward visits by Scottish professionals in these fields. The Council arranges a number of high-level specialist courses and summer schools each year for overseas participants.

BRITISH GAS SCOTLAND, Granton House, 4 Marine Drive, Edinburgh EH5 1YB; T.-031-559 5000.

Founded: 1947.
Regional Chairman: R.W. Hill; Regional Secretary: A.J. Hyne; Director of Engineering: L. Pott; Director of Finance: D.M. Dewar;

Director of Personnel: J.J. Walmsley; Director of Marketing: R.M. Currie.
Regional administration of British Gas plc, serving Scotland. Supplying gas to over 1 million customers, retailing and servicing appliances from showrooms and depots situated at the centres of population.

BRITISH GEOLOGICAL SURVEY, (BGS), Murchison House, West Mains Road, Edinburgh EH9 3LA; T.-031-667 1000.

Founded: 1835.
Programmes Director - UK North: Dr R.W. Gallois.
The principal Government body for the systematic acquisition and interpretation of geological data. Publishes geological maps of the United Kingdom and its Continental Shelf, and provides geological advice to Government departments, local authorities, public bodies, industry, universities and individuals. The Edinburgh office is responsible for geological surveying in Scotland, Northern Ireland, northern England, and the whole of the United Kingdom Shelf area, including hydrocarbon resources. Earthquakes in the United Kingdom are monitored, and other geophysical work includes global seismic and geomagnetic research. There is a public reference library and a sales desk.

BRITISH HORSE SOCIETY (SCOTTISH COMMITTEE), (BHS), Slates Farm, Kilmacolm, Renfrewshire PA13 4SX; T.-050 587 2682.

Chairman: Mrs H. Coward; Development Officer (Scotland): W.A. Bowes.
Incorporates the Pony Club. Aims are to promote the interests of horse and pony breeding, to further the art of riding and driving and to encourage horsemanship and the welfare of horses and ponies.

BRITISH LINEN BANK LTD, PO Box 49, 4 Melville Street, Edinburgh EH3 7NB; T.-031-453 1919.

Founded: 1746.
Governor: J.E. Boyd; Deputy Governor: Thomas W. Walker; Chief Executive: Ian F. Brown; Deputy Chief Executive: Ian Macpherson; Secretary: J.W. Robertson.
Merchant bank providing a full range of services including: corporate finance, investment, fund management, leasing, deposit facilities, term loans.

BRITISH MEDICAL ASSOCIATION, (BMA), 7 Drumsheugh Gardens, Edinburgh EH3 7QP; T.-031-225 7184/7.

Founded: 1832.
Chairman, Scottish Council: Dr A.G.R. Law, JP; Scottish Secretary: Mr A.J. Vallance-Owen.
Exists to promote the medical and allied sciences and, through its trade union role, to represent the interests of the medical profession in Scotland.

BRITISH RAIL (SCOTTISH REGION), (ScotRail), ScotRail House, 58 Port Dundas Road, Glasgow G4 0HG; T.-041-332 9811.

Founded: 1948.
General Manager: J.S. Cornell; Deputy General Manager: V.A. Chadwick; Director, Public Affairs: J.S. Boyle; Provincial Manager (ScotRail): C.R. Leah; Freight Manager: D.G.E. Clayton; Parcels Manager: R. Buick.
With a £350 million turnover and 15,000 employees, ScotRail plays an important role in the Scottish economy. Operates 1,500 trains a day and carries 46 million passengers a year (143 million passenger miles). Railfreight runs 200 trains a day, moving 12 million tonnes per annum into and out of 50 terminals and 190 private sidings.

BRITISH RED CROSS SOCIETY, SCOTTISH BRANCH, (BRCS), Alexandra House, 204 Bath Street, Glasgow G2 4HL; T.-041-332 9591.

Founded: 1870.
Chairman of Council: Mrs I.R. Readman; Vice-chairman of Council: Miss S. Dixon-Carter; General Secretary: Lt Col W.W. Kerr; Assistant General Secretary: C.W. Newman.
Non-denominational, non-political, non-racist, independent voluntary organisation formed to work for the relief of pain and suffering throughout the world. Over 200 million members worldwide.

BRITISH STEEL CORPORATION, Ravenscraig Works, Motherwell ML1 1SW; T.-Motherwell 66211.

Founded: 1957.
Works Director: J.G. Dunbar.
Iron and steel manufacturers.

BRITISH TECHNOLOGY GROUP, (BTG), 87 St. Vincent Street, Glasgow, G2 5TF; T.-041-221 1820.

Manager, Scotland: Colin Dale.
Public sector organisation which promotes and commercialises new technology arising from academic institutions. Technology transfer is brought about either through licensing to established companies, or by sponsoring and funding start-up companies. Also provides finance for companies which want to develop their own new technology.

BRITISH TELECOM.
East of Scotland District, 19 Canning Street, Edinburgh EH3 8TH; T.-031-229 2525. District General Manager: Mr W.A. Furness; District Accountant: Miss J. Sweeney; District Engineer: Mr W.M. Oliver; District Marketing Manager: Mr K.B. Runcorn.
North of Scotland District, Caledonian House, 232 Union Street, Aberdeen AB9 2BB; T.-0224 752000. District General Manager: Paul Duffin; District Accountant: Robin Lochhead; District Marketing Manager: Clive Pratt.
West of Scotland District, Westergate, 11 Hope Street, Glasgow G2 6AB; T.-041-220 1234. District General Manager: Doug Soutar; District Accountant: Mr I. Tarbet; District Engineer: Mr E. O'Neill; District Marketing Manager: Mr L. Thompson.

BRITISH VETERINARY ASSOCIATION, c/o Veterinary Division, West of Scotland Agricultural College, Ayr KA6 5AE; T.-0292 520468.
Founded: 1923.
President: W. Beswick; Secretary/Treasurer: C.L. Wright.
Fosters the interests of the veterinary profession in Scotland.

BRITISH WATERWAYS BOARD, Canal House, Applecross Street, Glasgow G4 9SP; T.-041-332 6936.
Founded: 1963.
Area Engineer (Scotland): D.J. Cochrane; Estate Officer (Scotland): P. Coyne; Area Leisure Officer (Scotland): M.C. Lindsay.
Has responsibility for the overall management of 2,000 miles of inland waterways in Scotland, England and Wales. Seeks to improve the use of the waterways for leisure, recreation and amenity, and freight transport, where appropriate. In Scotland, the board's waterways are the Caledonian and Crinan Canals (both open to navigation) and the Forth and Clyde, Union, and Monkland Canals (navigable in parts).

BRITISH YOUTH COUNCIL (SCOT-

LAND), Atholl House, 2 Canning Street, Edinburgh EH3 8EG; T.-031-229 6111.
General Secretary: Mr M. Lazarowicz.

BRITOIL plc, 301 St Vincent Street, Glasgow G2 5DD; T.-041-204 2525.
Founded: 1982.
Chairman: Sir Philip Shelbourne; Chief Executive: David Walker; Managing Director: Malcolm Ford.
Main activity: oil and gas exploration and production. Turnover (1985): £1,800 million.

BUILDING STANDARDS ADVISORY COMMITTEE, (BSAC), Scottish Development Department, Building Control Division, New St Andrew's House, Edinburgh EH1 3SZ; T.-031-556 8400, Ext. 5952.
Founded: 1959.
Chairman: Mr R.C. Young.
Advises and makes recommendations to the Secretary of State on building standards regulations.

THE BURNS FEDERATION, Dick Institute, Elmbank Avenue, Kilmarnock KA1 3BU; T.-0563 26401.
Founded: 1885.
Honorary Secretary and Treasurer: William A. Anderson; President: Dr J. Connor; Senior Vice-president: Mrs E. Logan; Junior Vice-president: Mrs A. Gaw; Assistant Secretary: Mrs M.G. Turner; Convener of Schools Competitions: J. Glass; Convener of Memorials: S.K. Gaw.
Main objects are: to encourage clubs and societies who honour Robert Burns; to strengthen the bond of fellowship among members of Burns clubs and kindred societies all over the world; to keep alive the old Scottish tongue; to encourage and arrange school children's competitions, in order to stimulate the teaching of Scottish history, literature, art and music; to mark with suitable inscriptions, repair or renew memorials to Robert Burns and his contemporaries. Membership: 364 clubs (with a total membership of around 35,000) and 250 individuals.

THE BURRELL COLLECTION, Pollok Park, 2060 Pollokshaws Road, Glasgow G43 1AT; T.-041-649 7151.
Keeper: Miss Rosemary Watt.
Given to the city of Glasgow in 1944 by Sir William Burrell (1861-1958), a Glasgow shipowner with a lifelong passion for art

collecting. The collection includes paintings, sculpture, tapestries, ceramics, stained glass, furniture, silver, metalwork and objets d'art of every kind, from three continents and virtually every period. After many years in store, the collection was eventually permanently housed by the City of Glasgow District Council in a new, purpose-built gallery.

THE BYRE THEATRE OF ST ANDREWS LTD, Abbey Street, St. Andrews KY16 9LA; T.-0334 76288.
Founded: 1933.
Administrator: Frank Chinn; Artistic Director: Adrian Reynolds; Chairman of Board: Alex B. Paterson.
Began in 1933 in a cow byre which, up to the late 1920s, had been part of Abbey Street dairy farm. In 1969, the old byre was demolished and the existing purpose-built theatre erected a short distance from the original site. Policy is to produce the best possible season of plays by a resident professional company, augmented by visiting companies and local amateurs.

C

CAITHNESS DISTRICT COUNCIL, Council Offices, Market Square, Wick, Caithness KW1 4AB; T.-0955 3761.
Founded: 1974.
Convener: John M. Young; Chief Executive: Mr A. Beattie; Director of Finance: Mr R.L. Bruce; Director of Technical Services: Mr M.G. Lunny; Director of Environmental Health: Mr R.G. Ferguson; Director of Leisure and Recreation: Mr J.W. Robertson. Political composition of council: Independent 15, Independent/Liberal 1. Population of district: 27,417.

CAITHNESS TOURIST BOARD, Tourist Office, Whitechapel Road, Wick KW1 4EA.
Founded: 1969.
President: Viscount Thurso of Ulbster; Area Tourist Officer: I. Sargent; Chairman: J. Green; Vice Chairman: J. Taylor; Treasurer: Mrs C. Scott.
Body with responsibility for all matters involving tourism in the area: marketing, advertising and promotion; production of area accommodation guide; promotional and informative literature; operating the tourist information centres; and representing the views of the trade to the national tourist board.

CAMANACHD ASSOCIATION, Algarve, Bad Abrach, Banavie, Fort William.
Secretary: Alastair MacIntyre.
Governing body of the game of shinty.

CAMBUSLANG COLLEGE, 6 Glasgow Road, Cambuslang, Glasgow G72 7BS; T.-041-641 6197/8.
Founded: 1948.
Principal: Mr N.J. Wright; Vice Principal: Mr O.C.G. Robbins; Industrial Liaison Officer: Mr D.F. Cameron.
Teaching staff of 125 in seven departments. Serves a large area of Lanarkshire and south east Glasgow with centres at East Kilbride, Hamilton and Wishaw in addition to the Cambuslang centre. Students attend full-time, block release, day release and evening, for vocational and non vocational courses.

THE CAMPING AND CARAVANNING CLUB, SCOTTISH REGION, c/o 70 Douglas Road, Longniddry, East Lothian EH32 0LJ; T.-0875 53292.
Chairman: W.R. Sangster; Vice Chairman: M. Smith; Secretary: A. Strachan; Treasurer: J.T. MacDonald.
Part of a national and international organisation for camping, caravanning and canoeing, with a total national membership of around 180,000, including a youth section. Provides comprehensive services for members, including running its own sites, arranging meets, foreign travel, insurance, technical information. Members are expected to conform to codes of conduct for camping and the organisation of meets. Represented in Scotland on the Association for the Protection of Rural Scotland, the Scottish Countryside Activities Council and the Scottish Youth Hostels Association.

CARBERRY TOWER, Musselburgh, Midlothian EH21 8PY; T.-031-665 3135.
Founded: 1963.
Wardens: Jock and Margaret Stein.
Residential centre of the Church of Scotland. Runs short-term courses.

CARDONALD COLLEGE, 690 Mosspark Drive, Glasgow G52 3AY; T.-041-883 6151/4, 041-883 1119.

Founded: 1971.
Principal: R.J. Bailey; Depute Principal: T.B. Wilson; Registrar: C.J. Kelly.
College of further education serving the south western district of Glasgow. Wide range of courses offered.

CARNEGIE BIRTHPLACE MUSEUM, ANDREW. See Andrew Carnegie Birthplace Museum.

CARNEGIE DUNFERMLINE TRUST, Abbey Park House, Abbey Park Place, Dunfermline KY12 7PB; T.-0383 723 638.
Founded: 1903.
Secretary and Treasurer: Fred Mann.
Established to bring 'more of sweetness and light...to the toiling masses' of Andrew Carnegie's native town. Pioneered, particularly in the first 20 years of the century, many social, recreational and cultural amenities, including a comprehensive health service for children 30 years in advance of the National Health Service. All the services which the trust established and administered for many years - swimming baths, district institutes and libraries, the Carnegie Hall, the music institute, craft school, playing fields and Pittencrieff Park - are now administered by the local authorities. Trust devotes its income of £200,000 a year to supporting and stimulating the activities of local clubs and societies and to sponsoring special projects of its own.

CARNEGIE HERO FUND TRUST, Abbey Park House, Abbey Park Place, Dunfermline KY12 7PB; T.-0383 723 638.
Founded: 1908.
Secretary and Treasurer: Fred Mann.
Provides financial assistance, if necessary, to the dependants of people who have died or to people who have been injured or who have incurred appreciable financial loss through performing acts of heroism in peaceful pursuits. Roll of heroes and heroines contains over 6,000 names and is on display in the Andrew Carnegie Birthplace Museum in Dunfermline. The trust has about 250 continuing beneficiaries, representing about 200 families living in Britain and in some instances abroad, most of whom receive a regular allowance or frequent grants for special purposes. The trust's annual income is around £100,000.

CARNEGIE TRUST FOR THE UNIVERSITIES OF SCOTLAND, 22
Hanover Street, Edinburgh EH2 2EN; T.-031-225 5817.
Founded: 1901.
Chairman: The Hon Lord Cameron, KT; Secretary and Treasurer: Prof J.T. Coppock.
Established by Andrew Carnegie to promote the interests of the Scottish universities. Makes research awards and scholarships to Scottish graduates and members of staff of Scottish universities, capital grants to universities, university fee assistance to Scottish school pupils, support to universities for staff travel.

CARNEGIE UNITED KINGDOM TRUST, 80 New Row, Dunfermline KY12 7EJ; T.-0383 721445.
Founded: 1913.
Secretary and Treasurer: Geoffrey Lord.
Charitable trust which supports innovatory schemes with national implications in amateur arts, community service and environment run by voluntary organisations registered as charitable. Priority given to national bodies.

CENTRAL ADVISORY COMMITTEE ON JUSTICES OF THE PEACE, St Andrew's House, Edinburgh EH1 3DE; T.-031-556 8501.
Chairman: The Rt Hon Lord Ross (Lord Justice Clerk); Secretary: A.F. Reid (Secretary of Commissions for Scotland).
Remit is to advise the Secretary of State as to problems arising in relation to the appointment and distribution of Justices of the Peace and the work of Justices of the Peace in general and of the District Court in particular. Sixteen members, apart from the chairman.

CENTRAL BUREAU FOR EDUCATIONAL VISITS AND EXCHANGES, 3 Bruntsfield Crescent, Edinburgh EH10 4HD; T.-031-447 8024.
Secretary, Scotland: J.R. Wake.

CENTRAL COLLEGE OF COMMERCE, 300 Cathedral Street, Glasgow G1 2TA; T.-041-552 3941.
Founded: 1962.
Principal: G.S. Barr; Depute Principal: R.C. Brown.
College of further education with 7,000 students.

CENTRAL OFFICE OF THE INDUSTRIAL TRIBUNALS (SCOTLAND), Saint Andrew House, 141

West Nile Street, Glasgow G1 2RU; T.-041-331 1601.
Founded: 1965.
President: R.C. Hay, WS; Secretary: A.J. Campbell.
Industrial tribunals are independent judicial bodies that have jurisdiction over a wide variety of matters in the employment field. They have permanent offices in the larger centres of population and sit in most parts of the country. Each has a legally qualified chairman, appointed by the Lord President, and two members appointed by the Secretary of State for Employment, one after consultation with employees' organisations and one after consultation with employers' organisations.

CENTRAL REGIONAL COUNCIL, Viewforth, Stirling FK8 2ET; T.-73111.
Founded: 1974.
Convener: Charles Sneddon, OBE, JP; Leader: James F.G. Anderson, CBE, OStJ, JP; Chief Executive: Eric Geddes; Director of Administration and Legal Services: Percival W. Buchanan; Director of Finance: John Broadfoot; Director of Planning: Frank Bracewell, OBE; Director of Architectural Services: Gerald M. Crossan; Director of Education: Ian Collie; Director of Roads and Transportation: Iain McCrindle; Director of Social Work: John A. Ross; Director, Personnel and Management Services Department: Peter V. Hay; Director of Water and Drainage: James T. Robertson; Director, Industrial Development Department: B.M. Nicholson; Firemaster: I.S.T. Adam; Chief Constable: Dr Ian T. Oliver, QPM.
Political composition of council: Labour 23, SNP 5, Conservative 4, Independent 1, Liberal/SDP Alliance 1. Population of region: 272,426.

CENTRAL SCOTLAND CHAMBER OF COMMERCE, Suite A, Haypark, Marchmont Avenue, Polmont, Falkirk FK2 0NZ; T.-Polmont 716868.
Founded: 1954.
President: A. Wilson; Secretary: H.B. Johnson.

CHARLES RENNIE MACKINTOSH SOCIETY, Queen's Cross, 870 Garscube Road, Glasgow G20 7EL; T.-041-946 6600.
Founded: 1973.
Chairman of Council: W. Leggat Smith; Director: Patricia Douglas; Joint Treasurers: Gordon and Efric McNeil.

Formed to promote an awareness of the Scottish architect, to encourage the conservation and improvement of his buildings and artefacts and to foster the development of interest in works by Charles Rennie Mackintosh and his contemporaries by means of meetings and lectures. In 1977, it negotiated a lease of Queen's Cross Church with the General Trustees of the Church of Scotland. With the help of grants from the Historic Buildings Council for Scotland, Glasgow District Council, Strathclyde Regional Council and the Scottish Development Agency, a major repair programme is now in hand to restore this, the only building for church purposes designed by Mackintosh which was actually built. Queen's Cross serves as an information centre with a small exhibition area, library and shop for enthusiasts. Membership: almost 1,500 worldwide.

CHARTERED INSTITUTE OF ARBITRATORS (ARBITERS), SCOTTISH BRANCH, c/o 40 Wellington Street, Glasgow G2 6RL; T.-041-221 3512.
Founded: 1964.
Chairman: James Miller, CBE; Vice-chairman: C.R. Ford; Honorary Secretary and Treasurer: J. Dietrichsen.

CHEST, HEART AND STROKE ASSOCIATION, (CHSA), 65 North Castle Street, Edinburgh EH2 3LT; T.-031-225 6963.
Founded: 1898.
Chairman, Scottish Executive Committee: Dr Norman W. Horne; Vice-chairman, Scottish Executive Committee: Sir John Crofton; Director, Scotland: Mrs Morag Younie.
Works for the prevention of chest, heart and stoke illness and gives practical help to patients suffering from these illnesses. This is accomplished by a programme of research, health education, welfare and rehabilitation. The first CHSA Volunteer Stroke Schemes were established in 1973. There are now 15 in Scotland with more to be established as finances allow. The schemes help in the rehabilitation of patients with speech and communication difficulties following a stroke.

CHRISTIAN SALVESEN PLC, 50 East Fettes Avenue, Edinburgh EH4 1EQ; T.-031-552 7101.
Founded: 1872.
Chairman: Sir Gerald Elliot; Managing Director: Barry E. Sealey; Director, Food

Services (Europe) Division: Joseph M. Barber; President, Merchants Refrigerating Company (USA): Alan J. Cole; Director, Marine Division: Robin S. Salvesen; Director, Industrial Services Division: Dr C. Masters.
Consists of four largely autonomous divisions (listed above) under a small central office operation. Food processing, freezing, storage, packing and distribution in Europe, the USA and the United Kingdom represent over two thirds of the company's turnover, with shipping and ship's management, generator hire, oil pollution control, tubing technology services and brick manufacture making up the balance. Turnover (1985-86): £295 million.

THE CHURCH OF SCOTLAND, 121 George Street, Edinburgh EH2 4YN; T.-031-225 5722.
Moderator-Elect of the General Assembly: Rev. Duncan Shaw; Principal Clerk of the General Assembly: Rev James Weatherhead; Secretary, Assembly Council: Mr I.D. Miller; Secretary, Department of Stewardship and Finance: Rev George Elliot; General Treasurer, Department of Stewardship and Finance: Mr W.G.P. Colledge; Joint Secretaries, Department of Ministry and Mission: Rev G.L. Lugton, Rev Ian B. Doyle; Secretary, Department of World Mission and Unity: Rev C. Wigglesworth; Secretary, Department of Social Responsibility: Rev Frank S. Gibson; General Secretary, Department of Education: Rev Alasdair J. Morton; Secretary, Department of Communication: Mr D. Bruce Cannon; General Secretary, Woman's Guild: Mrs Lorna M. Paterson.
Scotland's national church with a communicant membership of 887,166. Functions through 1,765 congregations in every part of Scotland. Parishes are grouped under 46 presbyteries and 12 synods. The supreme court, the General Assembly, meets annually in Edinburgh in May in the presence of the Lord High Commissioner representing The Queen. The church's work in caring for the elderly, the handicapped and the needy, at home and overseas, is conducted through various departments. Information about these and other activities is available from the Department of Communication at the above address.

CITIZENS' THEATRE, Gorbals Street, Gorbals, Glasgow G5 9DS; T.-041-429 5561.
Founded: 1945.
Chairman of Board: Mr W.L. Taylor; Artistic Director: Giles Havergal; Director: Mr R.D. MacDonald; Director/Designer: Philip Prowse; General Manager: Paul Bassett.
Innovative theatre company dedicated to the production of British and European classic drama. The theatre management wishes to make productions accessible, both artistically and financially, to as wide an audience as possible. Low seat price policy is operated together with a wide range of concessions. Normal season comprises six productions and one Christmas show.

CLACKMANNAN COLLEGE OF FURTHER EDUCATION, Branshill Road, Alloa FK10 3BT; T.-0259 215121.
Founded: 1968.
Principal: Mr W. Scott; Registrar: Mr A. Steele.
College with 1,300 students.

CLACKMANNAN DISTRICT COUNCIL, The Whins, Alloa FK10 3SA; T.-0259 722160.
Founded: 1974.
Convener: James Millar; Chief Executive: Ian F. Smith; Director of Environmental Health: William Cunningham; Director of Finance: Robert Dunbar; Director of Housing: Philip Jones; Director of Technical Services: Stewart Fowler.
Political composition of council: Labour 9, SNP 2, Conservative 1. Population of district: 47,809.

CLASSICAL ASSOCIATION OF SCOTLAND, (CAS), Department of Classics, King's College, Aberdeen AB9 2UB.
Founded: 1902.
Honorary President: Emeritus Prof W.S. Watt; Chairman of Council: Prof P.G. Walsh; Honorary Treasurer: Dr M.H.B. Marshall; Honorary Secretary: T.E.V. Pearce.
Exists to foster an interest in the civilisation and literature of Ancient Greece and Rome. Membership open to university and school teachers and anyone else interested. Around 160 members. Meetings held twice a year in one of the four ancient Scottish universities - St. Andrews, Glasgow, Aberdeen or Edinburgh.

CLINTERTY AGRICULTURAL COLLEGE, Kinellar, Aberdeen AB5 0TN; T.-0224 79 393.
Founded: 1968.

Principal: John Telfer; Farms Director and Depute Principal: Adrian D. Devonshire. Provides agricultural education at craft level for agriculture, agricultural engineering and horticulture students on full-time and part-time basis; for apprentices; those on YTS and others. Has agriculture day release course centres throughout Grampian region and in Inverness. All courses use SCOTVEC national certificate modules. Residential facilities in addition to normal college and farm provision. Residence essential on full-time courses.

CLYDEBANK COLLEGE, Kilbowie Road, Clydebank G81 2AA; T.-041-952 7771.
Founded: 1965.
Principal: William Greenock; Depute Principal: Robert C. Langlands; Registrar: John U. Mackay.
Operates vocational and non-vocational further education courses and modular programmes. Eight departments and around 6,000 students (day and evening) and 440 teaching and non-teaching staff (day and evening).

CLYDEBANK DISTRICT COUNCIL, District Council Offices, Clydebank G81 1TG; T.-041-941 1331.
Founded: 1974.
Provost: David S. Grainger, JP; Chief Executive and Administrative Officer: J.T. McNally; Director of Environmental Services and Senior Depute Chief Executive: J.O. Sayers; Director of Finance and Depute Chief Executive: G.E. Walker.
Political composition of council: Labour 11, Conservative 1. Population of district: 50,500.

CLYDE PILOTAGE AUTHORITY, 16 Robertson Street, Glasgow G2 8DU; T.-041-221 4046.
Pilot Master: Captain Lewis W. Black.

CLYDE PORT AUTHORITY, (CPA), 16 Robertson Street, Glasgow G2 8DS; T.-041-221 8733.
Founded: 1966.
Chairman: R.W. Easton; Managing Director: J. Mather; Secretary: G.P. Johnston; Harbour Master: Capt D.B. McMurray; Financial Manager: P. Lamb.
Encompasses the 450 square miles of the River Clyde, its estuary and sea lochs - a deep and sheltered natural harbour containing the port facilities of Ardrossan, Hunterston, Greenock and Glasgow.

CLYDE RIVER PURIFICATION BOARD, (CRPB), Rivers House, Murray Road, East Kilbride, Glasgow G75 0LA; T.-035 52 38181.
Founded: 1975.
Chairman: Cllr A. MacLean, JP; Director: Mr D. Hammerton; Depute Director: Mr D.W. Mackay; Clerk: Mr S.F. Hamilton, JP; Director of Finance: Mr W. English.
Independent body of 51 members, including, in equal proportion, regional councillors, district councillors and those appointed directly by the Secretary of State. Responsible for maintaining or restoring the cleanliness of rivers and tidal waters in an area approximately that of Strathclyde Region. Pollution of rivers and the sea arises from discharges of industrial and farm wastes, untreated domestic sewage, by spillage of chemicals and oils, and by diverse other means including vandalism, poaching, and the careless use of pesticides. The board's staff of scientists license dischargers, investigate incidents, and report offenders to the procurator fiscal.

CLYDESDALE BANK PLC, 30 St Vincent Place, Glasgow G1 2HL; T.-041-248 7070.
Founded: 1838.
Chairman: Sir Eric Yarrow; Chief General Manager: A. Richard Cole-Hamilton; Deputy Chief General Manager: Robert A. Laurenson; General Managers: Robert C. Legge, D. Ritchie Robertson, John W. McKinlay.
Offers full range of domestic and international banking facilities including advice on setting up in business. Operates a network of 380 branches with specialised offices in Glasgow, London, Edinburgh and Aberdeen.

CLYDESDALE DISTRICT COUNCIL, District Offices, South Vennel, Lanark ML11 7JT; T.-Lanark 61331.
Founded: 1974.
Convener: Miss M.T. Hodgson; Chief Executive: Peter W. Daniels; Director of Administration and Legal Services: D.J. Liddell; Director of Finance and Management Services: D.S.H. Anderson; Director of Planning and Technical Services: W. Graham U'ren; Director of Recreational Services: Roderick I.D. Mair; Director of Housing: Thomas Orr; Director of Environmental Health: James Hamilton, JP.
Political composition of council: Labour 6, Independent 4, SNP 3, Progressive 2, Inde-

pendent Labour 1. Population of district: 58,246.

THE CLYDESDALE HORSE SOCIETY OF GREAT BRITAIN & IRELAND, (CHS), 24 Beresford Terrace, Ayr KA7 2EG; T.-0292 281650.
Founded: 1877.
President: David L. Picken; Vice President: Tom Brewster; Honorary Presidents: John Lang, William Murdoch, James C. Picken; Honorary Treasurer: Thomas W. Clark.
Exists to promote the breeding of Clydesdale horses and the interests of their breeders. Around 600 members in the United Kingdom, with sister societies in the USA, Canada, Australia and New Zealand. Thirty horses exported each year, mainly to North America.

CLYDE VALLEY TOURIST BOARD, South Vennel, Lanark ML11 7JT; T.-0555 2544.
Founded: 1979.
Chairman: Cllr James Swinburne; Honorary Treasurer: Cllr Robert French; Tourism Manager: Scott Armstrong.
The Board is a partnership between the Scottish Tourist Board, the three district councils of Hamilton, Motherwell and Clydesdale and the local tourist trade. Produces a wide variety of publications including an accommodation guide, and has a trade membership of around 250 businesses. Main objectives are to attract visitors to the area, provide a comprehensive information service and encourage the development of tourist facilities.

CLYDE YACHT CLUBS' ASSOCIATION, (CYCA), Anchor House, Blackhall Lane, Paisley PA1 1TA; T.-041-887 8296.
Founded: 1898.
Chairman: G.B. Fleming; Vice Chairman: I.P.C. MacKenzie; Honorary Secretary: M.J. MacDonald; Honorary Treasurer: C.G. Rae.
Run by yachtsmen to serve yachtsmen on the Clyde and west coast of Scotland, from Girvan in the south to Armadale in Skye, in the north. The executive committee is elected from among the membership of the 33 constituent clubs, and has a nominee from the Clyde Port Authority and by the Queen's harbourmaster.

COATBRIDGE COLLEGE, Kildonan Street, Coatbridge ML5 3LS; T.-0236 22316.
Founded: 1890.
Principal: Edward J. Dowdalls; Depute Principal: Francis Burns; Registrar: George W. Stewart.
College of further education with 3,500 students.

COATS PATONS PLC, 155 St Vincent Street, Glasgow G2 5PA; T.-041-221 8711.
Founded: 1960.
Chairman: W.D. Coats.
Manufacturers and merchants of threads, yarns, knitting wools and garments. Turnover (1985): £1,076 million.

THE COCKBURN ASSOCIATION (The Edinburgh Civic Trust), 15 North Bank Street, Edinburgh EH1 2LP; T.-031-225 5085.
Founded: 1875.
President: The Hon Lord Cameron, KT; Chairman of Council: John Pinkerton, QC; Vice-chairman: Kenneth Newis, CB, CVO; Secretary: Oliver Barratt; Honorary Treasurer: Robin M. Martin, WS.
Objectives are: the maintenance and improvement of the amenity of the City of Edinburgh and its neighbourhood; and the protection and preservation of the city's landscape and historical and architectural heritage. Membership (around 1,200) is open to all who support these objectives. Life and annual membership available. Illustrated newsletter is normally published twice yearly, and varied activities are arranged.

THE COCKBURN CONSERVATION TRUST, 15 North Bank Street, Edinburgh EH1 2LP; T.-031-225 5085.
Founded: 1978.
Chairman: P.W. Simpson; Secretary: O.W. Barratt.
Acquires, restores and sells neglected buildings of historic or architectural interest in Edinburgh. Can restore buildings for any appropriate purpose but most of its work is on predominantly residential properties. It is a company, limited by guarantee, with charitable status, and works closely with the Cockburn Association.

THE COLLEGE OF PIPING, 16-24 Otago Street, Glasgow G12 8JH; T.-041-334 3587.
Founded: 1944.
Principal: Seumas MacNeill; Honorary Secretary: MacGregor Kennedy; Honorary

Treasurer: Hugh A. MacCallum.
Teaches about 100 students in evening classes in Glasgow and Edinburgh. Around 20 students, from North and South America, China, Japan and countries of Europe, receive instruction during the day. The College is a centre of piping information for the world. Publishes *Piping Times* (a monthly magazine) and seven books.

COLLINS PLC, William. See William Collins PLC.

COMANN AN LUCHD ION-NSACHAIDH, (CLI), 111 Academy Street, Inverness IV1 1LX; T.-0463 234138.
Chairman: Hector Mackenzie.
Organisation for adult learners of Gaelic.

COMHAIRLE NAN EILEAN (Western Isles Islands Council), Sandwick Road, Stornoway PA87 2BW; T.-0851 3773.
Founded: 1974.
Convener: Alexander Matheson; Chief Executive: Dr George Macleod; Director of Administration and Legal Services and Depute Chief Executive: Robert J.C. Barnett; Director of Finance and Depute Chief Executive: Donald G. Macleod; Director of Education: Neil R. Galbraith; Director of Architectural Services: John F. Paterson; Director of Engineering Services: Colin Macaulay; Director of Consumer Protection and Environmental Health: Hamish Fraser; Director of Social Work: Norma Macleod.
Non-political authority (30 members). Population of area: 31,500.

COMHAIRLE NAN SGOILTEAN ARAICH, (The Scottish Association of Gaelic Nursery Schools and Playgroups), (CNSA), 111 Academy Street, Inverness IV1 1LX; T.-0463 225469.
National Development Officer: Finlay MacLeod; Organising Secretary: Keith Scammell.
A national charitable organisation providing Gaelic-medium pre-schooling throughout Scotland. Services include the training of play leaders. Membership includes 27 playgroups, 11 mother and toddler groups and *Padraig Am Bus Trang*, a playbus providing Gaelic-medium pre-schooling and other facilities in and around Glasgow (but which is available to other areas during summer months).

COMMISSIONER FOR LOCAL ADMINISTRATION IN SCOTLAND, (Ombudsman), 5 Shandwick Place, Edinburgh EH2 4RG; T.-031-229 4472.
Founded: 1975.
Commissioner: R.G.E. Peggie, CBE; Secretary: Kenneth Bratton.
Investigates complaints of injustice caused by maladministration by local authorities, new town development corporations (regarding housing only), the Scottish Special Housing Association, water development boards, river purification boards and certain committees.

COMMISSIONERS OF NORTHERN LIGHTHOUSES, (Northern Lighthouse Board), 84 George Street, Edinburgh EH2 3DA; T.-031-226 7051.
Founded: 1786.
General Manager: Cdr J.M. Mackay, MBE; Secretary: Mr I.A. Dickson; Engineer-in-Chief: Mr J.H.K. Williamson.
Concerned with the operation and maintenance of lighthouses, buoys and beacons in Scotland and the Isle of Man.

COMMISSION OF THE EUROPEAN COMMUNITIES, 7 Alva Street, Edinburgh EH2 4PH; T.-031-225 2058.
Representative for Scotland: Stanley Budd; Documentalist/Librarian: Diana Hart.
Supplies information about the European Communities to enquirers from the press, television and radio, local authorities, businessmen and investors, schools and universities, etc. Maintains links with those bodies in Scotland particularly concerned with Community affairs, and aims to ensure that Scotland's particular problems and potential are known in Brussels.

COMMISSION FOR LOCAL AUTHORITY ACCOUNTS IN SCOTLAND, 18 George Street, Edinburgh EH2 2QU; T.-031-226 7346.
Founded: 1973.
Chairman: Prof John R. Small; Controller of Audit: Robert K. Simpson; Secretary: Keith Ferguson.
Independent statutory body, established by the Local Government (Scotland) Act 1973. Responsible for arranging the audit of all Scottish local authorities. Its chief executive, the Controller of Audit, makes statutory reports to the commission on major matters arising from the audits, such as unlawful expenditure or losses arising from misconduct. The commission may make recom-

mendations, including surcharge, to the Secretary of State for Scotland, in regard to matters raised by the Controller of Audit.

THE COMMITTEE OF SCOTTISH CLEARING BANKERS, 19 Rutland Square, Edinburgh EH1 2DD; T.-031-229 1326.
Secretary: John C. Sutherland.
Central point of contact in matters affecting member banks collectively, but not matters affecting banks individually or competitively. Also responsible for formulating and expressing a Scottish clearing bank view on relevant subjects, either on its own initiative or in response to a request or invitation.

COMMON SERVICES AGENCY FOR THE SCOTTISH HEALTH SERVICE, (CSA), Trinity Park House, South Trinity Road, Edinburgh EH5 3SE; T.-031-552 6255.
Founded: 1974.
Chairman: Sir Simpson Stevenson; Secretary: J.R.Y. Mutch; Treasurer: J.W. Morrison.
Established to provide certain specialist services to the National Health Service in Scotland. Discharges its function through its headquarters and the following divisions: Building Division, Communicable Diseases (Scotland) Unit, Dental Estimates Division, Scottish Health Education Group, Information Services Division, Central Legal Office, Management Education and Training Division, Prescription Pricing Division, Scottish Ambulance Service, Scottish Health Service School of Catering, Scottish Blood Transfusion Service, Supplies Division, Scottish Hospital Advisory Service, Scottish Antibody Production Unit. In addition, there are specialist advisory services such as domestic, laundry and catering.

COMMONWEALTH GAMES COUNCIL FOR SCOTLAND, c/o Secretary, 139 Old Dalkeith Road, Edinburgh EH16 4SZ; T.-031-664 1070.
Founded: 1929.
Chairman: A. Campbell, MBE; Vice Chairman: E.S. Murray, OBE; Secretary: G.A. Hunter, OBE, SBStJ; Treasurer: S. Coghill.
Sole object is to select and fund the Scottish team to compete at all Commonwealth Games.

COMMONWEALTH INSTITUTE, SCOTLAND, 8 Rutland Square, Edinburgh EH1 2AS; T.-031-229 6668.
Chairman: Prof George Shepperson; Director: Charles Carrol; Education Officer: W. Norman Henderson.
Educational body which provides information about the Commonwealth, its member nations, and world issues which affect everyone. Sponsored by the Foreign and Commonwealth Office.

COMMUNIST PARTY OF GREAT BRITAIN, SCOTTISH COMMITTEE, (CP), 44 Carlton Place, Glasgow G5 9TW; T.-041-429 2558.
Founded: 1920.
Secretary: Jack Ashton; Chairman: Bob Sommerville; Industrial Organiser: John Kay; Organiser: Douglas Chalmers; Glasgow Secretary: Frances Lockhart; Secretary, Young Communist League: Iain Chalmers.
Aim is to achieve a socialist Britain in which the means of production, distribution and exchange will be socially owned and utilised in a planned way for the benefit of all. Scottish membership: 3,100, organised in 97 branches. Weekly newspaper: 7 Days.

COMUNN NA GAIDHLIG, (CNAG), 111 Academy Street, Inverness IV1 1LX; T.-0463 234138.
Chairman: Rev Father Malcolm MacLellan; Vice Chairman: Rev Jack MacArthur; Director: John Angus MacKay; Development Officer: Donald John MacLeod.
Concerned with the promotion of the Gaelic language. Has a co-ordinating and developmental role, working with both public and voluntary bodies.

CONFEDERATION OF BRITISH INDUSTRY, SCOTLAND, Beresford House, 5 Claremont Terrace, Glasgow G3 7XT; T.-041-332 8661.
Founded: 1965.
Chairman: Mr J.M. Little, CBE; Vice-chairman: Mr W.B. Miller, OBE; Director: Mr J. Davidson.
Represents the interests of industry and commerce with government, local government, EEC and foreign governments. Membership covers every sector of industry and commerce, together with employer organisations, trade associations and nationalised industries. Also provides a forum in which members may develop business contacts, in the form of seminars, conferences and meetings. Authoritative data on the economy, industrial relations, employment policy, trading opportunities, company law, education and training and other subjects of significance to business is

available to assist members. CBI Scottish Council, consisting of 40 elected members and 15 co-opted members, guides the work of the CBI, Scotland, and influences the CBI in the development of its United Kingdom policy initiatives. Membership open to all corporate bodies, including partnerships, but not available to individual or sole traders.

CONGREGATIONAL UNION OF SCOTLAND, (CUS), PO Box 189, Glasgow G1 2BX; T.-041-332 7667.
Founded: 1897.
General Secretary: Rev Robert Waters; Honorary Treasurer: Robert B. Copleton; Chairman: F. Jeff Fowkes; President: Rev John Arthur.
Scottish church denomination of over 100 local churches, which operates on the principle of the responsibility of every member and each local congregation to raise its own funds, pay its own minister and pursue its own mission in the community. Identifies with the Scottish, British and World councils of churches, the World Alliance of Reformed Churches and the Council for World Mission.

CONSULTATIVE COMMITTEE ON THE CURRICULUM, (CCC), Room 4/21, New St Andrew's House, Edinburgh EH1 3SY; T.-031-244 4509.
Founded: 1965.
Chairman: Sir James Munn, OBE; Secretary: David R. McNicoll.
Advisory body to the Secretary of State for Scotland. Principal function is to promote the development of the school curriculum and to provide advice to central Government, education authorities and schools on the subject. Chairman and members are selected for their individual contribution and not as delegates of other bodies. Majority are from the education profession but others reflect community, parental and industrial interests. The CCC and its substructure of committees and working parties are supported by a secretariat and by officers of the Scottish Curriculum Development Service in Dundee, Edinburgh and Glasgow.

CONSULTATIVE COMMITTEE ON FRESHWATER FISHERIES, Chesser House, Gorgie Road, Edinburgh EH11 3AW; T.-031-443 4020.
Chairman: Mr J. Reid.
Concerned with the making of protection orders for freshwater fishings.

CONVENTION OF SCOTTISH LOCAL AUTHORITIES, (COSLA), Rosebery House, 9 Haymarket Terrace, Edinburgh EH12 5XZ; T.-031-346 1222.
Founded: 1975.
President: Cllr Ken Fagan; Vice-president: Cllr Eric Milligan; Secretary General: Roy MacIver.
Membership consists of all local authorities in Scotland: nine regional councils, 53 district councils and three islands councils. Watches over, protects and promotes the respective interests, rights, powers and duties of its member authorities and obtains, considers and disseminates information on matters of importance and interest to member authorities.

CO-OPERATIVE UNION LIMITED, SCOTTISH SECTION, 95 Morrison Street, Glasgow G5 8LP; T.-041-429 2556.
Founded: 1868.
Chairman: W.R. Smith.
Employers' association for retail co-operative societies and the Co-operative Wholesale Society in Scotland.

COUNCIL FOR BRITISH ARCHAEOLOGY SCOTLAND, (CBA Scotland), c/o Royal Museum of Scotland, York Buildings, 1 Queen Street, Edinburgh EH2 1JD.
Founded: 1946.
President: Edwina V.W. Proudfoot; Secretary: Trevor Cowie; Treasurer: Robin C. Callander.
Independent voluntary organisation whose object is to further the cause of archaeology in Scotland. Members are local archaeological, historical and amenity societies, museums and other bodies, as well as individuals interested in Scotland's past. Registered as a charity. Membership: 205.

COUNTRYSIDE COMMISSION FOR SCOTLAND, (CCS), Battleby, Redgorton, Perth PH1 3EW; T.-0738 27921.
Founded: 1968.
Chairman: J. Roger Carr; Vice Chairman: John M.S. Arnott; Director: Michael J. Taylor; Deputy Director: Thomas Huxley; Secretary: William B. Prior; Information Officer: Roderick I. Fairley.
Government agency with responsibilities relating to the conservation and enhance-

ment of the natural beauty and amenity of the Scottish countryside, provisions for public access and enjoyment, and a concern for the economic well-being of rural communities. Provides advice to central and local Government on planning and land use issues, and offers grants for recreational and amenity schemes. Issues wide range of free and priced publications.

COURIER & ADVERTISER, 7 Bank Street, Dundee DD1 9HU; T.-0382 23131.
Founded: 1926.
Daily newspaper circulating in city of Dundee and Tayside and Fife regions.

COURT OF THE LORD LYON, HM New Register House, Edinburgh EH1 3YT; T.-031-556 7255.
Lord Lyon King of Arms: Malcolm R. Innes of Edingight, CVO, WS; Lyon Clerk and Keeper of the Records: Mrs Elizabeth A. Roads.
One of the minor courts of Scotland, subject to appeal to the Court of Session and the House of Lords, with jurisdiction in questions of heraldry, the right to bear arms, succession to chiefships of clans and families in Scotland. The Lord Lyon grants armorial bearings to Scots and those of Scots descent domiciled in the Commonwealth and such armorial bearings are protected by statute. He judicially establishes rights to existing arms.

COURT OF SESSION, Parliament House, 11 Parliament Square, Edinburgh; T.-031-225 2595.
Principal Clerk of Session and Justiciary: A.M. Campbell.
Supreme civil court in Scotland.

CRAIGIE COLLEGE OF EDUCATION, Beech Grove, Ayr KA8 0SR; T.-0292 260321.
Founded: 1964.
Principal: Peter C. McNaught; Vice-principal: Richard L. Peddie; College Secretary: Robert T. Nisbet.
Provides pre- and in-service courses for teachers in the South West of Scotland. In association with the University of Strathclyde, it offers the degree of Bachelor of Education and the one-year postgraduate certificate for students already possessing a degree. A number of special qualifications are also offered including a one-year course leading to a special qualification for the teaching of infants and nursery children; a one-term course leading to a special qualification as a teacher in a nursery school; upper-primary associateships; remedial qualifications. The college also contributes in the fields of community education, social work, and related professions.

CROFTERS COMMISSION, 4-6 Castle Wynd, Inverness IV2 3EQ; T.-0463 237231.
Founded: 1955.
Chairman: A. MacLeod; Vice Chairman: I.G. Munro; Secretary: I.A. Macpherson.
Established by the Crofters (Scotland) Act with the principal duties of re-organising, developing and regulating crofting in the seven crofting counties of Scotland and keeping under general review all matters relating to crofters and crofting conditions.

CROSSROADS (SCOTLAND) CARE ATTENDANT SCHEMES, 24 George Square, Glasgow G2 1EG; T.-041-226 3793.
Founded: 1979.
President: Sir W. Ferguson Anderson; Chairman: Sir Robin MacLellan; Vice Chairman: Jack C. Rogers; Honorary Vice-president: Douglas G. Wood; Managing Director: Alexander G. Murray; Secretary/Treasurer: James A. Whittle.
Offers the help of a part-time care attendant to enable a caring relative or friend to have a break from constant supervision of frail elderly or severely handicapped and chronically ill people living at home. A reliable care attendant can be the crucial factor in determining whether or not a disabled or elderly person is able to go on living at home. Most of Scotland is covered by 39 schemes, with more developing.

CROWN OFFICE, 5-7 Regent Road, Edinburgh EH7 5BL; T.-031-557 3800.
Lord Advocate: Rt Hon Lord Cameron of Lochbroom, QC; Solicitor-General for Scotland: Peter Lovat Fraser, QC, MP; Crown Agent (Deputy Secretary): I. Dean; Deputy Crown Agent: J.D. Lowe; Establishment Officer (Principal): T. McKirdy.
Responsible for the public prosecution of crime in Scotland. All prosecutions in the High Court of Justiciary are conducted by Crown Counsel instructed by the Crown Office. In the Sheriff and District Courts, prosecutions are conducted by the Procurator Fiscal Service, which is administered by the Crown Office.

CULZEAN CASTLE AND COUNTRY PARK, Maybole, Ayrshire KA19 8LE; T.-06556 274/269.
Founded: 1945.
Administrator and Joint National Trust for Scotland Representative in Ayrshire: Michael L. Tebbutt; Joint National Trust for Scotland Representative in Ayrshire: Hazel Tebbutt; Deputy Administrator and Principal, Country Park: Gordon S. Riddle; Area Surveyor West: Alan J. Willoughby.
Attracts, as the major property of the National Trust for Scotland, some 300,000 visitors annually. Aims to preserve and interpret Culzean Castle and its policies for all time for the benefit of the visiting public.

CUMBERNAULD COLLEGE, Town Centre, Cumbernauld G67 1HU; T.-0236 731811/2/3.
Founded: 1976.
Principal: T.J. McGrenary; Registrar: G. Waters.
College of further education with 1,400 students.

CUMBERNAULD DEVELOPMENT CORPORATION, Cumbernauld House, Cumbernauld; T.-0236 721155.
Founded: 1956.
Chief Executive: Brig D.W. Anderson.
Exists for the planning and construction of the new town. With a population of 49,500 and over 200 companies in the town, a steady growth rate has been maintained since designation. The corporation is the catalyst for this growth: its experts in the fields of estates, architecture, engineering, finance and public relations are geared not only towards attracting new industry and commerce to the town, but also to maintaining as close a link as possible with companies already in the town.

CUMBERNAULD AND KILSYTH DISTRICT COUNCIL, Council Offices, Bron Way, Cumbernauld G67 1DZ; T.-Cumbernauld 22131.
Founded: 1974.
Provost: James Pollock; Chief Executive and Director of Finance: James Hutton; Director of Administration and Legal Services: James Gildea; Director of Recreation and Leisure: Daniel McGowan; Director of Technical Services: John Stark.
Political composition of council: Labour 8, SNP 4. Population of district: 62,970.

CUMBERNAULD AND KILSYTH ENTERPRISE TRUST, Enterprise Centre, 5 South Moor Head Road, Cumbernauld; T.-02367 38010.
Director: Ian Long.

CUMBERNAULD THEATRE TRUST LTD, Cumbernauld Theatre, Kildrum, Cumbernauld G67 2BN; T.-023 67 37235/6.
Founded: 1979.
Chairman: William Taylor; Vice-chairman: Cllr Craig Combe; Director: Robert Robson; Administrator: David Taylor.
Professional and community theatre offering a mixed programme featuring productions by its own resident company and visiting drama companies, youth theatre, all forms of music, film, popular entertainment, drama workshops, dance and educational and community drama projects. Aims to serve its community and offer presentations and participatory activities of the highest standard. Two theatres, cafe and two bars.

CUMBRAE NATIONAL WATERSPORTS TRAINING CENTRE, (CNWTC), Burnside Road, Largs KA30 8RW; T.-674666.
Principal: M.R. Barratt; Deputy Principal: A. Anderson; Chief Instructor: H. Maclean.
Variety of water sports coached, including dinghy sailing cruising, board sailing, canoeing, and sub-aqua diving. Courses conducted at all levels.

CUMNOCK AND DOON ENTERPRISE TRUST, (CADET), 46 Townhead Street, Cumnock KA18 1LD; T.-0290 21159/25203.
Founded: 1984.
Chairman: Alex Macdonald; Director: Alex Neil.
Established to create employment and new industry in the Cumnock and Doon Valley area.

CUMNOCK AND DOON VALLEY DISTRICT COUNCIL, Council Offices, Lugar, Cumnock KA18 3JQ; T.-0290 22111.
Founded: 1974.
Convener: D. Shankland; Chief Executive and Director of Administration: D.T. Hemmings; Director of Finance: K.W. Inch; Director of Planning and Architectural Services: A.C. Morris; Director of Environmental Health and Cleansing: A.J. Paton.
Political composition of council: Labour 10.

Population of district: 44,300.

CUNNINGHAME DISTRICT COUNCIL, Cunninghame House, Irvine KA12 8EE; T.-0294 74166.
Founded: 1974.
Convener: Teresa Beattie; Chief Executive: Bernard Devine; Director of Administration: James D.G. Gordon; Director of Finance: Ian L. Herd; Director of Technical Services: Lewis Dickens; Director of Housing: Robert Lindsay; Director of Leisure: David P. Webster; Director of Environmental Health: William Tulloch; Director of Cleansing: William Cowan.
Political composition of council: Labour 23, Conservative 5, Independent 2. Population of district: 137,094.

CYSTIC FIBROSIS RESEARCH TRUST, SCOTTISH COUNCIL, 39 Hope Street, Glasgow G2 6AE; T.-041-226 4244.
Founded: 1964.
Chairman: Mr D.M. Fortune; Treasurer: Mr W. Munro; Secretary: Mrs J.S. Deeley.
Exists to finance research to find a complete cure for cystic fibrosis and, meanwhile, to improve upon current methods of treatment. Forms branches and groups throughout the United Kingdom to help and advise parents with the everyday problems of caring for CF children. Aims to educate the public about the disease and thereby, through increased knowledge, help to promote earlier diagnosis in young children. Five branches in Scotland: Aberdeen; Dundee and Perth; Edinburgh and South East Scotland; Glasgow and South West Scotland; Highland.

D

DAILY RECORD, 40 Anderston Quay, Glasgow G3 8DA; T.-041-248 7000.
Founded: 1885.
Editor: Bernard Vickers.
Daily newspaper circulating throughout Scotland.

THE DAVID LIVINGSTONE CENTRE, Station Road, Blantyre, Glasgow G72 9BT; T.-0698 823140.
Founded: 1926.
Chairman: Fred McDermid; Vice Chairmen: Mrs Elspeth J. Murdoch, Mr G. Paton; Secretary: Mr A.M. Ferguson; Treasurer: Mr D. Macleod; Warden: Bill Cunningham.
Charitable trust committed to the restoration and preservation of the tenement building in which David Livingstone was born, as a memorial illustrating his work and an example to succeeding generations. Contains a vast number of relics relating to Livingstone, a social history section and an Africa Pavilion illustrating modern Africa. Grounds with gardens, play apparatus, souvenir shop, cafe and picnic area. Visited by 30,000 to 40,000 people annually.

DAVID LIVINGSTONE INSTITUTE OF OVERSEAS DEVELOPMENT STUDIES, (DLIODS), McCance Building, University of Strathclyde, 16 Richmond Street, Glasgow G1 1XQ; T.-041-552 4400.
Founded: 1973.
Director: Prof James Pickett; Deputy Director: Dr Eric Rahim.
University research institute concerned primarily with the economic and social problems of poor countries. Has undertaken considerable research on the choice of industrial techniques in developing countries, the employment problems in such countries, and work on agriculture. Has been funded in substantial part by the British Government, the United Nations and the EEC. Has facilities which enable postgraduate students to read for degrees by research.

DAWSON INTERNATIONAL PLC, Kinross KY13 7DH; T.-Kinross 63521.
Founded: 1972.
Executive Directors: R.A.B. Miller (Chairman and Chief Executive), D.L.D. Blackburn, J.D. Embrey, G.A. Smith, J.B. Waterton, B.S. Faulkner, P. Kemp; President: Sir Alan Smith CBE, DSC; Secretary: H. Somerville.
Specialist textile manufacturers, operating in world markets. The group is best known for its luxury knitwear and brand names which include Pringle of Scotland, Braemar, and Ballantyne. Turnover (1985): £285.194 million.

DENNY BONNYBRIDGE PROJECT, 42 Stirling Street, Denny FK6 6DJ; T.-Denny 825574.
Local enterprise trust.

DEPARTMENT OF AGRICULTURE AND FISHERIES FOR SCOTLAND,

Chesser House, 500 Gorgie Road, Edinburgh; T.-031-443 4020.
Secretary: L.P. Hamilton; Private Secretary: G.R. Ritchie.
Responsible for the promotion of agriculture and the fishing industry in Scotland. On the agricultural side, this includes participation in negotiations on agricultural policy at both United Kingdom and European Community level, oversight of support arrangements for commodities, and the provision of direct assistance to eligible producers. The supervision of educational, advisory and research services, the administration of a variety of schemes for the improvement of land, farm stock and crops, the development of crofting and the management of a large area of agricultural land which is in public ownership comes within its remit. As regards fisheries, duties include participation in international arrangements for conservation and other aspects of fishing and in European Community negotiations on fisheries policy, financial support for the fishing industry, assistance for fishery harbours, scientific research and the protection of Scottish fisheries by the department's fleet of fishery cruisers.

DEPARTMENT OF EMPLOYMENT, Office for Scotland, Pentland House, 47 Robb's Loan, Edinburgh EH14 1UE; T.-031-443 8731.
Benefit Manager, Scotland: Mr M. Rowe; Principal: Mr A.G. Dodds; Operations Manager: Mr G.P. McCluskey.
The Benefit Manager, Scotland, is responsible for the payment of benefits to the unemployed in Scotland through a network of local offices linked to the DHSS Computer Centre in Livingston. The Principal is responsible for personnel, industrial relations, use of staff resources, staff training, staff welfare, adjudication and fraud work. The Operations Manager is in charge of management services, monitoring standards of performance, employment protection measures, budgeting and accommodation.

DEPARTMENT OF HEALTH AND SOCIAL SECURITY, (DHSS), Central Office for Scotland, Argyle House, 3 Lady Lawson Street, Edinburgh EH3 9SH; T.-031-229 9191.
Controller for Scotland: R. Walton.

THE DESIGN COUNCIL, SCOTLAND, 72 St. Vincent Street, Glasgow G2 5TN; T.-041-221 6121.
Founded: 1944.
Chief Executive: Mr W. Deeprose.
Exists for the promotion by all practicable means of the standard of design in the products of British industry.

DISABLEMENT INCOME GROUP SCOTLAND, (DIG Scotland), ECAS House, 28-30 Howden Street, Edinburgh EH8 9HW; T.-031-667 0249.
Founded: 1966.
Chairman: Mr J.F. McGregor; Vice-chairman: Mr B. Parker; General Secretary: Mrs Muriel Smith.
Aims to secure the financial rights and general welfare of disabled people. Provides a welfare benefits service with domiciliary visiting. Makes grants in projects carried out by disabled communities throughout Scotland. Carries out research aimed at assisting disabled people in their fight to lead a full life, and gives grants in cases of hardship. Has branches or steering groups in 14 areas of Scotland with a membership of over 2,000 people.

THE DISTILLERS COMPANY plc, 33 Ellersly Road, Edinburgh EH12 6JW; T.-031-337 7373.
Founded: 1877.
Chairman, Management Committee: J.M. Connell; Company Secretary: E. Campbell.
Produces and sells potable distilled products. Principal products include: Scotch whiskies, London gins, vodkas, cognacs, bourbons, Pimm's, carbon dioxide, yeast and food products for the catering trade.

THE DUKE OF EDINBURGH'S AWARD, 69 Dublin Street, Edinburgh EH3 6NS; T.-031-556 9097.
Founded: 1956.
Chairman, Scottish Committee: John V. Hamilton; Secretary for Scotland: Col C.H.K. Corsar; Assistant Secretary: Peter T. MacLellan.
Offers a programme of leisure activities to all young people between the ages of 14 and 25. Activities include the training for and giving of voluntary service, expeditions (training given), the development of personal skills, and the participation in, and improvement of, performance at all manner of physical activities. The scheme is not competitive. What is required is the best possible endeavour by each participant. Those with physical and mental handicaps therefore have as much chance of getting an award as those who have no disabilities.

DUMBARTON DISTRICT COUNCIL, Crosslet House, Argyll Avenue, Dumbarton G82 3NS; T.-65100.
Founded: 1974.
Convener: Peter McCann; Chief Executive Officer: Lachlan MacKinnon; Director of Administration and Legal Services: J.N.S. MacEwan; Director of Finance: J.G. Ritchie; Director of Planning and Development: J. Webster; Director of Architectural Services: J. Oliver; Director of Housing Services: J. Pollock; Director of Environmental Health Services: A.B. Miller; Director of Civic Amenities: J. McErlane.
Political composition of council: Labour 10, Conservative 2, Independent 1, Non-political 1, SDP/Liberal Alliance 1, SNP 1. Population of district: 79,100.

DUMBARTON ENTERPRISE TRUST, Unit 2/2, Vale of Leven Industrial Estate, Dumbarton G82 3PA.
Director: R. Risk.

DUMFRIES ENTERPRISE TRUST, Heathall, Dumfries DG1 1FE; T.-0387 56229.
Director: Cyril Rankin.

DUMFRIES AND GALLOWAY COLLEGE OF TECHNOLOGY, Heathhall, Dumfries DG1 3QZ; T.-0387 61261.
Founded: 1961.
Principal: Mr J.W.M. Neil; Depute Principal: Mr I.D. Penn; Assistant Principal: Mr P.A. Hay.
Provides further and higher education in a wide range of disciplines. The main campus is situated two miles north of Dumfries and there are residential facilities. Major outcentre is planned for Stranraer in 1988.

DUMFRIES AND GALLOWAY HEALTH BOARD, Nithbank, Dumfries DG1 2SD; T.-0387 53181.
Founded: 1974.
Chairman: Mr J.A. McIntyre; General Manager: Michael D. Cook; Chief Administrator: Mr R.B.K. MacGregor; Chief Administrative Medical Officer: Dr J.F. Kirk; Chief Area Nursing Officer: Miss E.A. Edwards; Treasurer: Mr D. McEachran.
Provides health care for the people of Dumfries and Galloway.

DUMFRIES AND GALLOWAY REGIONAL COUNCIL, Council Offices, Dumfries DG1 2DD; T.-0387 53141.
Founded: 1974.
Convener: John V.M. Jameson; Chief Executive: Neil W.D. McIntosh; Director of Administration and Law: George M. Sinclair; Director of Finance: J.C. Stewart; Director of Education: J.K. Purves; Director of Architecture: John Henderson; Director of Physical Planning: A.H. Dobbie; Director of Roads and Transportation: H.D.B. Murray; Director of Water and Sewerage: J. McLean Cameron; Director of Social Work: T. McMenamay; Director of Economic Development: Leslie T. Jardine; Director of Information Technology: Dr J. Bruce Irving; Director of Consumer Protection: G.M. Smith; Chief Constable: J.M. Boyd, QPM; Firemaster: J.B. Stiff.
Political composition of council: Non-political/Non-party 14, Labour 7, SNP 5, Independent 4, Liberal/SDP Alliance 4, Others 1. Population of region: 146,562.

DUMFRIES AND GALLOWAY TOURIST BOARD, (DGTB), Douglas House, Newton Stewart, Wigtownshire DG8 6DQ; T.-0671 3401.
Founded: 1983.
Director: Andrew Llanwarne; Chairman: Tom Gillespie.
Responsible for marketing its area worldwide, for encouraging tourism locally, for operating 10 tourist information centres and administering a membership of approximately 900.

DUNCAN OF JORDANSTONE COLLEGE OF ART, Perth Road, Dundee DD1 4HT; T.-0382 23261.
Founded: 1896.
Principal: Mr Myer Lacome; Vice-principal: Dr Christopher Carter; Secretary: Mr Garnet Reid.
One of the Scottish Central Art Institutions. Offers a range of full-time undergraduate and postgraduate courses, all of which are professionally orientated with the main emphasis on professional practice. Also offers numerous part-time non-vocational courses.

DUNCRAIG CASTLE COLLEGE, Plockton, Ross-shire IV52 8UA; T.-059 984 229.
Founded: 1947.
Principal: Miss D.J. Whan.
Duncraig Castle and its estate were bequeathed to the education authority in 1945, and since then it has functioned as a residential educational establishment for girls, giving training in domestic science,

homecraft, and catering. Since 1960, Duncraig has been recognised as a college of further education. Has around 40 students.

DUNDEE ART GALLERIES AND MUSEUMS, McManus Galleries, Albert Square, Dundee DD1 1DA; T.-0382 23141.
Founded: 1867.
Curator: Mr A.B. Ritchie; Assistant Curator: Miss L.M. Thoms; Keeper of Art: Miss C. Young; Keeper of Human History: Mrs J. Murray; Keeper of Natural History: Mr R. Brinklow; Extension Services Offficer: Mr C. Dingwall.
Comprises four separate buildings in the care of the City of Dundee District Council. The McManus Galleries in Albert Square contain the art galleries and local history displays. Barrack Street Museum contains natural history displays. Broughty Castle Museum has displays on local history, whaling, local wildlife and military history. The Mills Observatory is Britain's only full-time public observatory and has telescopes and displays on astronomy and space exploration.

DUNDEE ASSOCIATION FOR SOCIAL SERVICE, (DASS), Castlehill House, 1 High Street, Dundee DD1 1TD; T.-0382 21545.
Founded: 1953.
Chairman: Don Cane; Vice-chairman: Susanta Sarkar; Honorary Treasurer: Alistair Gunn; Chief Executive and Secretary: Malcolm May.
Aims to promote and sustain the development of voluntary action in Dundee and district through: servicing voluntary and community organisations, linking and co-ordinating developments and activities, co-operating with local and public authorities, and encouraging self-help activity in the community. Numerous publications.

DUNDEE COLLEGE OF EDUCATION, Gardyne Road, Dundee DD5 1NY; T.-0382 454433.
Founded: 1906.
Acting Principal: Dr D.R.A. Keatch; Acting Vice-principal: W. Shearer; Secretary: M. McCarry; Assistant Secretary: H.P.P. Steel.
Offers training in teaching, community education and social work.

DUNDEE COLLEGE OF FURTHER EDUCATION, 30 Constitution Road,

Dundee DD3 4TB; T.-0382 29151.
Principal: Craig Brown.
Formed by the amalgamation of the former Dundee College of Commerce and Kingsway Technical College.

DUNDEE COLLEGE OF TECHNOLOGY, Bell Street, Dundee DD1 1HG; T.-0382 27225.
Founded: 1888.
Principal: Dr H.G. Cuming, CBE; Vice-principal: W.J. Emond; College Secretary: J.R. Smith, OBE; Depute Secretary and Registrar: C.M. McConnach.
Scottish Central Institution with three faculties. Offers full-time and part-time courses of vocational higher education at postgraduate, first degree, diploma and certificate level in a wide range of disciplines. 2,700 students.

DUNDEE DISTRICT COUNCIL, CITY OF, City Chambers, Dundee DD1 3BY; T.-0382 23141.
Founded: 1974.
Lord Provost: Thomas Mitchell; Chief Executive: James F. Hoey; Director of Administration: Michael Brown; Director of Finance: Alexander Stephen; Director of Housing: Russell Rowbotham; Director of Arts and Recreation: Allan Booth.
Political composition of council: Labour 25, Conservative 13, SDP/Liberal Alliance 3, SNP 2, Independent Conservative 1. Population of district: 177,674.

DUNDEE INDUSTRIAL ASSOCIATION LTD, (DIA), Meadow Mill, West Henderson Wynd, Dundee DD1 5BY; T.-0382 26001/2.
Founded: 1983.
Chairman: James Millar; Managing Director: David Morrison; Company Secretary: Steven Baillie; Property Manager: Mary Core.
Registered enterprise agency whose objectives are to reduce unemployment and create development in Dundee. Has two main areas of operation: the provision of business advice to start-up or existing businesses, and the provision of office and factory units to small businesses at reasonable rents and easy in, easy out terms.

DUNDEE REPERTORY THEATRE, Tay Square, Dundee DD1 1PB; T.-0382 27684 (Administration), 0382 23530 (Box Office).
Founded: 1939.

Chairman, Board of Directors: Prof S.G.G. MacDonald; Theatre Director: Robert Robertson; General Manager: Tom Gardner.

Repertory company providing dramatic entertainment of all kinds and acting as the venue for a variety of other arts activities, including music, dance and art exhibitions.

DUNDEE, UNIVERSITY OF, Nethergate, Dundee DD1 4HN; T.-0382 23181.

Founded: 1967.

Chancellor: The Rt Hon The Earl of Dalhousie, KT, GCVO, GBE, MC; Principal and Vice-chancellor: A.M. Neville, MC; Deputy Principal and Vice-principal: Prof W.D.P. Stewart; Deputy Principal: Prof A.E. Vardy; Rector: M.G. Bruce; Dean of the Faculty of Medicine and Dentistry: Prof P.D. Griffiths; Dean of the Faculty of Science: Prof J.D. Lambert; Dean of the Faculty of Law: Prof A.B. Wilkinson; Dean of the Faculty of Engineering and Applied Science: Prof A.F. Newell; Dean of the Faculty of Arts and Social Sciences: Dr D.B. Swinfen; Dean of the Faculty of Environmental Studies: A. Roberts; Secretary: R. Seaton.

Six faculties: Medicine and Dentistry; Science; Law; Engineering and Applied Science; Arts and Social Sciences; Environmental Studies. There are 57 academic departments, offering a wide and flexible range of undergraduate studies. Many of the courses are strongly vocational and provide the academic training for particular professions. At postgraduate level, specialist degree and diploma courses are available in branches of medicine, dentistry, pure science, law, engineering, education, and social sciences. Research work is undertaken throughout the university.

DUNDEE, UNIVERSITY OF, CENTRE FOR CONTINUING EDUCATION, The University, Nethergate, Dundee DD1 4HN; T.-0382 23181, Ext. 4128.

Founded: 1985.

Director: Prof Donald A. Bligh.

Includes the university departments of Education and Extra-mural Education and has responsibility for postgraduate teaching in education, mainly from the MEd and PhD degrees, and for the long-established programme of extra-mural courses in Dundee and Tayside organised by the university in liaison with Tayside Regional Council. It is also responsible for a range of post-experience courses, mainly for professional up-dating by private industry and the public sector.

DUNFERMLINE COLLEGE OF PHYSICAL EDUCATION, (DCPE), Cramond Road North Edinburgh EH4 6JD; T.-031-336 6001.

Founded: 1905.

Principal: Jean A. Carroll; Vice Principal: Brian S. Duffield; Assistant Principal: R. Ramsey Bone; College Secretary: Alexander S. Adam.

Offers the only graduate course in Scotland for women students of physical education. Also offers graduate and postgraduate courses in physical education, leisure and recreation, and a range of diploma and certificate courses and short in-service courses for teachers, leisure professionals, coaches etc. It is a centre for research and houses the Centre for Leisure Research which specialises in research in education, leisure, recreation, tourism and public policy for a range of public and private bodies.

DUNFERMLINE DISTRICT COUNCIL, City Chambers, Dunfermline; T.-0383 722711.

Founded: 1974.

Provost: Robert Mill, JP; Chief Executive: G. Brown; Director of Administration: F.M. Coutts; Director of Finance: J. Donaldson; Director of Technical Services: L.J. Walker; Director of Planning: I. Connon; Director of Housing: A. Davidson; Director of Environmental Health: K.N. Fraser; Director of Leisure, Recreation and Amenities: T.W. Robson; Director of Libraries, Museums and Art Galleries: J.K. Sharp.

Political composition of council: Labour 23, Liberal/SDP Alliance 6, Conservative 2, SNP 2, Communist 1. Population of district: 126,000.

DUNFERMLINE AND WEST FIFE CHAMBER OF COMMERCE, 10 Viewfield Terrace, Dunfermline KY12 7JH; T.-0383 721156.

Founded: 1900.

President: Alexander Punler; Vice President: John R. Richards; Secretary and Treasurer: Alan M. Stewart.

Represents the views of commerce and industry in the Dunfermline and West Fife area and provides a range of services to benefit members. Has around 150 members.

DUNOON AND COWAL TOURIST

BOARD, Information Centre, Dunoon PA23 7HL; T.-0369 3785.
Founded: 1969.
Chairman: Ian R. Taylor; Tourism Manager: Iain F. Clason.
Exists for the promotion of tourism in the area.

E

EARL HAIG FUND (SCOTLAND), Haig House, 1 Fitzroy Place, Glasgow G3 7RJ; T.-041-221 8141.
Founded: 1920.
President: Major The Earl Haig, OBE, KStJ; Chairman: Col C.H.K. Corsar, OBE, TD; Area Chairmen: Lt Col A.R. Ewing, TD (Glasgow), Col T.D. Purdie, TD (Edinburgh); Area Honorary Treasurers: Major J.F.deW. Duvoisin, TD (Glasgow), Mr J. Grier (Edinburgh).
Registered charity devoted to helping ex-servicemen, their widows and ex-servicewomen who are in need or distress. Responsible for the production of poppies at Lady Haig's poppy factory in Edinburgh and their distribution throughout Scotland at the time of remembrance. Also runs ex-servicemen's eventide homes in Edinburgh and Glasgow.

EAST KILBRIDE BUSINESS CENTRE, 10th Floor, The Plaza Tower, East Kilbride; T.-03552 38456.
Director: Burt Miller.
Local enterprise trust.

EAST KILBRIDE DEVELOPMENT CORPORATION, (EKDC), Atholl House, East Kilbride, Glasgow G74 1LU; T.-03552 41111.
Founded: 1947.
Chairman: J. Allan Denholm; Managing Director: George B. Young; Director of Development: George Grassie; Director of Finance: Hugh Stevenson.
In 40 years, East Kilbride has grown from a quiet village of less than 2,500 people, to Scotland's sixth largest town, with a population of over 72,000. The rapid growth of Scotland's first new town has been planned to integrate the living, commercial, and industrial developments with the surrounding countryside.

EAST KILBRIDE DISTRICT COUNCIL, Civic Centre, East Kilbride G74 1AB; T.-East Kilbride 28777.
Founded: 1974.
Provost: George McKillop; Chief Executive: W. Gordon McNay; Director of Finance and Management Services: Kenneth Love; Director of Administration and Legal Services: James M. Gallagher; Director of Planning and Technical Services: David McNidder; Director of Environmental Health and Housing: Hugh D. Henry; Director of Recreation and Leisure Services: Timothy P. Cruttenden.
Political composition of council: Labour 14, Conservative 2. Population of district: 82,524.

EAST LOTHIAN ANTIQUARIAN AND FIELD NATURALISTS' SOCIETY, Haddington House, Haddington, EH42 1LT; T.-0368 63335.
Founded: 1924.
Honorary President: Sir David Ogilvy, Bt; Honorary Secretary: Stephen A. Bunyan.
Founded for the study of the antiquities, archaeology, local history and natural history of East Lothian and for the collection and publication of relevant documentary evidence. Has a programme of lectures and excursions. Membership is open to all interested.

EAST LOTHIAN DISTRICT COUNCIL, Council Buildings, Court Street, Haddington EH41 3HA; T.-062 082 4161.
Founded: 1974.
Chairman: Thomas Wilson; Chief Executive: David B. Miller; Director of Administration: Malcolm Duncan; Director of Finance: John Lindsay; Director of Architectural Services: Ian G. Campbell; Director of Physical Planning: David G.B. Duncan; Director of Environmental Health: J.B. Cunningham; Director of Housing: T.C. Bathgate; Director of Leisure, Recreation and Tourism: R.A.P. Mellor.
Political composition of council: Labour 11, Conservative 6. Population of district: 82,160.

EAST LOTHIAN TOURIST BOARD, Brunton Hall, Musselburgh EH21 6AF; T.-031-665 3711.
Chief Tourism Officer: L. Abbie.

EAST OF SCOTLAND COLLEGE OF AGRICULTURE, West Mains Road, Edinburgh EH9 3JG; T.-031-667 1041.
Founded: 1901.

Principal: Prof P.N. Wilson; Vice Principal: J.L. Beveridge; Secretary and Treasurer: D.S. Land; Head of Extension Services: K.V. Runcie; Head of Animal Division: Prof C.T. Whittemore; Head of Crop Division: Prof J.C. Holmes; Head of Agricultural Resource Management: Prof S.B. Dent; Head of Microbiology Division: Prof J.F. Wilkinson; Veterinary Division: A.O. Mathieson; Farms Director: Dr W.J.M. Black.
Provides agricultural education at diploma and higher diploma levels as part of a teaching programme undertaken jointly with the University of Edinburgh. Also operates an advisory service, and undertakes an extensive programme of agricultural research.

EASTWOOD DISTRICT COUNCIL, Council Offices, Eastwood Park, Rouken Glen Road, Giffnock, Glasgow G46 6UG; T.-041-638 6511.
Founded: 1974.
Provost: J.M. Edmondson; Chief Executive Officer: M.D. Henry; Director of Finance: W.R. Crosbie; Director of Planning and Technical Services: R.C. Bowman.
Political composition of council: Conservative 10, Ratepayers/Residents Association 2. Population of district: 55,069.

EDINBURGH ARCHITECTURAL ASSOCIATION, 15 Rutland Square, Edinburgh EH1 2BE.
Founded: 1858.
Professional association.

EDINBURGH ART CENTRE, CITY OF, 2 Market Street, Edinburgh EH1 1DE; T.-031-225 2424, Ext. 6650.
Keeper of Fine Art Collections: Ian O'Riordan; Assistant Keeper of Fine Art Collections (Temporary Exhibitions): Lesley Woodbridge.
Houses the city's fine art collection comprising over 3,000 works. In addition to exhibitions of the collection, a diverse programme of temporary exhibitions from the United Kingdom and abroad continues throughout the year, catering for a wide range of tastes and interests.

EDINBURGH BIBLIOGRAPHICAL SOCIETY, c/o National Library of Scotland, George IV Bridge, Edinburgh EH1 1EW; T.-031-226 4531.
Founded: 1890.
President: P.B. Freshwater; Secretary: I.C. Cunningham.
Promotes and encourages bibliographical studies.

EDINBURGH BOOK FESTIVAL, 25a South West Thistle Street Lane, Edinburgh EH2 1EW; T.-031-225 1915.
Founded: 1983.
Chairman: Lord Balfour of Burleigh; Director: Jenny Brown; Children's Fair Organiser: Valerie Bierman; Honorary Treasurer: D. Ainslie Thin.
Biennual event held during the first fortnight of the Edinburgh Festival in Charlotte Square Gardens. Celebration of books and writing with thousands of books on display from Britain and abroad, a children's fair, and author events such as readings, discussions, demonstrations and signings. Aims to encourage and attract all readers. It is supported by the Scottish Arts Council and is registered as a charity.

EDINBURGH CENTRE OF RURAL ECONOMY, (ECRE), Bush Estates, Penicuik, Midlothian EH26 0PJ; T.-031-445 2161.
Founded: 1948.
Chairman: Mr Q. Brown; Vice Chairman: Prof P.N. Wilson; Secretary and Factor: Dr R.H.M. Nisbet.
Company limited by guarantee established jointly by the University of Edinburgh, the Department of Agriculture and Fisheries for Scotland and the East of Scotland College of Agriculture to further research, development and teaching in agricultural, veterinary and environmental sciences. Manages and services the Bush Estate for the benefit of members.

EDINBURGH CHAMBER OF COMMERCE, 3 Randolph Crescent Edinburgh; T.-031-225 5851.
Chief Executive: D.M. Mowat, JP.

EDINBURGH CITY MUSEUMS AND ART GALLERIES, Huntly House Museum, 142 Canongate, Edinburgh EH8 8DD; T.-031-225 2424, Ext. 6689.
Founded: 1976.
City Curator: Herbert Coutts; Assistant City Curator: Derek Janes; Keeper of Fine Art Collections: Ian O'Riordan; Keeper of Childhood Collections: John Heyes; Keeper of Social History Collections: Helen Clark.
Administers: Huntly House (local history, applied art, Haig personalia collections), Canongate Tolbooth (tartan collection and brass rubbing centre), Museum of Childhood (childhood collection), Lady Stair's

House (personalia collections relating to Scottish literary figures), City Art Centre (fine art collection and temporary exhibitions), Lauriston Castle (Edwardian country house with extensive applied art collections), Queensferry Museum (local history collections), Scott Monument and Nelson Monument.

EDINBURGH CIVIC TRUST. See The Cockburn Association.

EDINBURGH COLLEGE OF ART, Lauriston Place, Edinburgh EH3 9DF; T.-031-229 9311.
Founded: 1909.
Principal: John L. Paterson; Vice Principal: W. Ferrie Wood; Secretary and Treasurer: John J. Nice.
One of the four Central Art Institutions in Scotland. Has 1,100 students.

EDINBURGH COUNCIL OF SOCIAL SERVICE, (ECSS), 11 St Colme Street, Edinburgh EH3 6AG; T.-031-225 4606.
Founded: 1868.
Chairman: Rev Norman Shanks; Vice Chairman: Maureen O'Neill; Honorary Treasurer: Michael Hathorn; Director: Edward Matthews; Assistant Director: Alan Rees.
Aims to encourage voluntary action within the community and enable voluntary organisations to come together for joint consultation on issues of common concern. Professional staff are available and the council provides a range of services including: Edinburgh Volunteer Exchange with its central recruiting agency; an information and advisory service; Edinburgh Community Transport (a community service for the elderly and disabled); duplicating and printing at low cost for voluntary and community groups. Publications: an annual report; *Link-Up* (a quarterly bulletin); *Red Book* (a directory of voluntary and statutory services in Lothian Region); *Charities Aid Fund Handbook*; occasional papers.

EDINBURGH CRIPPLE AID SOCIETY, (ECAS), 28-30 Howden Street, Edinburgh EH8 9HW; T.-031-668 3371.
Founded: 1903.
Chairman: Donald Semple; Treasurer: Thomas Michael Galloway; Executive Secretary: Mrs J. Morag McLafferty.
Voluntary organisation providing services and facilities for the physically handicapped in Edinburgh and Lothians. Services

include the Dial A Cab scheme operated with a standard taxi charged at a flat rate per journey with the society subsidising the balance. Three passengers may travel with the disabled client and there are 1,800 registered clients. ECAS House is a leisure and recreation centre where clients, together with able-bodied friends, can enjoy a variety of cultural and sports activities.

EDINBURGH CYRENIAN TRUST, 20 Broughton Place, Edinburgh EH1 3RX; T.-031-556 4971/7507.
Founded: 1968.
Chairperson: Dr J.V. Basson; Central Treasurer: Paul Kenny; Chairperson, Farm Committee: John Carson; Chairperson, Hostel Committee: Helen Cook.
Charitable, voluntary organisation running projects for the single homeless and rootless in the Lothians. Works with young people (18-30) who have been labelled as offenders or mentally ill, those rejected by society and those who cannot cope with the pressures and demands of society. The bulk of the work is carried out by full-time residential volunteers living in communities with the residents. Currently has two projects: a city community in Edinburgh, and a farm community in West Lothian.

EDINBURGH DISTRICT COUNCIL, CITY OF, City Chambers, High Street, Edinburgh EH1 1YJ; T.-031-225 2424.
Founded: 1974.
Lord Provost: Rt Hon John McKay, JP; Chief Executive: M.M. Duncan; Director of Administration: W. Blyth; Director of Finance: A. Hepburn; Director of Technical Services: R. Cooper; Director of Physical Planning: N. Fort; Director of Housing: J.M. Wilson; Director of Economic Development and Estates: W. Ross; Director of Cleansing Services: A. McCreath; Director of Recreation: B.M. Connolly; Director of Environmental Health: R.A. Carson; Director of Personnel and Management Services: D.B. Hughes; Director of Public Relations and Tourism: A.A. Fyall.
Political composition of council: Labour 34, Conservative 22, Liberal/SDP Alliance 4, SNP 2. Population of district: 439,672.

EDINBURGH FESTIVAL FRINGE, 170 High Street, Edinburgh EH1 1QS; T.-031-226 5257.
Founded: 1947.
Administrator: Mhairi MacKenzie-Robin-

son; Assistant Administrator: Patricia Emblem.

Started as a spontaneous addition to the first Edinburgh International Festival and is now the largest cultural event in the world. The Edinburgh Festival Fringe Society was formed in 1959 to co-ordinate publicity and ticket sales. The 'Fringe' is an annual co-operative of independent artists and managements doing their own thing at their own financial risk and on their own initiative. Runs for three and a half weeks each year in August.

EDINBURGH GEOLOGICAL SOCIETY, c/o British Geological Survey, Murchison House, West Mains Road, Edinburgh EH9 3LA; T.-031-667 1000.
Founded: 1834.
Honorary Secretary: Mr A.A. McMillan; President: Dr E.N.K. Clarkson; Treasurer: Mr W.G.W. Harper; Editorial Board Convener: Mr D. Grant; Excursions Secretary: Mr S.I. Hogarth; Lectures Secretary: Dr A.H.F. Robertson.
Objectives include the stimulation and encouragement of public interest in geology and the advancement of geological knowledge by such means as public lectures, conferences, excursions, exhibitions, the maintenance of a geological library, the publication of the *Scottish Journal of Geology* jointly with the Geological Society of Glasgow, and other publications including excursion guides and maps. Has 580 members, both amateurs and professionals, about 300 of whom live in Scotland.

EDINBURGH HOSPITAL BROADCASTING SERVICE, (EHBS), 69 Hanover Street, Edinburgh EH2 1EE; T.-031-225 4646 (7pm - 10pm).
Founded: 1962.
Chairman: R.G. Allan; Treasurer: A.K. Cunningham.
Registered charity providing hospital radio entertainment, via British Telecom landlines, to 10 hospitals across the city. On air 7pm until 10pm, with daytime programmes at weekends and all day broadcasts on Christmas Day and New Year's Day. Staffed entirely by volunteers who are involved in programmes, maintaining equipment, office administration, hospital visiting, maintaining the record library and fund raising.

EDINBURGH INTERNATIONAL FESTIVAL, 21 Market Street, Edin-
burgh EH1 1BW; T.-031-226 3001.
Founded: 1947.
Festival Director: Frank Dunlop, CBE; Associate Director: Sheila Colvin; General Manager: Christopher Barron.
Largest celebration of the arts in the world. Held for three weeks every August. Its programme of music, opera, theatre, dance and the visual arts attracts the finest international performers to Edinburgh each year.

EDINBURGH JUNIOR CHAMBER OF COMMERCE, 3 Randolph Crescent, Edinburgh; T.-031-225 5851.
Founded: 1946.
President: Dick Allan; Senior Vice President: Jim Clark; Junior Vice President: Eddie Lafferty; Secretary: Valerie Gordon; Treasurer: Roland Boyd.
Leadership and training organisation open to people under 40 who are engaged in an executive or professional capacity in, or associated with, commerce or industry in the Edinburgh area and the south east of Scotland. Affiliated to the Edinburgh Chamber of Commerce and Manufactures and to Junior Chamber Scotland.

EDINBURGH MATHEMATICAL SOCIETY, (EMS), Department of Mathematics, University of Edinburgh, The King's Buildings, Edinburgh EH9 3JZ; T.-031-667 1081.
Founded: 1883.
President: Dr P. Heywood; Vice-president: Dr R.M.F. Moss; Secretaries: Dr J. Martin, Mr C.J. Shaddock; Treasurer: Dr A.C. McBride; Editor of Proceedings: Dr C.M. Campbell.
Founded for 'the mutual improvement of its members in the Mathematical Sciences, pure and applied'. Three main activities: meetings, publication of proceedings, and a four-yearly colloquium held in St Andrews. Eight meetings held each session, half in Edinburgh University and the remainder in other Scottish universities. One volume of the proceedings is published each year in three parts, appearing in February, June and October, and containing research articles and book reviews.

THE EDINBURGH MILITARY TATTOO, 22 Market Street, Edinburgh EH1 1QB; T.-031-225 1188.
Founded: 1950.
Producer: Lt Col L.P.G. Dow, OBE; Business Manager: Major B.A.S. Leishman.
Presented jointly by the City of Edinburgh District Council and Army HQ Scotland.

Annual event held during the Edinburgh International Festival on the Castle esplanade. Attended by over 200,000 people each year, from all parts of the world. Programme includes music of the massed pipes and drums of the Scottish regiments. The participation of foreign units does much to contribute to the international flavour, and around 30% of the spectators come from overseas.

EDINBURGH NEW TOWN CONSERVATION COMMITTEE, (ENTCC), 13A Dundas Street, Edinburgh EH3 6QG; T.-031-556 7054.

Founded: 1970.
Chairman: Sir Alan Hume, CB; Vice-chairman: Patrick Simpson; Director: Desmond Hodges, OBE; Assistant Director: James Clark; Finance Officer: Mary Storrar.
Offers encouragement, technical advice and grant assistance to proprietors undertaking external repairs to listed buildings in Edinburgh's new town conservation area. Grants of £4.5 million have been recommended since 1972 towards conservation contracts valued at over £6 million. The committee operates a salvage scheme for building materials and fittings to be reused throughout the city and has produced a maintenance manual, *The Care and Conservation of Georgian Houses*. Also offers a series of walks through Georgian Edinburgh each summer.

EDINBURGH OLD TOWN TRUST, c/o Arthur Young, 7 Abercromby Place, Edinburgh EH2; T.-031-556 8641.

Director: Muir Morrison.
Local enterprise trust.

EDINBURGH SPIRITUALIST SOCIETY, 34 Albany Street, Edinburgh EH1 3QH; T.-031-556 1749.

Secretary: Mrs K. Conroy.
Promotes the philosophy of spiritualism.

EDINBURGH, UNIVERSITY OF, Old College, South Bridge, Edinburgh EH8 9YL; T.-031-667 1011.

Founded: 1583.
Chancellor: Prince Philip, Duke of Edinburgh, KG, KT, PC, OM, GBE; Principal and Vice-chancellor: J.H. Burnett; Rector: A. MacPherson; Vice-principals: Prof W. Cochran, Prof C.P. Brand; Dean of the Faculty of Arts: Prof R.E. Asher; Dean of the Faculty of Divinity: Rev Prof J.P. Mackey; Dean of the Faculty of Law: Prof D.N. Mac-Cormick; Dean of the Faculty of Medicine: Prof R.E. Kendell; Dean of the Faculty of Music: Prof M. Tilmouth; Dean of the Faculty of Science: Prof E.A.V. Ebsworth; Dean of the Faculty of Social Sciences: Prof Michael Anderson; Dean of the Faculty of Veterinary Medicine: Prof A. Iggo; Secretary to the University: A.M. Currie, OBE.
The University of Edinburgh was originally the College of Edinburgh or The Tounis College, founded in 1583 by the Town Council of Edinburgh, under general powers granted by the Charter of King James VI. From the first, the College possessed the privilege of conferring degrees. Gradually, in succeeding Acts, the College came to be styled the University; but it remained under the control and patronage of the Town Council until 1858 when, by the Universities Act, all the universities of Scotland received new and autonomous constitutions. Today, the university confers degrees in eight faculties: Arts, Divinity, Law, Medicine (including Dentistry), Music, Science, Social Sciences, Veterinary Medicine. It is one of the largest unitary, non-collegiate universities in Britain, offering not only every principal subject taught in any British university, but also an unmatched range of undergraduate and postgraduate courses. There are 8,628 full-time undergraduate and 1,402 postgraduate students, including students from some 90 countries around the world.

EDINBURGH, UNIVERSITY OF, DEPARTMENT OF EXTRA-MURAL STUDIES, 11 Buccleuch Place, Edinburgh EH8 9JT; T.-031-667 1011.

Director: Mr B.C. Skinner; Administrator: Miss B.M. Stevens.
Provides on average 300 educational opportunities for adults each year with an enrolment of about 10,000 annually. It provides weekly courses, both day and evening, throughout three terms; weekend schools and conferences; special courses; certificate courses; summer schools and study tours. Enrolment is open to anyone over 18 and there are no entrance qualifications. Full prospectuses are available.

EDINBURGH VENTURE ENTERPRISE TRUST, (EVENT), Hanover Buildings, Rose Street, Edinburgh EH2 2YQ; T.-031-226 5783.

Founded: 1983.
Chairman: J.M.B. Macmillan; Vice Chairman: C.A. Fraser; Director: P.J. Duke; Assistant Director: J.F. Jacobs.

Enterprise trust offering specialist financial and business advice to companies requiring assistance or individuals setting up in business. Free service sponsored by local companies.

EDINBURGH VOLUNTEER EXCHANGE, (EVE), 48 Dalry Road, Edinburgh EH11 2BA; T.-031-346 0540.

Founded: 1975.
Joint Organisers: Maggie MacLeod, Nan McKenna, Mary Weir.
Objectives are: to provide an information, advice and placement service for both potential volunteers and agencies working with volunteers, to promote good practice in working with volunteers and to encourage people to consider their own needs and the needs of their community when looking for suitable voluntary work. Operates a 'job shop' to allow user agencies to contact the public. Gives information on on-going and one-off voluntary opportunities in Edinburgh.

EDINBURGH WALK-IN NUMERACY CENTRE, (EWINC), 67 Bread Street, Edinburgh EH3 9AH; T.-031-229 0382.

Founded: 1982.
Chairman of the Directors: Dr Ralph Jordinson; Company Secretary: Simon Bracher; Centre Manager: Mrs Rosalind Richardson.
Offers free and informal tuition in any area of numeracy, from basic number recognition to calculus, if required. Increased funding has allowed micro-computing to be included in the programme. Funded by Manpower Services Commission, the centre is a community programme. Employs 33 paid staff who provide support for the volunteer tutors and students. Some staff work in community centres in the Edinburgh area.

EDUCATIONAL BROADCASTING COUNCIL FOR SCOTLAND, (EBCS), BBC, Broadcasting House, 5 Queen Street, Edinburgh EH2 1JF; T.-031-225 3131.

Chairman: Gordon Kirk; Secretary/Senior Education Officer: Ms Jacqueline Johnston; Education Officers: Donald Gunn, John Russell.
Advises the BBC on the provision of appropriate educational broadcasts to Scotland, conducts research, issues publications and generally acts as the official link between the educational world and the BBC.

THE EDUCATIONAL INSTITUTE OF SCOTLAND, (EIS), 46 Moray Place, Edinburgh EH3 6BH; T.-031-225 6244.

Founded: 1847.
President: Kathleen Finn; General Secretary: John D. Pollock; Depute General Secretary: Robert Beattie; Organising Secretary: Frederick L. Forrester; Further and Higher Education Secretary: Jack Dale.
Founded for the purpose of 'increasing the efficiency of teachers, improving their conditions and raising the standard of education in general'. Generally concerned with the promotion of sound learning and the interests and welfare of teachers. Recognised as a trade union. Has 43,500 members in all sectors of education.

THE ELECTRICAL CONTRACTORS' ASSOCIATION OF SCOTLAND, 23 Heriot Row, Edinburgh EH3 6EW; T.-031-225 7221.

Founded: 1900.
President: Douglas Kelly; Vice-president: Patrick Feeney; Immediate Past President: Robert Taylor; Director and Secretary: Daniel D.W. Montgomery.
Represents almost 600 electrical contracting firms employing 14,000 people. Main services for members cover industrial relations, apprenticeship matters, training courses, technical and contractual matters, marketing and general management services. In conjunction with the EETPU, it regulates wages and conditions for the industry through the Scottish Joint Industry Board. Employs 22 staff at its Edinburgh headquarters.

ELECTRICITY CONSULTATIVE COUNCIL FOR THE NORTH OF SCOTLAND DISTRICT, 24 Marshall Place, Perth PH2 8AG; T.-0738 36669.

Founded: 1947.
Chairman: Mrs C.A.M. Davis; Deputy Chairman: Mr J. Kelly; Secretary: Mr D.D. McDonald.
Established to protect the interests of electricity consumers in the North of Scotland Hydro-Electric Board's area. Deals with matters associated with the generation and supply of electricity including tariffs, appliance sales and servicing etc. Local committees have been established to ensure that local views and circumstances are fully represented.

ELMWOOD AGRICULTURAL AND TECHNICAL COLLEGE, Carslogie

Road, Cupar, Fife KY15 4JB; T.-0334 52781.
Founded: 1953.
Principal: W.A. Wilson; Depute Principal: W.S.F. Fyfe; Registrar: K.M. Ovenstone.
Responsible for a wide range of full-time, day release and evening classes. Some of the agricultural, horticultural and engineering courses are unique to the college.

ENGLISH-SPEAKING   UNION, (E-SU), 22 Atholl Crescent, Edinburgh EH3 8HQ; T.-031-229 1528.
Founded: 1954.
Chairman, Scottish National Committee: Robert C. Cumming; Vice-chairmen, Scottish National Committee: James Miller, Martin Sinclair; Director: Brian Gorman; Assistant Director: Judith Fleming.
Voluntary, non-political organisation concerned with promoting greater friendship and understanding between the peoples of the Commonwealth and the USA. Operates a programme of exchanges, scholarships, and awards and organises fund-raising events through the membership.

EPILEPSY ASSOCIATION OF SCOTLAND, (EAS), 48 Govan Road, Glasgow G51 1JL; T.-041-427 4911.
Chairman: John G. Craig, TD; Chief Executive Officer: James Caddie; Development Officer: Mrs Vivien Cairnie; Appeals and Publicity Officer: Mrs Ann Furst.
Registered charity promoting the welfare of people with epilepsy. Offers advice and information to families and individuals. Provides training on epilepsy to professional personnel and develops self-help groups for individuals and their families throughout Scotland. Organises clubs, holiday camps and in Glasgow runs the Seaborn Centre and Seaborn Workshop. Sponsors research into epilepsy and aims to inform and educate the entire population about epilepsy. Has offices in Glasgow and Edinburgh.

THE EPISCOPAL THEOLOGICAL COLLEGE, EDINBURGH, Rosebery Crescent, Edinburgh EH12 5JT; T.-031-337 3838.
Founded: 1810.
Principal: Rev Canon John Armson; Vice-principal: Rev Geoffrey Payne; Tutor: Dr Philip West; Chaplain: Rev Dr Gregor Duncan; Bursar: John Mottram.
Training college of the Scottish Episcopal Church. Normally admits students (men and women) who have been sponsored for training for ministry by a bishop of the Anglican communion. Students may concurrently read for a divinity degree at Edinburgh University, or study internally for church examinations. Studies are pursued in the context of a community life, which includes daily worship together with pastoral links with local concerns.

EQUAL OPPORTUNITIES COMMISSION, (EOC), 249 West George Street, Glasgow G2; T.-041-226 4591.
Founded: 1975.
Scottish Officer: Ronald Miller; Executive Officer: Jane MacKenzie.
Provides a confidential advice service on all matters relating to sex discrimination and equal pay. This service is available to individuals, employers, and trade unions and is free of charge.

ERSKINE HOSPITAL. See Princess Louise Scottish Hospital.

ESK VALLEY COLLEGE, Newbattle Road, Dalkeith EH22 3AE; T.-031-663 1951.
Principal: John Lisgo; Registrar: J.B. Nimmo.
College of further education.

ETTRICK   AND   LAUDERDALE DISTRICT COUNCIL, PO Box 4, Council Chambers, Paton Street, Galashiels TD1 3AS; T.-Galashiels 4751.
Founded: 1974.
Provost: Andrew L. Tulley, JP; Chief Executive and Director of Administration: Charles M. Anderson; Director of Environmental Services: Michael Halls; Director of Finance: Duncan M. Brown; Director of Housing: James M. Blacklaws.
Political composition of council: Independent 8, Non-party 5, Conservative 1, Labour 1, SNP 1. Population of district: 33,296.

EVENING EXPRESS, Lang Stracht, Mastrick,   Aberdeen   AB9   8AF; T.-0224 690222.
Founded: 1879.
Editor: Richard Williamson.
Evening newspaper circulating in Aberdeen and surrounding district.

EVENING NEWS, 20 North Bridge, Edinburgh EH1 1YT; T.-031-225 2468.
Founded: 1873.
Editor: Ian A. Nimmo.
Evening newspaper circulating in Edinburgh and the East of Scotland.

EVENING TELEGRAPH & POST, 9 Bank Street, Dundee DD1 9HU; T.-0382 23131.
Founded: 1905.
Evening newspaper circulating in Dundee and surrounding district.

EVENING TIMES, 195 Albion Street, Glasgow G1 1QP; T.-041-552 6255.
Founded: 1876.
Editor: George McKechnie.
Evening newspaper circulating in Glasgow and the West of Scotland.

F

FACULTY OF ACTUARIES IN SCOTLAND, 23 St Andrew Square, Edinburgh EH2 1AQ; T.-031-557 1575.
Founded: 1856.
President: J.M. Macharg; Vice Presidents: J.R. Gray, D.W. Williams, W. Proudfoot, W.M. Morrison; Honorary Treasurer: A. Neill; Honorary Secretaries: E.S. Robertson, J.M. Souness; Secretary: W.W. Mair.
Professional body of actuaries in Scotland, but containing a substantial number of members practising in England and overseas. Concerned with the maintenance of professional standards in life assurance and pensions and with the education and training of actuarial students, with the promotion of research on actuarial matters and the furtherance of public knowledge of the actuarial profession.

THE FACULTY OF ADVOCATES, Advocates' Library, Parliament House, Edinburgh.
Founded: c.1532.
Dean: J.A.D. Hope, QC; Vice-dean: J.A. Cameron, QC; Treasurer: A.C.M. Johnston, QC; Clerk: P.B. Cullen; Keeper of the Advocates' Library: J.T. Cameron, QC.
Professional body to which all those practising before the supreme courts of Scotland and holding the office of advocate must belong. Responsible for the qualification, training, and discipline of advocates, and provides services for them, including a copyright law library. The exact date of the establishment of the faculty is unknown, but advocates were known to exist before 1532.

FALKIRK COLLEGE OF TECHNOLOGY, Grangemouth Road, Falkirk FK9 2AD; T.-0324 24981.

Founded: 1962.
Principal: W.L.E. Henderson; Depute Principal: R. McF. Wales; Assistant Principal: Dr J.M. Sharp.
A major establishment of further and higher education in central Scotland. Courses range from training courses for industrial workers to higher diploma, degree equivalent and final professional courses. Specialist facilities include a unique industrial chemistry installation and a working foundry.

FALKIRK DISTRICT COUNCIL, Municipal Buildings, Falkirk FK1 5RS; T.-Falkirk 24911.
Founded: 1974.
Provost: John Docherty, OStJ, JP; Chief Executive Officer and Director of Administration and Legal Services Department: J.P.H. Paton; Director of Finance: W. Weir; Director of Planning: W.F. Frame; Director of Architectural Services: G.M. Robb; Director of Housing: P. Craig; Director of Environmental Health: M. MacDonald; Director of Amenity and Recreation: D.J.G. Mould; Director of Libraries and Museums: A.H. Howson; Director of Direct Works: P.B. Young.
Political composition of council: Labour 24, SNP 7, Conservative 2, Independent 2. Population of district: 143,798.

FALKIRK ENTERPRISE ACTION TRUST, (FEAT), Suite A, Haypark, Marchmont Avenue, Polmont FK2 0NZ; T.-0324 716173.
Founded: 1983.
Director: John M. Jackson; Assistant Director: Peter White; Secretary: Herbert B. Johnson.
A private sector initiative supported by public and private funds. Basic objectives are the stimulation of economic activity in the Falkirk district through practical and expert assistance in the creation of new business and the preservation and expansion of existing business organisations. This is achieved by offering a free and confidential counselling service, promotion of suitable training courses, exhibitions, seminars, managing an office complex and, eventually, managed workshops. Clients are assisted in the preparation of business plans, finding premises and funds, and are guided through the regulations, including taxation, which they face.

FIFE HEALTH BOARD, (FHB), Glenrothes House, North Street,

Glenrothes KY7 5PB; T.-0592 754355.
Founded: 1974.
Chairman: John C. Balfour, OBE; General Manager: Mr J. Leigh; Chief Administrative Medical Officer: Dr R. Gardiner; Chief Area Nursing Officer: Mrs S. McDade; Secretary: Mr I.G. Dorward; Treasurer: Mr M. Murray. Consists of 21 members. Responsible for the provision of health care services in Fife Region, an area with a population of around 344,019. Controls 17 hospitals, 10 day hospitals/centres, 19 health centres, 45 clinics and is responsible for an annual budget of £100 million. Employs a total staff of 7,500.

FIFE REGIONAL COUNCIL, Fife House, North Street, Glenrothes KY7 5LT; T.-Glenrothes 754411.
Founded: 1974.
Convener: Mr R. Gough; Chief Executive: Dr John Markland; Director of Administration: Mr W. Breslin; Director of Finance: Mr D.T. Mitchell; Director of Architectural Services: Mr J.D.T. Cowling; Chief Constable: Mr W.McD. Moodie; Director of Economic Development and Planning: Mr W.G. Taylor; Director of Education: Mr M. More; Director of Engineering: Mr J.T. Rowson; Firemaster: Mr J. Thomson; Director of Information Processing Services: Mr I.B. Ramage; Director of Manpower Services: Mr W. Muir; Director of Social Work: Mr A.J. Bowman; Director of Supplies: Mr J.J. McHugh; Director of Trading Standards and Consumer Protection: Mr E. Abrahams; Director of Works: Mr J.T. Thomson.
Political composition of council: Labour 30; SDP/Liberal Alliance 8; Conservative 4; SNP 2, Communist 1, Independent 1. Population of region: 344,019.

FINLAY PLC, JAMES. See James Finlay PLC.

FJC LILLEY plc, 331 Charles Street, Glasgow G21 2QX; T.-041-552 6565.
Founded: 1954.
Chairman: C. White; Group Managing Director: D.C. Neill; Assistant Managing Director: D.E. Beardsmore; Group Financial Director: S.G. Robson; Main Board Director and Managing Director of MOW (Holdings) Ltd: J.C.K. Murray.
Holding company for a group of companies engaged in building and civil engineering construction and ancillary activities. With headquarters in Glasgow, Lilley undertakes projects in the United Kingdom, Africa, Middle and Far East and in America where it owns subsidiary companies. Employs 6,500

and has an annual turnover of around £350 million.

FOOD INTOLERANCE NUTRIENT DEFICIENCY, (FIND), 59 Barrington Drive, Glasgow G4 9ES; T.-041-339 3705.
Chairperson: A. Good; Secretary: Mrs Jessie Campbell.
Exists to further the study of the causes of food intolerance and its relation to disease, and research into the effects of vitamins and trace elements in physical and psychiatric illness.

THE FORESTRY COMMISSION, (FC), 231 Corstorphine Road, Edinburgh EH12 7AT; T.-031-334 0303.
Founded: 1919.
Chairman: Sir David Montgomery; Deputy Chairman and Director General: George Holmes; Secretary: Peter Clarke.
Has the legal status of, and functions as, a Government department. Reports directly to forestry ministers, to whom it is responsible for advice on forestry policy and for the implementation of that policy in Great Britain. Differs from the usual Government departments of state in that there is a statutorily appointed chairman and board of commissioners (four full-time and seven part-time). As the forestry authority, the commission is also responsible for several regulatory functions in connection with plant health, felling licences, forest research and administering grants for private woodlands. As the forestry enterprise, the commission has a primary responsibility to provide timber.

FORTH PORTS AUTHORITY, Tower Place, Leith, Edinburgh EH6 7DB; T.-031-554 4343.
Founded: 1968.
Chairman: W.A.C. Thomson; Vice Chairman: F.M. Cook; Managing Director: H.M. Thompson; Director (Engineering and Marine): P.C. Clutterbuck; Finance Director: W.W. Murray; Secretary: G. Renwick; Personnel Manager: A.C. Morrison; Chief Harbourmaster: Captain A.R.C. Childs; Port Manager, Grangemouth and Fife Ports: J.R. Grant; Port Manager, Leith: T.S. Skinner.
Statutory port authority responsible for the operation and management of the ports of Burntisland, Grangemouth, Granton, Kirkcaldy, Leith, Methil and the River Forth. Activities also include stevedoring, warehousing, estate management, shiptowage, and shipping agency. The authority

is the largest multi-purpose port authority in Scotland, with a cargo throughput in 1985 of 29,010,000 tonnes. Turnover for 1985 was £25.939 million. The authority and its wholly owned subsidiaries employ 970 people.

FORTH RIVER PURIFICATION BOARD, Colinton Dell House, West Mill Road, Colinton, Edinburgh; T.-031-441 4691.
Founded: 1975.
Director: W. Halcrow.
Promotes the cleanliness of the River Forth and tributaries, and the Forth estuary, under Part II of the Control of Pollution Act 1974.

FORTH VALLEY HEALTH BOARD, 33 Spittal Street, Stirling FK8 1DX; T.-0786 63031.
Founded: 1974.
Chairman: Mr L.J.M. Hynd; General Manager: Mr A.R. Robertson; Acting Secretary: Mr C.C. Denton; Treasurer: Mr D.F. Hird; Chief Administrative Medical Officer: Dr J.L. Graham; Chief Area Nursing Officer: Mr J.G. Sutherland.
Responsible for the provision of all health services within Central Region, an area with a population of approximately 272,400. Has 6,600 employees. The area is divided into four units with offices in Stirling, Falkirk and Larbert. Manages a total of 13 hospitals, with 3,500 beds, and 13 health centres.

FORTH VALLEY TOURIST BOARD, Burgh Halls, The Cross, Linlithgow, West Lothian EH49 7AH; T.-0506 843306.
Founded: 1983.
Tourist Officer: Alison Connell; Assistant Tourist Officer: Helen Cheyne.
Covers the districts of Dunfermline, Falkirk and West Lothian.

FORT WILLIAM AND LOCHABER TOURIST BOARD, Travel Centre, Fort William, Inverness-shire; T.-0397 3781.
Founded: 1969.
Chairman: I. Milton; Area Tourist Officer and Secretary: B.L. Simpson; Assistant Tourist Officer: Mrs E.W.B. Howie.
Exists for the promotion of tourism in the area.

FRASER OF ALLANDER INSTITUTE, (FAI), University of Strathclyde, Curran Building, 100 Cathedral Street, Glasgow G1 1XQ;
T.-041-552 4400.
Founded: 1975.
Director: Prof J.W. McGilvray; Research Director: Dr I.H. McNicoll; Senior Research Fellows: Dr F.J. Harrigan, Dr B. Ashcroft.
Carries out applied research on the Scottish economy. Gives impartial comment on Scottish economic affairs. Has 15 research and support staff and is funded by Strathclyde University, grants, contracts and sponsorships. Produces *Economic Commentary* and *Scottish Business Survey* (quarterly) and provides a business forecasting service twice yearly.

FRASERBURGH LTD, Dover Lodge, 117 Charlotte Street, Fraserburgh; T.-0346 27764.
Managing Director: Ron Taylor.
Local enterprise trust.

FREE CHURCH OF SCOTLAND, The Mound, Edinburgh EH1 2LS; T.-031-226 5286.
Founded: 1843.
General Treasurer: Iain D. Gill; Moderator-Designate, 1987: Rev Fergus A.J. Macdonald; Clerk of Assembly: Rev Principal C. Graham; Assistant Clerk of Assembly: Rev A.P.W. Fraser.
A Christian Church professing the doctrines of the Westminster Confession of Faith. It is organised in some 170 local churches throughout Scotland for pastoral care and evangelical outreach, operates two eventide homes, supports Christian missions overseas in India, South Africa and Peru, and co-operates with the Christian Witness to Israel in the evangelisation of Jewish people.

FREE PRESBYTERIAN CHURCH OF SCOTLAND, 13 Kingsborough Gardens, Glasgow G12 9NH; T.-041-339 0553.
Founded: 1893.
Clerk of Synod: Rev Donald MacLean; Moderator of Synod: Rev D.B. MacLeod; Church General Treasurer: W.D. Fraser.
Presbyterian church in historic, doctrinal and governmental descent from the Reformed Church of Scotland. Subordinate standard is the Westminster Confession of Faith. Foreign mission in Zimbabwe and congregations in Canada, Australia and New Zealand.

FRESHWATER FISHERIES LABORATORY, Faskally, Pitlochry,

Perthshire PH16 5LB; T.-0796 2060.
Founded: 1948.
Officer in Charge: Dr R.G.J. Shelton.
Responsible to the Director of Fisheries Research for Scotland for advice to the Secretary of State on all aspects of Scottish fisheries for salmonid and other migratory or freshwater fishes. Outstations are maintained at Montrose, Almondbank (near Perth), Abergeldie (near Ballater) and Peninver (near Campbeltown).

FRIENDS OF THE EARTH (SCOTLAND), 53 George IV Bridge, Edinburgh EH1 1EJ; T.-031-225 6906.
Founded: 1979.
Joint Co-ordinators: Xanthe Jay, Andrew Kerr.
Campaigns for the rational use of the earth's resources.

G

GALLOWAY CATTLE SOCIETY OF GREAT BRITAIN AND IRELAND, 131 King Street, Castle Douglas, Kirkcudbrightshire   DG7   1LZ; T.-Castle Douglas 2753.
Founded: 1877.
Chairman: F. Hunter Blair; Breed Secretary: Mr C.R. Graves.
Promotes the Galloway cattle breed, services members and manages the Galloway herd book.

GARNOCK VALLEY DEVELOPMENT EXECUTIVE, 44 Main Street, Kilbirnie KA25 7BY; T.-0505 685455.
Founded: 1984.
Chairman: Tom Dickie; Managing Director: Bill Dunn; Project Co-ordinator: Iain Parkin; Training Manager: Jim McIvor.
Supports existing businesses in the area, aims to attract new business, encourage local initiatives and any other measures to improve the performance of the local economy.

GAS CONSUMERS' COUNCIL, 86 George Street, Edinburgh EH2 3BU; T.-031-226 6523.
Founded: 1986.
Councillor for Scotland: Col W.A. Dalziel, CBE, TD, JP; Manager - Scotland: Mr E.M. Robson.
Body representing the interests of gas consumers (and potential consumers) in Scotland.

GENERAL ACCIDENT FIRE & LIFE ASSURANCE CORPORATION plc, (GAFLAC), Pitheavlis, Perth PH2 0NH; T.-0738 21202.
Founded: 1885.
Chairman: G.R. Simpson; Deputy Chairmen: The Rt Hon The Earl of Airlie, D.A. Blaikie; Chief General Manager: B.C. Marshall.
One of Britain's largest insurance organisations with almost 65% of its total premium income derived from sources outside the United Kingdom. Formed in Perth, it is now represented in around 45 countries and employs some 17,000 people worldwide. Involved in all forms of life and non-life assurance, including marine and aviation. Employs 8,700 in the United Kingdom, 2,000 of these in Scotland. With a stock market capitalisation of around £1,600 million (subject to fluctuation) it is the third largest composite insurance company in the United Kingdom and Scotland's third largest company.

GENERAL REGISTER OFFICE FOR SCOTLAND, (GRO(S)), New Register House, Edinburgh EH1 3YT; T.-031-556 3952.
Founded: 1855.
Registrar General for Scotland: Dr C.M. Glennie; Deputy Registrar for Scotland: J.N. Randall; Principals: G.F. Baird (Census), I.G. Bowie (Computer Services), A.M. Titterington (Registration); Statisticians: D.A. Orr (Population), D. Salmond (Vital Events).
Supervises the local registration of births, marriages and deaths and publishes statistics of vital events and of population estimates. Also responsible for carrying out the census in Scotland and for maintaining the National Health Service Central Register for Scotland.

THE GENERAL TEACHING COUNCIL FOR SCOTLAND, (GTC), 5 Royal Terrace, Edinburgh EH7 5AF; T.-031-556 0072.
Founded: 1966.
Chairman: John Anderson; Vice Chairman: Rose A. Galt; Registrar: David I.M. Sutherland.
Functions are: to keep under review standards of education, training and fitness to teach appropriate to people entering the teaching profession; to consider and make recommendations to the Secretary of State on matters, other than remuneration and conditions of service, relating to the supply

of teachers; to establish and keep a register of teachers and to determine whether in any particular case under its disciplinary powers registration is to be withdrawn or refused.

THE GEOLOGICAL SOCIETY OF GLASGOW, c/o Department of Applied Geology, University of Strathclyde, Glasgow G1 1XJ; T.-041-552 4400, Ext. 2470.

Founded: 1850.
President: Dr J. Lawson; Honorary Secretary: Dr B.R. Bell; Vice Presidents: Dr M.C. Keen, Dr W.E. Tremlett; Membership Secretary: Mrs A. Lawson; Treasurer: Miss D.M. Blake.
Promotes geology to amateurs and professionals in the West of Scotland. Holds lectures, undertakes field excursions and acts as a general forum for the subject. Membership is around 500 and members receive the *Scottish Journal of Geology* as part of their subscription.

THE GIRL GUIDES ASSOCIATION (SCOTLAND), 16 Coates Crescent, Edinburgh EH3 7AH; T.-031-226 4511.

Founded: 1910.
Chairman of the Council for Scotland: The Baroness Carnegy of Lour; Scottish Chief Commissioner: Mrs G.D.M. Reid; General Secretary: Miss A.K. James; Deputy General Secretary: Miss S.M. McCulloch.
Provides a programme embracing a wide range of leisure-time activities and interests. While these are enjoyable in themselves, they have an underlying educational purpose: to develop individual character based on the values expressed in the Promise and Law. There are over 88,600 members in Scotland, and guiding has spread to over 100 countries.

THE GIRLS' BRIGADE SCOTLAND, (GB), Boys' Brigade House, 168 Bath Street, Glasgow G2 4TQ; T.-041-332 1765.

Founded: 1893.
National President: Miss S. MacFarlane; National Vice Presidents: Miss M.C. Coutts, Miss J.T. Morrison; National Training Officer: Mrs S. Buchan; Brigade Secretary: Miss H.R. McLeod.
Christian organisation for girls between the ages of 5 and 17, offering a programme designed to enable growth in the spiritual, educational, physical and service spheres of the girls' lives. Aims to train girls for a Christian life in the home, church and community through a varied programme. It is an operating authority for the Duke of Edinburgh's Award Scheme. It has a forum composed of brigaders and young officers between 16 and 25 years old to discuss issues relevant to themselves and the future policy of the organisation. Total membership in Scotland: 18,000.

GLASGOW ASSOCIATION OF SPIRITUALISTS, 6-7 Somerset Place, Glasgow G3 7JT; T.-041-332 4626.

Founded: 1866.
President: Mr C.R. Morton; Vice Presidents: Mrs D. Mitchell, Mr A. Adie, Mr B. Hastie, Mrs F. Keenan.
Aims to propagate spiritualism. Membership: 300.

GLASGOW BOARD OF JEWISH EDUCATION, 28 Calderwood Road, Glasgow G43 2RU; T.-041-637 7409.

Founded: 1895.
Chairman: Henry Tankel; Vice Chairman: Dr Kenneth Collins; Joint Honorary Treasurers: Malcolm Livingstone, Jeffrey Gladstone; Joint Honorary Secretaries: Dr Gerald Gordon, Dr Walter Sneader.
An educational charity providing Jewish education at all levels to the Jewish community in Glasgow and the surrounding area.

GLASGOW BUDDHIST CENTRE, 329 Sauchiehall Street, Glasgow G2; T.-041-333 0524.

Founded: 1973.
Chairman and Secretary: Susiddhi; Mitra Convener: Dharmavira; Secretary of Co-operative: Amoghavajra.
The 11 ordained Buddhists who run the centre teach meditation and Buddhist studies, work in producer co-operatives, live in communities and generally try to express Buddhist attitudes and ideals in their lives. They also encourage other people to do the same.

GLASGOW CHAMBER OF COMMERCE, 30 George Square, Glasgow G2 1EQ; T.-041-204 2121.

Founded: 1783.
President: H.L.I. Runciman; Deputy President: David R. Campbell; Secretary: Ewan Marwick; Assistant Secretaries: Roderick Baird, Louise M. Donnelly, Robert MacKay.
Serves business interests throughout the West of Scotland, and has 2,600 firms in membership. Makes representations on matters of interest; provides an information

service; deals with export documentation and trade enquiries; publishes a monthly journal and a Scottish trade directory; runs trade missions.

GLASGOW COLLEGE OF BUILDING AND PRINTING, 60 North Hanover Street, Glasgow G1 2BP; T.-041-332 9969.
Founded: 1972.
Principal: David McEwan; Depute Principal: William Duthie; Assistant Principal: James Rice; Academic Registrar: John K. Graham; Industrial Liaison Officer: John E. Kerr; Registrar: Julie Blackburn.
Offers full-time degree or diploma courses for students preparing for careers in building, interior design and surveying, and part-time courses for students in technical, supervisory and administrative posts in the construction and allied industries and professions. Courses are also offered for those employed in printing and publishing, graphic design and photography and audio visual communications.

GLASGOW COLLEGE OF FOOD TECHNOLOGY, 230 Cathedral Street, Glasgow G1 2TG; T.-041-552 3751.
Founded: 1973.
Principal: Dr W.R. Bannatyne; Depute Principal: J. McCabe.
Provides a comprehensive range of full-time and part-time courses in catering, hotel mangement, tourism, and food technology up to higher diploma level. Courses in bakery and meat trades are also offered. Has 4,500 students.

GLASGOW COLLEGE OF NAUTICAL STUDIES, (GCNS), 21 Thistle Street, Glasgow G5 9XB; T.-041-429 3201.
Founded: 1968.
Principal: T. Ireland.
In addition to the courses required for training Merchant Navy personnel, the college offers a large range of courses which have no connection with the maritime world. These include advanced courses in engineering, electronics, industrial measurement and process control, and multidisciplinary engineering. There are also certificate courses in these and other subjects.

GLASGOW COLLEGE OF TECHNOLOGY, (GTC), 70 Cowcad-
dens Road, Glasgow G4 0BA; T.-041-332 7090; Telex: 779341.
Founded: 1971.
Director: Dr N.G. Meadows; Chairman: Mr M.J. Wotherspoon; Depute Director: Dr N.K. Buxton; Senior Assistant Director: Mr K.S. Reader; Assistant Directors: Dr P.W. Bush, Dr K.C. Clements-Jewery; College Secretary: Mr A.R. Irons.
The sixth largest institution of higher education in Scotland. Offers a wide range of vocational postgraduate, degree, Higher National Diploma and Certificate, and professional courses, both full-time and part-time, to some 7,000 students, 50% of whom follow the 16 degree or honours degree courses validated by the Council for National Academic Awards. A Scottish Central Institution, the college is a focus of research, consultancy and short training courses, and, separately and in collaboration with other organisations, meets demands at local, national and international level.

GLASGOW COUNCIL FOR VOLUNTARY SERVICE, (GCVS), 11 Queen's Crescent, Glasgow G4 9AS; T.-041-332 2444.
Founded: 1974.
Chairperson: Vicky Jack; Director: Colin Williams.
Encourages and supports the development of voluntary and community organisations, and initiatives within the voluntary sector. Practical help offered includes: advice, consultation and support to new and existing groups; a library with newspaper cutting and enquiry services; informal training events; support and advice on employment projects; payroll service and book-keeping advice for those organisations employing staff; secretarial, photocopying and duplicating services; a sports and arts project providing trained instructors.

GLASGOW DISTRICT COUNCIL, CITY OF, City Chambers, George Square, Glasgow G2 1DU; T.-041 221 9600.
Founded: 1974.
Lord Provost: Robert Gray, OStJ, JP; Leader of the Council: Patrick Lally; Town Clerk and Chief Executive: Steven F. Hamilton, JP; Director of Architecture and Related Services: William D. Worden; Director of Building and Works: Brian J. Gallagher; Director of Corporate Services: Robert S. Hoyle; Director of Operations: Frederick L. Harrison; Director of Building Control: Rob

McGowan; Director of Cleansing: John Dagg; Director of Computer Services: Derrick S. Norris; Director of Environmental Health: James Jackson; Director of Finance: William J. English; Director of Halls and Theatres: Thomas Malarkey; Director of Housing: Paul Mugnaioni; Director of Libraries: Andrew Miller; Director of Museums and Art Galleries: Alasdair A. Auld; Director of Parks and Recreation: Keith J. Fraser; Director of Personnel: James Weir; Director of Planning: James H. Rae.

Political composition of council: Labour 59, Conservative 5, Liberal/Alliance: 2. Population of district: 760,955.

GLASGOW HERALD, 195 Albion Street, Glasgow G1 1QP; T.-041-552 6255.

Founded: 1782.
Editor: Arnold Kemp.
Daily newspaper circulating throughout Scotland.

GLASGOW JEWISH REPRESENTATIVE COUNCIL, 49 Coplaw Street, Glasgow G42; T.-041-423 8917.

Founded: 1914.
President: Dr W. Sneader; Vice-president: Mrs J. Tankel; Treasurer: Mr H. Livingston; Secretary: Dr K. Collins.
Representative organisation of 50 affiliated Jewish organisations in Strathclyde, responsible for representing the Jewish community in public matters. Co-operates with other Jewish organisations in educational matters.

GLASGOW JEWISH WELFARE BOARD, 49 Coplaw Street, Glasgow G42 7JE; T.-041-423 8916.

Founded: 1866.
Joint Honorary Chairmen: Albert Tankel, Marcus I. Green; Joint Honorary Treasurers: Melville A. Robinson, Jeffrey Gladstone; Honorary Secretary: Trevor Schuster Davis.
Registered charity dedicated to the care of the elderly, the sick and the underprivileged of the Jewish faith. Financial support given as necessary. Social clubs for the lonely. Advice and help for the troubled.

GLASGOW JUNIOR CHAMBER OF COMMERCE, (GJCC), 30 George Square, Glasgow G2 1EQ; T.-041-204 2121.

Founded: 1937.
Chairman: D.B. Wilson; Vice Chairman: R.C.P. Whitson; Honorary Secretary: A.J.

Currie; Honorary Treasurer: W.I.M. Sommerville.
Voluntary leadership development organisation for young people between the ages of 18 and 40. Has an active membership of approximately 250 involved in a wide range of projects, many of which are of direct benefit to the community. Affiliated to Junior Chamber Scotland and Junior Chamber International. The oldest and the largest junior chamber in the United Kingdom.

GLASGOW MARRIAGE GUIDANCE COUNCIL, 27 Sandyford Place, Sauchiehall Street, Glasgow; T.-041-248 5249.

Founded: 1947.
Objective is to foster the success and stability of marriage as the foundation of family life and of the well-being of society by: providing a confidential counselling service for people with difficulties in marriage or other personal relationships; providing an educational service in relationships for young people, engaged and married couples, and parents; selecting and training men and women for this work; publishing and distributing literature on marriage and family life; co-operating with other agencies in related fields and assisting with, and providing courses and conferences for, ministers of religion, teachers, youth leaders and others.

GLASGOW MUSEUMS AND ART GALLERIES, Kelvingrove, Glasgow G3 8AG; T.-041-334 1134.

Director: Alasdair A. Auld.
Comprises the Museum and Art Gallery at Kelvingrove; the Burrell Collection (see separate entry); Museum of Transport, Kelvin Hall, Glasgow (reopening, Spring 1988) (Keeper: Alastair R. Smith); People's Palace Museum, Glasgow Green, Glasgow G40 1AT (Depute Keeper, Local History: Elspeth King); and other smaller museums.

GLASGOW OLD PEOPLE'S WELFARE ASSOCIATION, (GOPWA), 7 Sandyford Place, Glasgow G3 7NB; T.-041-221 9924/5.

Founded: 1948.
Chairman: D.M. Kerr; Vice-chairman: G.W.R. Carlisle; Honorary Treasurer: R.F. Lochhead; Director: J.W.W. Stevenson.
Formed to promote 'the general welfare of old people in the City of Glasgow'. Administers over 120 clubs and day centres, two residential homes, one sheltered housing conversion and a number of projects aimed

at giving older people support within the community. Approximately 12,000 members with over 1,000 volunteer helpers and staff.

GLASGOW OPPORTUNITIES, (GO), 7 West George Street, Glasgow G2 1EQ; T.-041-221 0955.
Founded: 1983.
Chairman: J.H.F. Macpherson; Director: G. Paterson.
An enterprise agency providing free, confidential business advice to people wishing to set up in business in Glasgow. Advice is also given to existing businesses wishing to expand.

GLASGOW SCHOOL OF ART, 167 Renfrew Street, Glasgow G3 6RQ; T.-041-332 9797.
Founded: 1840.
Director: Professor Anthony Jones.
A Scottish Central Institution which offers degree courses to virtually all its full-time students. One of the largest colleges of art in Britain.

GLASGOW, UNIVERSITY OF, Glasgow G12 8QQ.
Founded: 1451.
Chancellor: Sir Alexander K. Cairncross, KCMG; Rector: Michael Kelly, CBE, JP; Principal and Vice-chancellor: Sir Alwyn Williams; Dean of Faculties: Robert A. Rankin; Vice-principals: John S. Gillespie, Alfred L. Brown, Michael R. Bond; Dean of the Faculty of Arts: Prof P.G. Walsh; Dean of the Faculty of Social Sciences: Patrick J. O'Donnell; Dean of the Faculty of Divinity: Dr J. Houston; Dean of the Faculty of Engineering: Prof Bryan E. Richards; Dean of the Faculty of Law and Financial Studies: Mr J.P. Grant; Dean and Adviser of Studies, Faculty of Medicine: Prof Donald Campbell; Dean of the Faculty of Science: Prof M.B. Wilkins; Dean of the Faculty of Veterinary Medicine: Prof J.A. Armour; Secretary of the University Court: Robert Ewen, OBE, TD; Registrar: J. Michael Black.
The university was founded by a bull of Pope Nicholas V on the application of William Turnbull, Bishop of Glasgow. Its charter provided for studies in theology, canon and civil law, arts and any other lawful faculty. Today, the university has the following faculties: Arts; Social Sciences; Divinity; Engineering; Law and Financial Studies; Medicine; Science; Veterinary Medicine. The 'old college' was situated in the High Street for more than four centuries

before the university moved to its present site on Gilmorehill in 1870. There are 10,000 full-time and 1,800 part-time students attending.

GLASGOW, UNIVERSITY OF, DEPARTMENT OF ADULT AND CONTINUING EDUCATION, 57-61 Oakfield Avenue, Glasgow G12 8LW; T.-041-339 8855, Ext. 394.
Founded: 1961.
Director: Prof Lalage Bown.
Exists to provide opportunities for adults to share in the ideas and knowledge in which the university deals.

GLASGOW & WEST HOSPITAL BROADCASTING SERVICE, (HBS GLASGOW), 342 Argyle Street, Glasgow G2 8LY; T.-041-221 4043.
Founded: 1969.
Chairman: Eric W.M. Simpson; Treasurer: Ian Oliphant; Programme Organiser: Alex Boyd; Technical Director: Ian McDougal.
Provides a broad base of programming specifically for patients in hospital. The major programme is the nightly request programme. Studio facilities include two 'self-op' DJ studios, a continuity studio and a music production studio. Has been the starting point for many of Scotland's top radio personalities.

THE GLASGOW AND WEST OF SCOTLAND ASSOCIATION OF THE INSTITUTION OF CIVIL ENGINEERS, c/o Babtie Shaw and Morton, 95 Bothwell Street, Glasgow G2 7HX; T.-041-204 2511.
Founded: 1884.
Chairman: W.S. McAlonan; Senior Vice-chairman: J.M. Dunbar; Honorary Secretary: G.G.T. Masterton; Honorary Treasurer: G.B. MacLean; Representative on Council: W.J. Barr.
Object is to foster and promote in the West of Scotland the art and science of civil engineering. Achieves this by: arranging lectures at which papers are presented and discussed; arranging visits to works of engineering interest; holding social functions to encourage friendship among members; providing information for those with a general interest in civil engineering or who wish to pursue it as a career. There is a section for junior members as well as specialist groups for those with a particular interest in hydrology, traffic and transportation, geotechnics and municipal engineer-

ing. Membership: 3,200.

GLASGOW AND WEST OF SCOTLAND BLOOD TRANSFUSION SERVICE, 80 St Vincent Street, Glasgow G2 5UA; T.-041-226 4111.

Founded: 1939.
Regional Director: Dr Ruthven Mitchell; Regional Donor Organiser: Ian Armour, TD. A division of the Common Services Agency of the Scottish Home and Health Department. Responsible for the collection, processing, storage and distribution of blood throughout Glasgow and the West of Scotland. More than 3,500 voluntary donations a week are required to supply hospitals in the area.

GLASGOW AND WEST OF SCOTLAND SOCIETY FOR THE DEAF, 158 West Regent Street, Glasgow G2 4RJ; T.-041-221 0794/5.

Founded: 1822.
Principal Officer: Gordon M. Chapman.
Aims to provide religious and secular instruction for the adult deaf in Glasgow and surrounding districts and to raise their social status. Visits the deaf in their homes, especially the sick and those in distress. Gives pensions to the aged and infirm. Provides premises for religious services on Sunday and on other occasions where the deaf may meet socially and for recreation. Interpreter provided when necessary. Accommodation provided for aged and infirm deaf. Membership: 1,200.

GLENROTHES AND BUCKHAVEN TECHNICAL COLLEGE, Stenton Road, Glenrothes, Fife KY6 2RA; T.-0592 772233.

Founded: 1968.
Principal: Mr T.J. Burness; Depute Principal: Mrs J.S.R. Johnston; Assistant Principal: Mr I.S. Ovens.
College of further education with 4,557 students.

GLENROTHES DEVELOPMENT CORPORATION, (GDC), Balbirnie House, Glenrothes, Fife KY7 6NR; T.-0592 754343.

Founded: 1948.
Chairman: Sir George Sharp, OBE, JP; Chief Executive: Martin Cracknell; Director of Administration and Legal Services: A.A. Dow; Development Director: John A.F. McCombie; Marketing Manager: John MacDonald.

New Town development corporation aiming to attract industrial and commercial investment and achieve population growth to 55,000 (1986: approximately 40,000). Rent free factories for up to two years and wide range of financial incentives. Glenrothes, now Fife's regional capital, has recently moved into tourism, exploiting its flying facilities, historic sites, bird watching and golf (100 courses in and around the town) for package holidays.

GLENROTHES ENTERPRISE TRUST, North House, North Street, Glenrothes; T.-0592 757903.

Director: Erik J. Hendry.

GOETHE-INSTITUT GLASGOW SCOTTISH-GERMAN CENTRE, Lower Meadway Building, 74 Victoria Crescent Road, Glasgow G12 9SG; T.-041-334 6116.

Founded: 1957.
Director: Dr Georg Heuser; Head of Language Department: Drs Ernst R. Rinke; Financial Administrator: James Sheffield.
Promotes the study of the German language abroad and international cultural co-operation.

GORDON DISTRICT COUNCIL, Gordon House, Blackhall Road, Inverurie, Aberdeenshire; T.-Inverurie 20981.

Founded: 1974.
Chairman: J. Presly; Chief Executive: M.C. Barron; Chief Solicitor: A. Grant; Director of Finance: A.J. Wilson; Director of Emvironmental Health: A. McKinnon; Director of Housing: P. Donaldson; Director of Planning: E. Geraldine Scott; Director of Recreation and Technical Services: J. Bruce.
Political composition of council: Independent 7, Conservative 3, Liberal/SDP Alliance 1, Liberal 1. Population of district: 70,000.

GORDON DISTRICT TOURIST BOARD, St Nicholas House, Broad Street, Aberdeen AB9 1DE; T.-0224 632727.

Founded: 1983.
Director: Gordon E. Henry; Chairman: Robert Graham; Treasurer: Andrew Wilson.
Principal activities are the development and promotion of tourism in Gordon District, the production of tourism literature and the operation of four seasonal tourist information centres.

GORDON HIGHLANDERS, REGIMENTAL HEADQUARTERS, Viewfield Road, Aberdeen AB1 7XH; T.-0224 318174.
Regimental Secretary: Major I.D. Martineau.

GOVAN INITIATIVE, Unit 27, Harmony Row, Govan, Glasgow; T.-041-440 0404.
Director: Mr A. Forbes.
Local enterprise trust.

GRAMPIAN HEALTH BOARD, (GHB), 1-7 Albyn Place, Aberdeen AB9 1RE; T.-0224 589901.
Founded: 1974.
Chairman: Mr C.W. Ellis; General Manager: Mr H. Fullerton; Secretary: Dr H.R.M. Wilson; Treasurer: Mr A. Wingfield; Chief Administrative Medical Officer: Dr M. Murchison; Chief Area Nursing Officer: Miss W. MacPherson.
Responsible for the provision of National Health Service care within the Grampian area. The area headquarters controls six units covering acute, maternity and child health, geriatric, psychiatric, community services and the West unit which covers Morayshire. The board employs a staff of over 12,000 and provides services for a population which is rapidly approaching 500,000. The major hospitals and specialist services for the area are based at Foresterhill in Aberdeen.

GRAMPIAN REGIONAL COUNCIL, Woodhill House, Ashgrove Road West, Aberdeen AB9 2LU; T.-0224 682222.
Founded: 1974.
Convener: Dr Geoffrey Hadley; Deputy Convener: David Anderson, MBE, JP; Chief Executive: J.D. Macnaughton; Depute Chief Executive: J.C. Liddell; Director of Law and Administration: Alan G. Campbell; Director of Finance: T.E. Carter, OBE; Director of Education: James A.D. Michie; Director of Architectural Services: Walter S. Scott; Director of Social Work: Miss M.C. Hartnoll; Chief Constable: Alexander G. Lynn; Firemaster: A.N. Morrison; Director of Manpower Services: A.C. McDougall; Director of Consumer Protection: J. Girdwood; Director of Roads: George Kirkbride; Director of Physical Planning: T.F. Sprott; Director of Water Services: I.D. Brown; Director of Estates: W.W. Murray; Director of Lighting: E. Wilkie.
Political composition of council: Labour 17, Conservative 16, SDP/Liberal Alliance 13, SNP 8, Independent 3. Population of region: 500,566.

GRAMPIAN TELEVISION, Queen's Cross, Aberdeen AB9 2XJ; T.-0224 646464.
Founded: 1961.
Chairman: Sir Iain Tennant, KT; Deputy Chairman: Dr Calum A. MacLeod; Chief Executive: Alex Mair, MBE; Financial Director: Donald H. Waters; Director of Operations: Robert L. Christie; Marketing Director: Neil R. Welling.
Britain's most northerly independent television company, serving a population of 1.28 million viewers in an area which stretches from Fife to Shetland. Produces a wide range of programmes with the help of studios and mobile crews in Aberdeen, Dundee and Inverness. Advertisers are served by sales offices in London, Aberdeen, Dundee, Inverness and Edinburgh.

GRAMPIAN TRANSPORT MUSEUM, (GTM), Alford, Aberdeenshire AB3 8AD; T.-0336 2292.
Founded: 1983.
Chairman: Mr C. Engel; Treasurer: Mr R. Milne; Secretary: Mr R. Gordon; Vice-chairman: Mr A. Gill; Curator: Mr M. Ward.
Independent, self-financing museum with charitable status. Administered by a voluntary association. The collection is drawn from the north of Scotland and exhibitions reflect the history of road and rail transport in the region. The museum is open daily from 1 April to 30 September. Attracts 30,000 visitors each season. Weekends during the season feature a programme of outdoor special events.

GREATER EASTERHOUSE PARTNERSHIP, 21 Arnisdale Place, Glasgow G34 9BW; T.-041-771 5591.
Director: Jim Graham.
Local enterprise trust.

GREATER GLASGOW HEALTH BOARD, 225 Bath Street, Glasgow G2 4JT; T.-041-204 2755.
Founded: 1974.
Chairman: Donald F. Macquaker; Vice Chairman: Dr John MacKay, OBE; General Manager: L.E. Peterken; Treasurer: A.M. Paterson; Chief Administrative Medical Officer: Dr G.D. Forwell; Chief Area Nursing Officer: Miss M.W. Aitken; Chief Administrative Dental Officer: R. McKechnie; Chief Administrative Phar-

maceutical Officer: Miss E.A. Meikle, OBE. Provides health service in the Greater Glasgow area. Employs approximately 37,000 staff. Covers following categories of hospital: general, geriatric, psychiatric, infectious diseases, maternity, mental deficiency, chronic sick, gynaecology, orthopaedic, neurological sciences, plastic surgery, chest, long-stay convalescence, general (children).

GREATER GLASGOW TOURIST BOARD, 35-39 St Vincent Place, Glasgow G1 2ER; T.-041-227 4885.
Chief Executive: Edward Friel.

GREENOCK CHAMBER OF COMMERCE, 64-66 West Blackhall Street, Greenock PA15 1XG; T.-Greenock 24533.
Founded: 1813.
President: B.A. Patrick; Vice-president: R.F. Beveridge; Secretary: E.J. Black; Treasurers: Henderson & Co, 73 Union Street, Greenock PA16 8BG.

H

HAMILTON DISTRICT COUNCIL, Town House, 102 Cadzow Street, Hamilton; T.-Hamilton: 282323.
Founded: 1974.
Provost: Sam Casserly, JP; Chief Executive: Alister Baird; Director of Finance: Spence Gray; Director of Housing: Andrew Martin; Director of Leisure and Recreation: Alan Whitfield; Director of Planning and Development: Gordon Gilfillan.
Political composition of council: Labour 17, Liberal 2, Conservative 1. Population of district: 107,122.

HANNAH RESEARCH INSTITUTE, (HRI), Ayr KA6 5HL; T.-0292 76013.
Founded: 1928.
Director: Prof M. Peaker; Deputy Director: Dr W. Banks; Heads of Departments: Dr W.W. Christie (Biological Chemistry), Dr D.G. Dalgleish (Physical Chemistry), Dr P.C. Thomas (Animal Nutrition and Production), Dr R.G. Vernon (Lactational Physiology and Biochemistry).
One of 15 Agricultural and Food Research Service institutes in Great Britain. Financed by a grant from the Department of Agriculture and Fisheries for Scotland. The research areas are agreed with the depart-ment on the scientific advice of the Agricultural and Food Research Council. There are 150 permanent staff, 100 of whom are in science grades. Two departments are concerned with animal science and three (comprising the Dairy Foods Division) with food science. The institute farm is used entirely for research. Direct contact with the dairy industry is maintained through the Consultative Panel for Milk Utilization.

THE HARRIS TWEED ASSOCIATION LTD, (HTA), Ballantyne House, 84 Academy Street, Inverness IV1 1LU; T.-0463 231270.
Founded: 1909.
Chief Executive: Donald John Mackay; Chairman: Calum A. MacLeod.
Producing Harris tweed is the major industry of the Western Isles, employing some 1,200 people. The association certifies, promotes and stamps Harris Tweed and protects the orb trade mark internationally.

HEADTEACHERS' ASSOCIATION OF SCOTLAND, (HAS), Park Cottage, 21 Victoria Place, Airdrie ML6 9BU; T.-62780.
Founded: 1936.
President: Gordon Wilson; Secretary: Percy J. Quinn.
Exists to promote education, particularly secondary education, in Scotland, to safeguard and promote the interests of headteachers in Scottish secondary schools, and to secure for those headteachers a fitting share in the making and implementing of policies which affect secondary education.

THE HERALDRY SOCIETY OF SCOTLAND, Limegrove, High Street, Gifford, Haddington, East Lothian EH41 4QU; T.-062 081 617.
Founded: 1977.
Chairman: Charles J. Burnett, CStJ; Secretary: William R.M. Adams, OStJ; Treasurer: Dr Christopher D. Green; Editor: R. John Malden; Membership Secretary: Stuart G. Emerson.
Exists to encourage the practice and study of heraldry in Scotland. Each year, the society arranges a programme of lectures, visits to places of heraldic and historic interest and social events. The society has close contacts with European heraldry societies and those in the Americas, Canada, Australia and New Zealand. The society's annual journal contains a wide range of heraldic articles and notes. Mem-

bership: approximately 500 worldwide.

HERIOT-WATT UNIVERSITY, Chambers Street, Edinburgh EH1 1HX; T.-031-225 8432. Riccarton Campus, Edinburgh EH14 4AS; T.-031-449 5111.

Founded: 1966.
Chancellor: The Rt Hon The Lord Thomson of Monifieth, KT, PC; Principal and Vice-chancellor: Dr T.L. Johnston; Vice-principal: Prof J. Rorke, CBE; Dean of Faculty of Science: Prof Robin J. Knops; Dean of Faculty of Engineerng: Prof Colin W. Davidson; Dean of Faculty of Economics and Social Studies: Prof Anthony Keenan; Dean of Faculty of Environmental Studies: Dr William F. Carmichael; Dean of Faculty of Art and Design: Dr Colin J. Bailey; Director of Administration and Secretary of the University: Duncan I. Cameron; Registrar and Deputy Secretary: David Sturgeon.
Technological university which has developed and maintains close links with Scottish industry and commerce. It has 3,758 students (full- and part-time) in five faculties. The university is located partly in central Edinburgh and partly on a campus at Riccarton, on the western boundary of the city, which will eventually house most of the university's departments. At Riccarton, the Research Park includes a number of high technology research and development projects.

HER MAJESTY'S STATIONERY OFFICE, (HMSO), 113 Rose Street, Edinburgh EH2 3DS; T.-031-225 6707.

Founded: 1906 (Edinburgh), 1786 (London).
Director: Gavin Turner.
Best known as the British Government publisher but in addition to its own publications, it provides a printing service for a wide range of official bodies in the United Kingdom, either from its own presses or by buying from the printing trade. Its largest business is in office supplies, ranging from pens and paper to photocopiers, audio equipment and micro computers. Since 1980 it has been a self-financing Government trading fund with an annual turnover of about £300 million.

HIGH COURT OF JUSTICIARY, Parliament House, 2 Parliament Square, Edinburgh EH1 1RF; T.-031-225 2595.

Principal Clerk of Session and Justiciary: A.M. Campbell.
Supreme criminal court in Scotland. Tries cases on indictment in Edinburgh and on circuit throughout the country.

THE HIGHLAND CATTLE SOCIETY, Blackchub, Keir, Thornhill, Dumfriesshire DG3 4DH; T.-0848 30438.

Founded: 1884.
President: A.J.M. Gibson; Vice-president: A.R. MacKay; Secretary: A.H.G. Wilson.
Objects are: 'to maintain unimpaired the purity of the breed of Highland cattle and to promote the breed and their wider use for commercial purposes'; to establish and maintain the herd book in which pedigrees are registered. Membership: 525 worldwide.

HIGHLAND FUND LTD, 39 St. Vincent Crescent, Glasgow G3 8NG; T.-041-248 4144.

Founded: 1954.
Chairman: Calum Ferguson; Secretary: Donald MacDonald.
Private organisation whose funds are raised by donation. It assists every aspect of Highland life by providing working capital at low interest rates and often without security.

HIGHLAND GEOLOGICAL CLUB, (HGC), c/o The Secretary, Berriedale, Kirkhill, Inverness; T.-0463 83 249.

Founded: 1983.
Honorary President: Sinclair Ross; Chairman: Donald MacDonald; Secretary/Treasurer: Anne Reynolds.
A group of around 50 enthusiastic amateur geologists. Runs a series of summer field trips and winter lectures which set out to explore the geology of the Highlands.

HIGHLAND HEALTH BOARD, Reay House, 17 Old Edinburgh Road, Inverness IV2 3HG; T.-0463 239851.

Founded: 1974.
Chairman: Mr J. McWilliam; General Manager: Mr R.R.W. Stewart; Chief Administrative Medical Officer: Dr A.R. Morrison; Treasurer: Mr J.C. Gray, OBE; Chief Area Nursing Officer: Miss E.M. Hood; Chief Administrative Dental Officer: Mr J.I. Tullis; Chief Administrative Pharmaceutical Officer: Mr M.M. Smith.
Health board.

HIGHLAND PERTHSHIRE DEVELOPMENT CO LTD, 1st Floor, Bank House, 82 Atholl Road, Pitloc-

hry PH16 5BL; T.-0796 2697.
Chief Executive: Dr R.G. Taylor.
Local enterprise trust.

HIGHLAND REGIONAL COUNCIL, Regional Buildings, Glenurquhart Road, Inverness IV3 5NX; T.-0463 234121.
Founded: 1974.
Convener: Alexander J. Russell; Chief Executive: R.H. Stevenson; Assistant Chief Executive: G. Bonner; Director of Law and Administration/Depute Chief Executive: H. Farquhar; Director of Architectural Services: A.M. Fulton; Director of Consumer Protection: D.G. Thompson; Director of Development: P. Mackintosh; Director of Education: C.E. Stewart; Director of Finance: J.W. Bremner; Director of Libraries and Leisure Services: H.W. Wilkinson; Director of Manpower Services: P.R. Thompson; Director of Planning: R.W.G. Cameron; Director of Roads and Transport: G.K.M. Macfarlane; Director of Social Work: J. Dick; Director of Water and Sewerage: J.D. Addly; Chief Constable: H.C. MacMillan; Firemaster: D. Grant.
Political composition of council: Others 24, Independent 13, Labour 7, Liberal 3, SNP 3, Conservative 2. Population of region: 198,617.

HIGHLAND RIVER PURIFICATION BOARD, Strathpeffer Road, Dingwall IV15 9QY; T.-Dingwall 62021.
Founded: 1975.
Chairman: N.W. Graesser; Director and River Inspector: D. Buchanan; Clerk to the Board: D.W. Martin; Treasurer: A.G. Imlah. Controls pollution of the rivers and tidal waters and conserves water resources within the area.

HIGHLANDS AND ISLANDS DEVELOPMENT BOARD, (HIDB), Bridge House, Bank Street, Inverness IV1 1QR; T.-0463 234171.
Founded: 1965.
Chairman: Robert Cowan; Deputy Chairman: Ronald D. Cramond; Secretary: J.A. Macaskill.
Principal source of public support for new industrial and commercial developments in the Highlands and Islands. Its central function is to provide finance on advantageous terms to encourage business development. Types of business covered include manufacturing and processing industries, crafts, tourism, agriculture and horticulture, fisheries and some service activities. The board's area covers about half of Scotland and includes Shetland, Orkney, the Western Isles, Highland Region, the Argyll and Bute district of Strathclyde Region, and the islands of Arran and the Cumbraes. Financed by the Scottish Office, it consists of seven board members appointed by the Secretary of State for Scotland, has a staff of about 250 and a wide range of discretionary powers.

HILL FARMING ADVISORY COMMITTEE FOR SCOTLAND, c/o Department of Agriculture and Fisheries for Scotland, Chesser House, 500 Gorgie Road, Edinburgh EH11 3AW; T.-031-443 4020.
Founded: 1947.
Chairman: Mr D. Essery.
Advises the Secretary of State for Scotland on the exercise of his powers under the Hill Farming Act 1946 and on any other matter relating to hill farming that may be referred to the committee.

HILL FARMING RESEARCH ORGANISATION, Bush Estate, Penicuik, Midlothian EH26 0PY; T.-031-445 3401.
Founded: 1954.
Chairman, Board of Management: J.A. Parry; Director: J. Eadie; Deputy Director and Head of Plants and Soils Department: Dr P. Newbould; Head of Animal Production Department: Dr T.J. Maxwell; Head of Animal Nutrition Department: Dr J. Milne.
Independent state-aided institute funded by the Department of Agriculture and Fisheries for Scotland. Its present remit is to improve the economic viability of meat production from the hills and uplands of the United Kingdom.

HISTORIC BUILDINGS COUNCIL FOR SCOTLAND, (HBC), 20 Brandon Street, Edinburgh EH3 5RA; T.-Direct Line 031-244 2940; Switchboard 031-556 8400.
Founded: 1953.
Chairman: The Marquess of Bute; Secretary: Mr I.G. Dewar.
Set up to advise the Secretary of State for Scotland on the making of grants for the repair and restoration of buildings of outstanding historic or architectural interest. Since 1972, it has also advised on the making of grants towards the preservation or enhancement of conservation areas. All grants are discretionary and are decided on

the merits of individual buildings, the schemes of work proposed and the financial resources of applicants, and are subject to annual allocation of funds. Executive responsibility for grants, listing and other statutory functions of the Secretary of State rests with the Scottish Development Department (Historic Buildings and Monuments Directorate), whose officials serve the council.

HM INDUSTRIAL POLLUTION INSPECTORATE FOR SCOTLAND, 27 Perth Street, Edinburgh EH3 5RB; T.-031-556 8400.

Chief Inspector: I.W.W. Wright; Deputy Chief Inspector: J.A. Hetherington.
Pollution control services, regulatory and advisory; hazardous wastes; air pollution control, radioactive waste management and control of radioactive substances; offensive trades.

HM INSPECTORATE OF CONSTABULARY (SCOTLAND), Scottish Office, St Andrew's House, Edinburgh EH1 3DE; T.-031-556 8501.£Q

Founded: 1857.
Her Majesty's Chief Inspector of Constabulary: Alexander Morrison, CVO, QPM; Her Majesty's Inspector of Constabulary: Robert Sim, MBE, QPM.
Undertakes annual inspections of the Scottish police forces and reports on the efficiency of each to the Secretary of State. Monitors the level and types of demands made upon the Scottish police service and seeks to ensure that the deployment and use of resources is proper and effective. Also offers professional advice on policing matters to the Scottish Office and maintains a liaison with police authorities and with police staff associations.

HOUSE OF FRASER plc, 69 Buchanan Street, Glasgow G1 3LE; T.-041-221 6401.

Chairman: Mr A. Fayed; Chief Executive: Mr B.L. Walsh.
Departmental store group retailing through 100 outlets in the United Kingdom, Eire and Denmark.

THE HOUSING CORPORATION IN SCOTLAND, Rosebery House, 9 Haymarket Terrace, Edinburgh EH12 5YA; T.-031-337 0044.

Founded: 1964.
Chairman of Scottish Committee: John D. Richards, CBE; Chief Officer - Scotland: Raymond K. Young.
Promotes, funds and supervises housing associations. Has three Scottish offices: a head office responsible for policy and programme, and two regional offices responsible for the day-to-day relations with housing associations - one in Glasgow dealing with Strathclyde and the other in Edinburgh dealing with the rest of Scotland.

HOWDEN GROUP PLC, 195 Scotland Street, Glasgow G5 8PJ; T.-041-429 4747.

Founded: 1854.
Chairman: R.C. Meech; Managing Director: J.D.H. Hume, CBE.
Specialises in the design, manufacture and installation of air, gas, and fluid handling equipment. Products include air preheaters, fans, gas circulators, wind turbine generators, blowers, heat exchangers, compressors, pumps, dust collectors and fabric filters. Turnover (1985): £224.132 million.

HUNTERIAN ART GALLERY, 82 Hillhead Street, Glasgow G12 8QQ; T.-041-330 5431.

Founded: 1807.
Director: Frank Willett; Deputy Director: Christopher Allan; Curators: Martin Hopkinson, Pamela Robertson.
This purpose-designed gallery displays internationally renowned collections of the works of the American painter, James McNeill Whistler and Glasgow architect and designer, Charles Rennie Mackintosh. A major feature is the reconstruction of the principal rooms from Mackintosh's own home. Also on display are notable 17th and 18th century paintings and a selection of Scottish paintings of the late 19th and 20th centuries. There is an outdoor sculpture courtyard, and exhibitions of Old Master and modern prints drawn from the largest public collection in Scotland are shown in a gallery which also houses an explanatory display of print techniques.

HUNTERIAN MUSEUM, University of Glasgow, University Avenue, Hillhead, Glasgow G12 8QQ; T.-041-330 4221.

Founded: 1807.
Director: Frank Willett; Senior Curator in Geology: Keith Ingham; Senior Curator in Archaeology: Euan MacKie; Curator of Coins: Donal Bateson; Design Officer: Ron Harrison; Curator in Geology: Graham

Durant; Curator in Archaeology: Lawrence Keppie.

Takes its name from William Hunter (1718-83), physician and medical teacher who bequeathed to Glasgow University his substantial collections. When it opened, it was Scotland's first public museum. Many additions have been made since Hunter's time, with the emphasis now on geology, archaeology and coins. Temporary displays are regularly mounted in a new temporary exhibitions area. Practical activities are arranged for school children. There is a small refreshment area and shop. Admission is free.

I

INDEPENDENT BROADCASTING AUTHORITY, (IBA), 123 Blythswood Street, Glasgow G2 4AN; T.-041-226 4436.
Founded: 1964.
Member for Scotland: John R. Purvis; Officer for Scotland: G.B. Marjoribanks; Senior Assistant Officer for Scotland: W.A. Jamieson; Assistant Officer for Scotland: V.M. McDowall.
The central body responsible for the provision of Independent Local Radio, Independent Television, Breakfast Television and Channel Four services in the United Kingdom.

INDUSTRY DEPARTMENT FOR SCOTLAND, New St Andrew's House, Edinburgh EH1 3TD; T.-031-556 8400.
Secretary and Chief Economic Adviser: Dr R.G.L. McCrone, CB; Private Secretary: Ms J. Hutchison.
Advises the Secretary of State for Scotland on industrial and economic development in Scotland. Discharges his responsibility for selective financial assistance to industry, for the promotion of industrial development within Scotland, for matters relating to energy policy and for the activities in Scotland of the Manpower Services Commission. The department is also responsible for policy in relation to the Scottish Development Agency, the Highlands and Islands Development Board, the Scottish Tourist Board, the Scottish electricity boards and the Scottish new towns.

INLAND REVENUE. See Board of Inland Revenue.

INQUIRY REPORTERS, 16 Waterloo Place, Edinburgh EH1 3DN; T.-031-556 8400.
Chief Reporter: A.G. Bell; Deputy Chief Reporter: W.D. Campbell.
Conducts public local inquiries and carries out site inspections under the Planning Acts and some other statutes.

INSTITUTE OF ANIMAL PHYSIOLOGY AND GENETICS RESEARCH, AFRC, Edinburgh Research Station, Roslin, Midlothian EH25 9PS; T.-031-440 2726.
Station Head: Dr R. B. Land; Secretary: A.I. Menzies.
The Edinburgh Research Station is concerned with the scientific study of biological processes and principles so that knowledge and expertise are available to facilitate the future development of the livestock industry. In particular, it is concerned with the genetic improvement of livestock.

INSTITUTE OF AQUACULTURE, University of Stirling, Stirling FK9 4LA; T.-0786 73171.
Founded: 1971.
Director: Prof Ronald J. Roberts; Deputy Director: Dr Randolph H. Richards; Head of Nutrition Unit: Prof Alan J. Matty; Head of Engineering Unit: Dr James F. Muir; Head of Aquatic Biotechnology Unit: Dr Michael T. Horne; Director of Studies: Dr Lindsay G Ross.
International research and postgraduate training institute dealing with all aspects of fish and shell fish culture. In addition to its basic scientific research programme and training courses, it also carries out a variety of evaluation, diagnostic and developmental remits for international agencies, Government institutions in the United Kingdom and overseas, and for industrial collaborators.

INSTITUTE OF BANKERS IN SCOTLAND, 20 Rutland Square, Edinburgh EH1 2DE; T.-031-229 9869.
Founded: 1875.
Secretary General: Brian McKenna; Director of Studies: A. Evan Williams; Administrative Secretary: Geraldine Stanton.
Exists for the education of bankers employed by the Scottish banks. Main activities are: examining trainee bankers, publishing literature on banking practice and *The Scotish Bankers' Magazine* (quar-

terly), and providing courses and lectures for qualified members. Membership: 11,000.

THE INSTITUTE OF CHARTERED ACCOUNTANTS OF SCOTLAND, 27 Queen Street, Edinburgh EH2 1LA; T.-031-225 5673.

Founded: 1854.
President: G.A. Anderson; Senior Vice-president: N. Lessels; Junior Vice-president: I.N. Tegner; Secretary: Eric Tait, MBE.
Oldest accountancy body in the world. Unique among accountancy bodies in educating its students as well as examining them. The professional designatory letters CA are exclusive in the British Isles to members of the institute. Most CAs (52%) work in industry and commerce, with 30% in practising firms of accountants. Publishes *The Accountant's Magazine* (monthly). Membership: 11,600.

INSTITUTE OF CHARTERED FORESTERS, (ICF), 22 Walker Street, Edinburgh EH3 7HR; T.-031-225 2705.

Founded: 1926.
President: Mr R.T. Gray; Vice President: Dr D.C. Malcolm; Editor: Dr Julian Evans; Secretary and Treasurer: Mrs Margaret W. Dick.
Established as the Society of Foresters of Great Britain and incorporated by Royal Charter in 1982. Objects are to maintain and improve the standards of practice and understanding of forestry, to promote the professional status of foresters in the United Kingdom and to be the representative of the profession. Keeps under review the needs of education, research and training, and offers examinations to members. The journal *Forestry* is published twice yearly and the institute publishes the results of practice and research in all aspects of forestry. A study tour and discussion meeting are held annually.

THE INSTITUTE OF GROUNDSMANSHIP - SCOTLAND AND NORTHERN IRELAND ZONE, 104 Roseburn Street, Murrayfield, Edinburgh EH12 5PF; T.-031-337 2800.

Founded: 1934.
Chairman: Andrew Murray; Secretary: William Elwood; Treasurer: George Skirving.
Founded as an educational body and to improve the standards of turfculture throughout the United Kingdom. Six branches within the zone: Aberdeen, Dundee, Edinburgh, Fife, Glasgow and Northern Ireland, accounting for 10% of the United Kingdom membership. A system of examinations is organised nationwide each year, aimed at enhancing the status of groundsmen and greenkeepers. Lectures, outings, seminars and social events are held both at branch and zone level. The highlight of the zone's activities is the *Scotsturf* indoor exhibition, held annually in November at Ingliston.

INSTITUTE OF WATER POLLUTION CONTROL, (SCOTTISH BRANCH), 129 Woodstock Avenue, Glasgow G41 3QZ; T.-041-889 5454.

Honorary Secretary: A.Y. Morton.
Professional body.

INSTITUTION OF GEOLOGISTS - EAST OF SCOTLAND BRANCH, c/o Frank Saynor & Associates, 5 Broughton Market, Edinburgh EH3 6NU.

Founded: 1978.
Chairman: Colin ·Braithwaite; Secretary: Brian Easton; Treasurer: Dick Robinson.
Has a membership of between 70 and 100 professional geologists in the East of Scotland. Aims to promote information and ideas in geology and assist in the education, training and advancement of geological knowledge. Each year, evening lectures are held on a variety of geological topics and members of the public are welcome to attend. Once a year, there is a field visit to a site of interest in the region.

INVERCLYDE DISTRICT COUNCIL, Municipal Buildings, Greenock PA15 1LX; T.-0475 24400.

Founded: 1974.
Provost: Sir Simpson Stevenson; Chief Executive: I.C. Wilson, JP; Director of Administration: J.R. Thompson; Director of Finance: R.N. McPherson, JP; Director of Housing: A. Craig; Director of Planning and Technical Services: J.S. Mackie; Director of Recreational Services: J.A. Douglas; Director of Environmental Health: P. Tait.
Political composition of council: Labour 11, Liberal 9. Population of district: 97,932.

INVERCLYDE ENTERPRISE TRUST LTD, Inverclyde Initiative Office, 64-66 West Blackhall Street, Greenock PA15 1XG; T.-0475 86240/24533.

Founded: 1984.
Chairman: Gerry Quigley; Trust Director: Ewen Macaulay; Project Officers: Elizabeth Cameron, Brian Warren.
Local enterprise agency providing free business advice in Inverclyde District. Funded partly by local companies and partly by Government, including the Scottish Development Agency.

INVERCLYDE NATIONAL SPORTS TRAINING CENTRE, (INSTC), Burnside Road, Largs KA30 8RW; T.-Largs 674666.

Principal: M.R. Barratt; Deputy Principal: A. Anderson.
Main role is to provide a residential base for the training of coaches, instructors and leaders. Also used extensively for the training of top sportsmen and women and many of Scotland's national squads. Runs a series of Sportsbreaks, short sports holidays offering coaching for participants at all levels in a range of sports.

INVERNESS COLLEGE OF FURTHER AND HIGHER EDUCATION (ICFHE), 3 Longman Road, Longman South, Inverness IV1 1SA; T.-0463 236681.

Founded: 1960.
Principal: W.J. Hedley.
Largest college in Highland Region, having over 4,000 students in full-time or part-time education. The Scottish School of Forestry is part of the college. Covers a wide range of abilities. Variety of courses available both by attending college and by distance learning schemes.

INVERNESS AND DISTRICT CHAMBER OF COMMERCE, 13A Island Bank Road, Inverness; T.-0463 233570.

Founded: 1893.
President: Peter Drummond; Secretary/Treasurer: Douglas W. Brookes, TD.

INVERNESS DISTRICT COUNCIL, Town House, Inverness IV1 1JJ; T.-0463 239111.

Founded: 1974.
Provost: A.G. Sellar; Chief Executive: B. Wilson; Director of Administration: T. McClenaghan; Director of Legal Services: D.R. Somerville; Director of Architectural and Technical Services: W. Hamilton; Director of Housing: D.I. MacKenzie; Director of Finance: A.G. Imlah; Director of Environ-

mental Health: R. Chisholm; Director of Cleansing: W. Fraser.
Political composition of council: Independent 18, Labour 8, Liberal 2. Population of district: 58,849.

INVERNESS, LOCH NESS AND NAIRN TOURIST BOARD, 23 Church Street, Inverness IV1 1EZ; T.-0463 234353.

Founded: 1971.
Chairman: Alistair McPherson; Vice-chairman: David Caldwell; Secretary and Area Tourist Officer: Mrs Jean Slesser.
Promotes the Inverness, Loch Ness and Nairn area as a tourist destination and services visitors to the area through four tourist information centres: Inverness, Nairn, Fort Augustus and Daviot Wood. Has accommodation booking service.

INVERNESS MUSEUM AND ART GALLERY, Castle Wynd, Inverness IV2 3ED; T.-0463 237114.

Founded: 1881.
Curator: Catharine Niven; Assistant Curators: Stephen Moran (Natural Sciences), Gillian Harden (Archaeology), David Stones (Social History); Conservation Officer: Marie Scally Noonan.
Run by Inverness District Council. Collections relate to the social and natural history, archaeology and culture of Inverness and the Highlands. There are new display galleries and the museum has an active programme of temporary exhibitions and events. Visitor facilities include a museum shop and coffee shop. Open Monday to Saturday, 9 am to 5 pm.

THE IONA COMMUNITY, Community House, Pearce Institute, Govan, Glasgow G51 3UT; T.-041-445 4561.

Founded: 1938.
Leader: Rev Ron Ferguson; Deputy Leader: Rev Margaret Stewart; Convenor of Council: Catherine Hepburn; Wardens, Iona Abbey: Rev Ian Galloway and Rev Kathy Galloway; Financial Administrator: Alison Macdonald; Finance Convenor: Malcolm May.
Ecumenical community of women and men bound together by a five-fold rule and seeking new ways of living the Gospel, wherever they are in the world. Activities include the support of unemployed youth volunteers living in areas of urban deprivation, workers in justice and peace and in urban mission. Iona Abbey and CAMAS Adventure Camp on Mull welcome guests to share in these living

communities. A new centre for youth work in Iona is being planned and building should start in 1987.

IRVINE DEVELOPMENT COR-PORATION, (IDC), Perceton House, Irvine KA11 2AL; T.-0294 214100.
Founded: 1966.
Chairman: Ross Belch; Managing Director: Tony Rickets; Commercial Director: Mike Thomson; Director of Technical Services: Ian Downs; Director of Finance and Administration: Jack Murdoch.
Established to increase the population of Irvine from 34,600 to 95,000. In 1986, the population stood at around 58,000 people. Further expansion depends on developing existing companies and attracting new industry and commerce. The corporation therefore offers financial incentives, advance factories, serviced sites, housing, and professional advice and assistance. A further function is to publicise the town's other attractions - the workforce, leisure environment, commercial and social facilities.

ISLE OF ARRAN TOURIST BOARD, Tourist Information Centre, Brodick Pier, Brodick, Isle of Arran; T.-0770 2140.
Chairman: A.R. Crawford; Area Tourist Officer: Jill M. Gardiner.
Exists for the promotion of tourism on the Isle of Arran.

ISLE OF SKYE AND SOUTH WEST ROSS TOURIST BOARD, Meall House, Portree, Isle of Skye IV51 9BZ; T.-0478 2137.
Chairman: J. MacDonald; Vice Chairman: K. Pittam; Treasurer: H. Andrew; Secretary and Area Tourist Officer: P.H. Turner.
Gives special attention to the needs of the area in relation to the promotion and development of tourism and provides information about the area. Also provides a booking service within the area.

J

JAMES FINLAY PLC, Finlay House, 10-14 West Nile Street, Glasgow G1 2PP; T.-041-204 1321.
Founded: 1750.
Chairman and Chief Executive: Sir Colin Campbell, Bt, MC.

International traders and financiers. Turnover (1985): £194.133 million

JAMES WATT COLLEGE, Finnart Street, Greenock PA16 8HF; T.-0475 24433.
Founded: 1973.
Chairman, College Council: Mr A. Paxton; Principal: Mr R. McAdam; Depute Principal: Mr D. Morrison; Registrar: Mr G. Blair.
Local authority college of further education. The six departments are integrated into an area consortium with local schools under the 16+ action plan. Serves as a community resource as well as a technical and vocational institution. Of particular note are developments in electronic and mechanical engineering, new technology courses, open learning provision and courses and facilities for those in the special needs category. In addition, a TVEI unit is housed on the premises.

JOHN MENZIES plc, Hanover Buildings, Rose Street, Edinburgh EH2 2YQ; T.-031-225 8555.
Founded: 1833.
Chairman: J.M. Menzies; Managing Director: F.R. Noel-Paton.
Wholesale and retail newsagents, booksellers, and stationers, and providers of library services. Turnover (1985): £546.9 million.

JOINT STANDING COMMITTEE OF ARCHITECTS, SURVEYORS AND BUILDING CONTRACTORS IN SCOTLAND, 9 Manor Place, Edinburgh EH3 7DN; T.-031-225 7078.
Chairman: R.S. Gray; Secretary: J.M. Ritchie.
Provides a medium whereby questions affecting the building industry in Scotland can be discussed, and a means of concerting action within the industry. Bodies represented are the Royal Incorporation of Architects in Scotland, the Royal Institution of Chartered Surveyors (Scottish Branch), the Scottish Building Employers' Federation, the Scottish and Northern Ireland Plumbing Employers' Federation, the Electrical Contractors Association of Scotland, the Scottish Decorators Federation, the Association of Consulting Engineers, the Scottish Board of the Federation of Associations of Specialists and Sub-Contractors, and the Heating and Ventilating Contractors Association.

JORDANHILL   COLLEGE   OF

EDUCATION, 76 Southbrae Drive, Jordanhill, Glasgow G13 1PP; T.-041-959 1232.
Founded: 1928.
Chairman, Board of Governors: Mr J.L. Brown; Principal: Dr T.R. Bone; Vice-principal: Dr J. McCall; College Secretary: Mr W.G. Charters.
The largest college of education in Scotland. Autonomous body administered by a Board of Governors and financed directly by the Scottish Education Department. Since it opened, it has trained large numbers of secondary and primary teachers and in the 1960s, new groups such as social workers, youth leaders and speech therapists were added. Embraces two institutions which might elsewhere have been separate colleges themselves: the Scottish School of Physical Education and the School of Further Education.

JUNIOR CHAMBER SCOTLAND, c/o National Secretary, Brunton Miller, 7 Colquhoun Street, Helensburgh G84 8AN; T.-0436 5323.
Founded: 1948.
National Secretary: Bill Cairns; National President: David Edmunds.
The national organisation to which local junior chambers are affiliated (34 throughout Scotland).

K

KEEP SCOTLAND BEAUTIFUL CAMPAIGN, Old County Chambers, Cathedral Square, Dunblane FK15 0AQ; T.-0786 823202.
Director: Douglas S. Wright; General Manager: R.N. Harper; Administration Manager: W.J.C. Rowan; Education Manager: W.S. Hall; Community Manager: C.R. Stewart; Training Manager: R. Shanks.
National agency for litter prevention. Has local projects in most parts of Scotland.

KILMARNOCK COLLEGE, Holehouse Road, Kilmarnock KA3 7AT; T.-Kilmarnock 23501.
Founded: 1966.
Principal: Mr P.A. Martin; Depute Principal: Mr J. Cleland; Assistant Principal: Mr M. Aird.
Further education college with annexes at Irvine and Ardeer. Four departments. Full-time, block release, day release, YTS and restart courses are offered as well as short industrial and ESF (European Social Fund) sponsored courses.

KILMARNOCK AND LOUDOUN CHAMBER OF COMMERCE, c/o Honorary Secretary, 23 The Foregate, Kilmarnock; T.-Kilmarnock 25104.

KILMARNOCK AND LOUDOUN DISTRICT COUNCIL, Civic Centre, John Dickie Street, Kilmarnock KA1 1BY; T.-0563 21140.
Founded: 1974.
Provost: T. Ferguson; Chief Executive: R.W. Jenner; Finance Manager: I.R. Smith; District Chief Environmental Health Officer: J. Riach; District Engineer: D.T. Maclean; District Chief Planning Officer: L. Guilford; District Architect: A. Innes.
Political composition of council: Labour 13, Conservative 3, SNP 1. Population of district: 82,000.

THE KILMARNOCK VENTURE, 30 The Foregate, Kilmarnock KA1 1JH; T.-0563 44602.
Founded: 1983.
Chairman: David Adam; Director: Alistair Ferguson.
Enterprise trust.

KINCARDINE AND DEESIDE DISTRICT COUNCIL, Viewmount, Arduthie Road, Stonehaven AB3 2DQ; T.-0569 62001.
Founded: 1974.
Convener: Donald J. Mackenzie; Chief Executive and Director of Finance and Administration: Thomas Hyder; Director of Legal Services and Depute Chief Executive: Keith G. Jones; Director of Environmental Health: Laurence Borthwick; Director of Planning and Development: Norman G. Marr; Director of Housing and Property: John D.V. Nicoll.
Political composition of council: Independent 7, Conservative 3, Liberal 1, SNP 1. Population of district: 46,788.

KINCARDINE AND DEESIDE TOURIST BOARD, 45 Station Road, Banchory AB3 3XX; T.-03302 2066.
Founded: 1983.
Chairman: Jack Emslie; Vice-chairman: Pat Greaves; Area Tourist Officer: Liz MacInnes; Treasurer: Mr T. Hyder.
Partnership between Kincardine and

Deeside District Council, the Scottish Tourist Board and the tourism industry in the district. There are tourist information centres in Braemar, Ballater, Aboyne, Banchory and Stonehaven throughout the season. Membership: 317.

KIRKCALDY COLLEGE OF TECHNOLOGY, St Brycedale Avenue, Kirkcaldy KY1 1EX; T.-Kirkcaldy 268591.
Founded: 1919.
Principal: D.A. Huckle; Depute Principal: D. Law; Assistant Principal: A. Blair; Acting Registrar: Mrs J. Fleming.
60% of the college's work is at higher certificate, higher diploma, and post higher diploma level, in engineering, building, management, communications, and science. Has 1,500 full-time and 3,500 part-time students.

KIRKCALDY DISTRICT CHAMBER OF COMMERCE, 288 High Street, Kirkcaldy KY1 1LB; T.-0592 262463.
Founded: 1825.
President: D. Macfie; Secretary: J.W. Brodie, JP.
Exists for the promotion and protection of the trade, commerce and industry of the district.

KIRKCALDY DISTRICT COUNCIL, Town House, Kirkcaldy KY1 1XW; T.-Kirkcaldy 261144.
Founded: 1974.
Convener: R. King; Director of Administration: J. Martin Smith; Director of Finance: Hugh Wilson; Director of Planning: Douglas M. Nelson; Director of Housing: Kenneth G. Fenwick; Director of Environmental Health: Stephen D. Rooke; Director of Architectural and Technical Services: J.I. Brodley; Director of Leisure and Recreation: A. Sneddon; Director of Works and Transport: Donald W. Swinney.
Political composition of council: Labour 29, Conservative 3, SDP/Liberal Alliance 3, SNP 2, Independent 2, Ratepayers' Association 1. Population of district: 149,423.

KYLE AND CARRICK DISTRICT COUNCIL, Burns House, Burns Statue Square, Ayr; T.-0292 281511.
Founded: 1974.
Provost: Gibson Macdonald; Chief Executive and Director of Administration: Ian R.D. Smillie; Director of Architectural Planning and Technical Services: William Gilmour;

Director of Finance: John F. Beaton; Director of Housing: John Small; Director of Parks and Recreation: David Roy; Director of Environmental Services: James McVie; Director of Libraries and Museums: Peter Hemphill.
Political composition of council: Labour 12, Conservative 11, Independent 2. Population of district: 113,324.

L

LABOUR PARTY, SCOTTISH COUNCIL, Keir Hardie House, 1 Lynedoch Place, Glasgow G3 6AB; T.-041-332 8946.
Founded: 1907.
Chairman: Bob Middleton; Vice Chairman: William Speirs; Treasurer: Norman F. Buchan, MP; Scottish Secretary: Helen Liddell; Scottish Organiser: James Allison.
Political party.

LANARKSHIRE HEALTH BOARD, 14 Beckford Street, Hamilton ML3 0TA; T.-0698 281313.
Founded: 1974.
Chairman: Mrs B.M. Gunn, OBE, JP; Vice Chairman: R.J. Logan, JP; General Manager: F. Clark; Treasurer: M. Docherty; Chief Administrative Medical Officer: Dr W.O. Thomson; Chief Area Nursing Officer: Miss E. Hastings.
Provides health services in local authority districts of Monklands, Cumbernauld, Motherwell, Clydesdale, Hamilton and East Kilbride, covering a population of 563,000. The board employs 11,561 staff and provides 5,285 beds in 23 hospitals. The budget for 1985-86 was £158.534 million.

LANARKSHIRE INDUSTRIAL FIELD EXECUTIVE, Old Town Hall, 1/11 High Road, Motherwell ML1 3HU; T.-Motherwell 66622.
Founded: 1983.
Chief Executive: Peter F. Agnew.
A business development agency committed to assisting in the creation of new jobs in Lanarkshire by encouraging business start-ups, developing existing companies, and attracting investment into the area from the United Kingdom and overseas.

THE LANDS TRIBUNAL FOR SCOTLAND, (LTS), 1 Grosvenor Crescent,

Edinburgh EH12 5ER; T.-031-2257996/7.
Founded: 1970.
President: The Hon Lord Elliott, MC; Members: William Hall, DFC, T. Finlayson, JP, W.D.C. Andrews, CBE, WS, K.O. Osborne, QC, J. Horsburgh, QC.
Independent judicial body with jurisdictions ranging from questions of land valuation, including tax appeals and compensation for compulsory purchase to allocating feu duties and discharging restrictive land obligations. Jurisdiction has been extended to include appeals against the Keeper of the Land Register and implementation of the Tenants' Rights (Etc) Scotland Act 1980. In 1985, it became an appellate body for complex valuation appeals. Consists of a legally qualified president and other members who are either lawyers or who are experienced in land valuation. Though based in Edinburgh, the tribunal is a travelling one.

LANGSIDE COLLEGE, 50 Prospecthill Road, Glasgow G42 9LB; T.-041-649 4991.
Founded: 1947.
Principal: J. Reilly; Depute Principal: J. Flynn.
College of further education with an annual student population of 5,400, of whom 1,400 are full-time. Serves as a local centre for industrial, commercial, general, and continuing education, as well as a community college providing a wide range of vocational and leisure activities by day and in the evening. Organised in seven departments.

LAUDER TECHNICAL COLLEGE, North Fod, Halbeath, Dunfermline KY11 5DY; T.-0383 726201.
Founded: 1899.
Chairman of College Council: Cllr Mrs J.H. Mackie, JP; Depute Principal: Peter S. Richardson; Assistant Principal: Frank Hughes.
College of further education with an annual student population of 4,600, providing further education to meet the industrial, commercial and social needs of West Fife.

THE LAW SOCIETY OF SCOTLAND, 26 Drumsheugh Gardens, Edinburgh EH3 7YR; T.-031-226 7411.
Founded: 1949.
Secretary: Kenneth W. Pritchard.
Governing body of the Scottish solicitor profession in Scotland. Membership: 7,243.

LEITH CHAMBER OF COMMERCE, 3 Randolph Crescent, Edinburgh EH3 7UD; T.-031-225 5851.
Secretary: D.M. Mowat, JP.

LEITH ENTERPRISE TRUST, 25 Maritime Street, Leith EH6 5PW; T.-031-553 5566.
Founded: 1984.
Chairman: R. Bruce Weatherstone; Executive Director: James A. Prettyman; Secretary: J. Malcolm-Smith.
Supported by three public sector and 43 private sector sponsors to provide a free advisory and assistance service for small businesses, both new and newly started in Leith. Work includes premises location, business planning, helping to find finance, and training.

LEITH NAUTICAL COLLEGE, 24 Milton Road East, Edinburgh EH15 2PP; T.-031-669 8461.
Founded: 1908.
Chairman, Board of Governors: R.S. Salvesen; Principal: Dr A. Watson, TD; College Secretary and Treasurer: Miss E. Johnston.
Recognised by the Department of Transport as a navigation and marine engineering school and by the Home Office as a radio telegraphy school. Also recognised as a training and examination centre for the Royal Yachting Association/Department of Transport courses leading to all yachtmaster certificates. SCOTVEC courses are offered in control and electronic engineering up to Higher National Diploma level. Specialist short courses deal with the handling of hazardous cargoes and the operation of semi-submersible vessels. The college is residential with a full range of sporting facilities.

LEVENMOUTH ENTERPRISE TRUST, Hawkslaw Development (Leven) Ltd, Riverside Road, Leven; T.-0333 26001.
Director: Mr Sandy Lawrie.

LEWS CASTLE COLLEGE, Stornoway, Isle of Lewis PA86 0XR; T.-0851 3311.
Founded: 1953.
Principal: Malcolm MacKay; Depute Principal: D.K. MacLeod; College Secretary: Edith MacLeod.
Further education college with 420 full-time students.

LILLEY plc, FJC. See FJC Lilley plc.

LIVE MUSIC NOW (SCOTLAND), (LMN), Ainslie House, 11 St Colme Street, Edinburgh EH3 6AG; T.-031-225 4606.
Founded: 1984.
Founder: Sir Yehudi Menuhin; Scottish Governor: Rt Hon Lady Polwarth; Scottish Representative: Carol Main.
Exists to take live music of high standard back into the community and to give young performers under the age of 27 the opportunity of professional engagements at the outset of their careers. Concerts are given in homes for the elderly or for children, hospitals, prisons, schools, private receptions - anywhere people are gathered together. Musicians are chosen for their ability to communicate verbally as well as musically.

LIVINGSTON DEVELOPMENT CORPORATION, Sidlaw House, Almondvale, Livingston, West Lothian; T.-0506 414177.
Founded: 1962.
Chairman: R.S. Watt; Deputy Chairman: W. Percy; Chief Executive: J. Wilson; Secretary and Legal Adviser: J. Ritchie; Chief Finance Officer: A. Kinnear; Commercial Director: J. Pollock.
With a population of almost 41,000, Livingston is the largest town in Lothian Region after the city of Edinburgh. The town is a primary economic growth point and some 15,000 jobs have been established on four main industrial parks, the town centre and other sites. Many of these are in electronics and other high technology industries, but most industrial sectors are represented in the town. The Almondvale Centre is becoming established as a sub-regional centre for a population of around 140,000.

LIVINGSTONE CENTRE, THE DAVID. See The David Livingstone Centre.

LIVINGSTONE INSTITUTE OF OVERSEAS DEVELOPMENT STUDIES, DAVID. See David Livingstone Institute of Overseas Development Studies.

LOCAL GOVERNMENT BOUNDARY COMMISSION FOR SCOTLAND, New St Andrew's House, Edinburgh EH1 3SZ; T.-031-556 8400 (Direct: 031-244 4058).
Founded: 1975.
Chairman: R.A. Bennett, CBE, QC; Deputy Chairman: G. Carlton, OBE; Secretary: E.M.C. Mackay.
Has two principal functions: reviewing local authority administrative areas, and reviewing the electoral arrangements for local government areas in Scotland.

LOCATE IN SCOTLAND (LIS) 120 Bothwell Street, Glasgow G2 7JP; T.-041-248 2700.
LIS is the division of the Scottish Development Agency responsible for inward investment and is staffed jointly by IDS personnel and Scottish Development Agency personnel.

LOCHABER DISTRICT COUNCIL, Lochaber House, High Street, Fort William PH33 6EL; T.-0397 2881.
Founded: 1974.
Chairman: Colin Neilson; Chief Executive: D.A.B. Blair; Director of Finance: A. MacKenzie; Director of Environmental Health Services: J. Cormack; Director of Architectural Services: M. McGruer.
Political composition of council: Independent 5, Labour 5, Non-affiliated 3, Independent Labour 2. Population of district: 19,395.

LOCH LOMOND, STIRLING AND TROSSACHS TOURIST BOARD, PO Box 30, Stirling; T.-Stirling 70945.
Founded: 1983.
Chairman: Cllr W. Neeson; Tourism Manager: James Fraser.
Promotes tourism within the District Council areas of Dumbarton, Stirling, and Clackmannan.

LOTHIAN COMMUNITY RELATIONS COUNCIL, 12A Forth Street, Edinburgh EH1 3LH; T.-031-556 0441.
Founded: 1971.
Chairman: Mr Yousaf Inait; Vice Chairman: John Dickie; Secretary: Mr Habib Hashmi; Treasurer: Mr Wali Tasar Uddin.
Main aims are the elimination of racial discrimination and the promotion of good community relations. Has over 70 member organisations including nearly all the main minority ethnic organisations. Work consists mainly of supporting the minority ethnic communities and campaigning for policy change as needed. Much of the work is in public education, in raising the awareness of racism and discrimination in society.

LOTHIAN HEALTH BOARD, (LHB), 11 Drumsheugh Gardens, Edinburgh EH3 7DQ; T.-031-225 1341.

Founded: 1974.
Chairman: R. Bruce Weatherstone, TD; General Manager: Winston J. Tayler; Secretary: Ross Mitchell; Treasurer: Derek F. Hardman; Chief Administrative Medical Officer: C. Brough; Chief Area Nursing Officer: D.J. MacDonald.
Responsible for the provision of health care services in an area coinciding with that of Lothian Region. Serves a population of some 750,000, maintains 36 hospitals, 26 health centres (with others planned), and more than 120 clinics and health units of differing types.

LOTHIAN REGIONAL COUNCIL, Regional Chambers, Parliament Square, Edinburgh EH1 1TT; T.-031-229 9292.

Founded: 1974.
Convener: James Cook; Vice-convener: Alexander Bell; Leader of Council: John Mulvey; Chief Executive: G.M. Bowie; Director of Finance: D.B. Chynoweth; Director of Planning: D.M. Jamie; Regional Secretary: R.L. Cowan; Director of Management and Information Services: Dr R.G. Musgrave; Director of Architectural Services: T.R. Hughes; Director of Trading Standards: J. Short; Director of Water and Drainage: L.K.W. Richards; Director of Education: W.D.C. Semple; Firemaster, Lothian and Borders: R. Edmonds; Director of Highways: P.J. Mason; Chief Constable, Lothian and Borders Police: W.G.M. Sutherland, QPM; Director of Social Work: R.W. Kent; Director of Transport: C. Evans.
Political composition of council: Labour 32, Conservative 13, SDP/Liberal Alliance 3, SNP 1. Population of region: 744,558.

LOW & BONAR PLC, Bonar House, Faraday Street, Dundee DD1 9JA; T.-0382 818171.

Founded: 1912.
Chairman: Sir Dermot de Trafford; Managing Director: R.J. Jarvis; Finance Director: W.L. Telfer.
Holding company with interests in packaging, plastics, textiles and electronics. Has operations in North America, Africa and Australia. Turnover (1985): £174.8 million.

LOW & COMPANY PLC, WILLIAM. See William Low & Company PLC.

M

THE MACAULAY INSTITUTE FOR SOIL RESEARCH, (MISR), Craigiebuckler, Aberdeen AB9 2QJ; T.-0224 318611.

Founded: 1930.
Chairman, Council of Management: Prof H.M. Keir; Director: Prof T.S. West; Secretary and Treasurer: Miss E.A. Piggott.
Combines practical studies of the soils of Scotland, designed to improve their fertility, with related research into various branches of soil science. Nine departments: spectrochemistry, soil organic chemistry, plant physiology, microbiology, soil fertility, statistics, soil survey, mineral soils and peat and forest soils.

MACKINTOSH SOCIETY, CHARLES RENNIE. See Charles Rennie Mackintosh Society.

MACLAURIN ART GALLERY, Rozelle House, Monument Road, Alloway, Ayr KA7 4NQ; T.-0292 45447/43708.

Founded: 1976.
Curator: Michael Bailey.
Kyle and Carrick District Council's museum and gallery department is based in Rozelle House. In addition to managing the collection of paintings and museum objects there, the staff provide a continuing programme of art exhibitions in its Maclaurin Art Gallery and in the smaller Rozelle House Gallery.

THE MALCOLM SARGENT CANCER FUND FOR CHILDREN, COMMITTEE FOR SCOTLAND, Drumwhill, Mossdale, by Castle Douglas DG7 2NL; T.-Laurieston 269.

President for Scotland: The Duke of Buccleuch and Queensberry, KT; Chairman: Sir Donald Cameron of Lochiel, KT, CVO; Honorary Treasurer: D. Bruce Pattullo; Administrative Secretary: Miss Venetia Fane; Trustee for Scotland: Dr O.B. Eden.
Helps children suffering from cancer in all its forms, including leukaemia or Hodgkins disease, either at home or in hospital, with grants which are given within 48 hours of the request for help being received for whatever the doctors and social workers deem vital for the well-being and comfort of their young patients. Grants given for travel, toys, holidays, heating, beds and bedding,

clothing, accommodation for parents near the hospital, extra nourishing foods etc. Has five 'Malcolm Sargent' social workers in Scotland: two based in the Royal Hospital for Sick Children in Edinburgh, two in the Royal Hospital for Sick Children in Glasgow, and one in Aberdeen Royal Children's Hospital, and it is one of these who should be contacted when a grant is needed for a child. All money raised in Scotland is kept in Scotland to help Scottish children.

MANPOWER SERVICES COMMISSION, OFFICE FOR SCOTLAND, (MSC), 9 St. Andrew Square, Edinburgh EH2 2QX; T.-031-225 8500.
Founded: 1974.
Chairman, Committee for Scotland: Sir James Munn, OBE; Director for Scotland: G.D. Calder; Assistant Director for Scotland: A.G. Proctor; Employment Manager, Scotland: J.G. Duncan; General Manager, Skills Training Agency: I. Fisher.
Runs the public employment and training services and advises the Government on manpower policies. Accountable to the Secretary of State for Scotland for its operations in Scotland, and is responsible for appointing a committee of 10 composed of three appointees from the CBI, three from the STUC, two from local authorities and one in education, plus a chairman, to advise on its Scottish operations. Its three operating divisions - employment, training, and the skills training agency - run the network of local Jobcentres, area offices, professional and executive recrutiment offices, employment rehabilitation centres and skillcentres, through which the commission provides a range of advisory services and schemes to help employers train and obtain workers, and to assist people to choose, train for and obtain employment.

MARGARET BLACKWOOD HOUSING ASSOCIATION LTD, Pritchard House, 32 Inglis Green Road, Edinburgh EH14 2ER; T.-031-443 7239.
Founded: 1972.
Chairman: Lord MacLehose of Beoch, KT, GBE, KCMG, KCVO; Vice Chairman: Mr A.G.L. Baxter; Director: Mr D.R.M. Gregory; Deputy Director: Mr A. Baird; Secretary: Mr J.D. Anderson; Finance Officer: Miss H.J. Fairlie.
Engaged in the construction and management of housing for physically disabled people. Funded by the Scottish Development Department and the Scottish Housing Corporation.

MARINE LABORATORY, PO Box 101, Victoria Road, Aberdeen AB9 8DB; T.-0224 876544.
Founded: 1882.
Director: Dr A.D. Hawkins; Deputy Director: D.N. MacLennan; Secretary: A. Beaton; Librarian: J.H. Burne.
Research laboratory of the Department of Agriculture and Fisheries for Scotland, covering marine research, and problems arising from and affecting fisheries. Most of the work is biological in character involving studies on the principal food fishes. Freshwater research is conducted at the Freshwater Fisheries Laboratory at Pitlochry.

MAYFEST LTD, 46 Royal Exchange Square, Glasgow G1 3AR; T.-041-221 4911.
Founded: 1983.
Festival Director: Di Robson; General Manager: William Kelly; Chairman: Jean McFadden; Vice-chairman: Alex Clark.
Glasgow's international arts festival. Features drama, dance, music, exhibitions, street events, community events and late night cabaret.

MEAT AND LIVESTOCK COMMISSION, (MLC), 3 Atholl Place, Perth PH1 5ND; T.-0738 27401.
Founded: 1967.
Chief Officer for Scotland: A. Donaldson; Chief Livestock Officer: G.M. McPherson; Chief Fatstock Officer: I.S. Wiggins.
Exists to improve the production and marketing of British cattle, sheep and pigs, and the meat they produce. Provides services, information and advice for livestock producers, auctioneers, slaughterers, wholesalers, manufacturers, retailers, caterers and consumers. Funded by statutory levies on all slaughter stock, fees as agents for the Intervention Board for Agricultural Produce and the Ministry of Agriculture, and payment received for services and publications.

MENTAL WELFARE COMMISSION FOR SCOTLAND, 22 Melville Street, Edinburgh EH3 7NS; T.-031-225 7034.
Founded: 1962.
Chairman: P.C. Millar, OBE; Secretary: Mr J.S. Graham.
Established under the Mental Health (Scotland) Act 1960, as amended by the Mental Health (Scotland) Act 1984. Exercises protective functions in respect of people who may, by reason of mental disorder, be incapable of adequately protecting them-

selves or their interests. Where those people are liable to be detained in hospital, or subject to guardianship under the provisions of the Act, the commission's functions include, in appropriate cases, the discharge of such patients.

METHODIST CHURCH, SYNOD IN SCOTLAND, c/o Secretary, Dormarky, Glasgow Road, Kilsyth, Glasgow G65 9AE; T.-0236 823135.
Chairman: Rev Alan P. Horner; Secretary: Rev E. Raymond Watker.

MID-ARGYLL, KINTYRE & ISLAY TOURIST ORGANISATION, The Pier, Campbeltown PA28 6EF; T.-0586 52056.
Area Tourist Officer: L. MacKinnon.
Promotes tourism in the area.

MIDLOTHIAN CAMPAIGN LTD, 115 High Street, Dalkeith EH22 1AX; T.-031-660 5849.
Director: Frank Binnie.
Local enterprise trust.

MIDLOTHIAN DISTRICT COUNCIL, 1 White Hart Street, Dalkeith EH22 1DE; T.-031-663 2881.
Founded: 1974.
Convener: D. Lennie; Chief Executive and Director of Administration: D.W. Duguid; Director of Finance: W.W. Lang; Director of Planning and Building Control: R.W. Maslin; Director of Recreation and Leisure: J.A.L. Gilfillan; Director of Environmental Health and Cleansing: I.F. Florence; Director of Housing: A.S. Adams.
Political composition of council: Labour 14, Liberal/SDP Alliance 1. Population of district: 81,453.

MONKLANDS DISTRICT COUNCIL, Municipal Buildings, Dunbeth Road, Coatbridge ML5 3LF; T.-Coatbridge 24941.
Founded: 1974.
Provost: Edward Cairns; Chief Executive and Director of Finance: James S. Ness; Director of Administration and Legal Services: Denis Ward; Director of Technical Services: Thomas Linney; Director of Planning and Development: Andrew I. Cowe; Director of Housing: Thomas McKenzie.
Political composition of council: Labour 18, Conservative 2. Population of district: 108,155.

MONKLANDS ENTERPRISE TRUST, Mill Street Industrial Estate, Upper Mill Street, Airdrie ML6 6JJ; T.-02364 69255.
Director: Marshall Martin.

MORAY COLLEGE OF FURTHER EDUCATION, (MCFE), Hay Street, Elgin IV30 2NN; T.-0343 3425.
Founded: 1971.
Principal: Donald MacPhail.
Offers a wide range of vocational and non-vocational education and training programmes. Higher National Diploma courses offered and other activities include advanced and non-advanced courses on a full-time, part-time or open learning basis.

MORAY DISTRICT COUNCIL, District Headquarters, High Street, Elgin IV30 1BX; T.-0343 3451.
Founded: 1974.
Chairman: E. Aldridge; Chief Executive and Director of Administration: J.P.C. Bell; Director of Finance: I.J. Stuart; Director of Housing and Technical Services: I.F. Potter; Director of Physical Planning and Development: R.A. Stewart; Director of Libraries: Miss M. Innes; Director of Environmental Health: W. Stables; Director of Recreation: R. Cherry.
Political composition of council: Non-political 10, Independent 5, SNP 2, Labour 1. Population of district: 85,500.

MORAY ENTERPRISE TRUST, 9 North Gildry Street, Elgin, Morayshire; T.-0343 49644.
Director: Bob Paterson.

MORAY FIRTH RADIO, (MFR), PO Box 271, Inverness IV3 6SF; T.-0463 224433.
Founded: 1982.
Managing Director: Thomas Prag; Programme Organiser: Brian Anderson; News Editor: Mike Hurry; Head of Sales: Rod Webster; Head of Finance: Neil Shaw; Non-executive Chairman: Alistair Gardner.
Independent local radio station covering the Moray Firth area from Fraserburgh to Wick. Broadcasts from Inverness to a population of nearly 250,000.

MORAY HOUSE COLLEGE OF EDUCATION, Holyrood Road, Edinburgh EH8 8AQ; T.-031-556 8455.
Founded: 1848.
Principal: Gordon Kirk; Vice-principal: Dr

Edmund A. Ewan; Assistant Principals: Mrs Pauline E. Brown, Hugh E. Perfect; Registrar: Dr David Jenkins; College Secretary: Stewart Dowie.

Offers a wide range of pre-service and in-service courses for a number of related professions: teaching, social work, community education, and educational psychology. Contains the Scottish Centre for Education Overseas (Director: James W. Morrison).

MOTHERWELL COLLEGE, Dalzell Drive, Motherwell ML1 2DD; T.-0698 59641.
Founded: 1967.
Principal: John Reid; Vice-principal: Robert M. Russell; Registrar: James Paterson; Secretary: Mrs Betsy Borland.
College of further education with 6,000 students.

MOTHERWELL DISTRICT COUNCIL, Civic Centre, Motherwell; T.-Motherwell 66166.
Founded: 1974.
Provost: John McGhee; Chief Executive and Director of Administration: John Bonomy; Director of Finance and Depute Chief Executive: John Milne; Director of Technical Services: Alexander R. Stewart; Director of Planning: Stanley Cook; Director of Housing: Richard Thomson; Director of Environmental Health: James Brownlie; Director of Leisure Services: Norman Turner.
Political composition of council: Labour 23, SNP 3, Conservative 2, Communist 1, Others 1. Population of district: 149,185.

MOTHERWELL ENTERPRISE TRUST, 28 Brandon Parade, Motherwell ML1 1UJ; T.-0698 69333.
Founded: 1983.
Chairman: Harry Porter, OBE; Executive Director: John Murphy.

MOUNTAIN BOTHIES ASSOCIATION, The Laigh House, Inveresk, near Musselburgh; T.-031-665 2055.
Chairman: Prof D. Mollison.

MOUNTAINEERING COUNCIL OF SCOTLAND, Rahoy Lodge, Gallinach Road, Oban, Argyll PA34 4PD.
Founded: 1971.
Secretary: Robin Shaw.
Fosters and promotes mountaineering in Scotland. Has 85 member clubs.

MOUNTAIN RESCUE COMMITTEE OF SCOTLAND, 5 Westfield Terrace, Aberdeen AB2 4RU; T.-0224 646995.
Chairman: Andrew Nicol; Honorary Treasurer: Andrew Wilson; Medical Officer: Dr Alastair MacGregor; Honorary Secretary: Malcolm Duckworth.
Central co-ordinating committee for all mountain rescue organisations in Scotland. The committee sets standards for training and distributes funds to teams. Around 30 rescue organisations are represented on the committee which is in turn represented on other national mountaineering and mountain rescue related bodies.

MULL LITTLE THEATRE, Dervaig, Isle of Mull; T.-06884 267.
Chairman: Chris Baker; Vice Chairman: David Pitman; Secretary: Jill Galbraith.
Britain's smallest professional theatre (38 seats). Summer season of plays begins in April.

MULTIPLE SCLEROSIS SOCIETY IN SCOTLAND, 27 Castle Street, Edinburgh EH2 3DN; T.-031-225 3600.
Founded: 1953.
Chairman: Mrs I.B. Reid; Vice-chairman: Lt Col F.R.N. Kerr, OBE, MC; Organising Secretary: Lt Col A.G. Bisset; Honorary Treasurer: Mr N.J. Pollock.
Two principal aims: to provide for the welfare of people with multiple sclerosis, and to fund medical research into its cause and finding a cure. The society's welfare function is exercised through a network of 38 branches which are all run by committees of volunteers. In addition, it provides holiday homes with full nursing service and self-catering holiday chalets designed for use by disabled people.

N

NAIRN DISTRICT COUNCIL, The Court House, Nairn IV12 4AU; T.-0667 52056.
Founded: 1974.
Provost: Lt Col Hugh McLean, MBE; Director of Law and Administration and Leisure and Recreation: Allan MacDonald Kerr; Director of Technical Services: Andrew Miller Cook; Director of Finance: W. John Anderson.
Political composition of council: Independent 9, Labour 1. Population of district: 10,180.

NAPIER COLLEGE, Colinton Road,

Edinburgh EH10 5DT; T.-031-444 2266.
Founded: 1964.
Chairman of Governing Body: Prof R.C.B. Aitken; Principal: W.A. Turmeau; Depute Principals: K.J. Anderson, I.H. Marker; Secretary and Academic Registrar: R.W. Stevenson; Information Officer: J.W. Dey.
Largest Scottish Central Institution and the fifth largest higher education establishment in Scotland, with 4,500 full-time and 3,500 part-time students. Courses cover professional studies, humanities, technology and science. Degrees, Higher National Diplomas, MPhil, PhD and research appointments are offered. Houses the Scottish Energy Centre, a small business unit, polymer laboratory, computer aided design centre and full industrial liaison and consultancy facilities. A sports dome caters for most sporting activities. Six college sites are based in the south west side of Edinburgh.

NATIONAL ASSOCIATION OF SCHOOLMASTERS AND UNION OF WOMEN TEACHERS (SCOTLAND), 34 West George Street, Glasgow G2 1DA; T.-041-332 2688.
Founded: 1933.
President: William Matthew; National Executive Member: Patrick O'Donnell; Scottish Secretary: John Duffy; Regional Official: James O'Neill; Convenor, Education Committee: Colin Wakeling; Convenor, Trade Union Committee: Roy Robertson.
Successor to the Scottish Schoolmasters Association. Affiliated to the TUC and STUC as well as to the ETUCE and IFFTU. Concerned with the salaries, conditions and welfare of teachers in all sectors of education, and in all parts of the United Kingdom.

NATIONAL ASSOCIATION FOR THE WELFARE OF CHILDREN IN HOSPITAL (SCOTLAND), 15 Smith's Place, Edinburgh EH6 8HT; T.-031-553 6553.
Founded: 1977.
National Co-ordinator: Mrs Julia Millar; Chairman: Mrs Elizabeth Bathgate.
Advises parents, professionals responsible for the care of children, and authorities responsible for the planning of hospital services of the special needs of sick children. Supports the provision of play facilities and facilities for parents to stay or visit their children as much as possible when in hospital. Information is provided for parents, children and professionals through leaflets, books, films, slides and talks and the provision of hospital playboxes. There are 11 groups in Scotland and around 200 members throughout Scotland who raise funds to provide equipment and information in their own areas. The above office is open 9.30am - 2pm, Tuesday, Wednesday and Thursday and a telephone answering machine is available at other times.

NATIONAL ASSOCIATION OF YOUTH ORCHESTRAS, (NAYO), Ainslie House, 11 St Colme Street, Edinburgh EH3 6AG; T.-031-225 4606.
Founded: 1961.
Honorary Chairman: Michael Rose; Honorary Vice-chairman: Brian Brown; Honorary Treasurer: Lucy Nattrass; Secretary: Carol Main.
Set up to represent youth and inter-school orchestras in the United Kingdom. Presents an annual festival of British youth orchestras in Edinburgh, organises an annual Anglo-German Youth Music Week, held in Germany and England in alternate years, and arranges courses, events and concerts in response to specific interests and needs. Publications include newsletters and a register of youth orchestras.

NATIONAL BIBLE SOCIETY OF SCOTLAND, (NBSS), 7 Hampton Terrace, Edinburgh EH12 5XU; T.-031-337 9701.
Founded: 1809.
President: Sir David McNee, QPM; Chairman: Rev Douglas Nicol; General Secretary: Rev Fergus Macdonald.
Charity which promotes the translation, production and distribution of the Bible, in whole or in part, into the languages of the world, at a level which ordinary people can understand and at a price which they can afford. Founder member of the United Bible Societies, a fellowship of 70 national bible societies working in over 150 countries.

NATIONAL BOARD FOR NURSING, MIDWIFERY AND HEALTH VISITING FOR SCOTLAND, 22 Queen Street, Edinburgh EH2 1JX; T.-031-226 7371.
Founded: 1983.
Chairman: Miss C.A. Asher; Deputy Chairman: Miss E.A. Edwards; Chief Executive Officer: Miss E.C. Coutts.
Provides training courses leading to registration as a nurse, midwife or health visitor and further training for those already

registered. Also provides an examination structure to enable people to become registered or to obtain additional qualifications. Investigates allegations of misconduct against nurses, midwives and health visitors.

NATIONAL COAL BOARD, SCOTTISH AREA. See British Coal.

NATIONAL DEAF BLIND AND RUBELLA ASSOCIATION, 168 Dumbarton Road, Glasgow G11 6XE; T.-041-334 9666/9675.
Founded: 1984.
Chairperson: Dr John Tulloch; Scottish Officer: Mrs Gillian Morbey.
The association, known as Sense-in-Scotland, seeks to promote awareness of the dual sensory disability of deafness and blindness. It promotes awareness through conferences, literature, talks, visits to homes and schools etc. It provides publicity for rubella vaccinations as the disease is still one of the major causes of deafness and blindness. Regular parents' meetings are held and counselling, advice and information is available. Holidays are provided and research is carried out into the incidence of deaf-blindness and the needs of deaf-blind children and adults. The association also campaigns for improved provisions by advising and assisting local authorities regarding the needs of deaf-blind people so that they can live as full and dignified a life as possible.

NATIONAL ENGINEERING LABORATORY, (NEL), East Kilbride, Glasgow G75 0QU; T.-East Kilbride 20222.
Founded: 1947.
Director: Dr D.A. Bell; Deputy Director: Mr H.L. Wunsch.
The United Kingdom national laboratory for mechanical engineering, and part of the Department of Trade and Industry. The largest organisation of its kind in the United Kingdom, with a staff or around 600. It has at its disposal many advanced and unique facilities and expertise appropriate to most industries in the field of mechanical engineering. Carries out research, design work, development, testing and measurement, and consultancy and troubleshooting in the following areas: mechanical engineering manufacture, process plant, oil

and gas (including offshore), vehicles, construction equipment, and metals and other materials.

NATIONAL FARMERS' UNION OF SCOTLAND, 17 Grosvenor Crescent, Edinburgh EH12 5EN; T.-031-337 4333.
Founded: 1913.
President: I.D. Grant; Vice Presidents: J.L. Goodfellow, J.A. Ross; Director and General Secretary: D.S. Johnston; Deputy General Secretary: R.I. Sandilands.
Watches over, protects, and promotes the interests of agriculture, horticulture, and aquaculture in all its branches, and encourages the development of the industry by such means as may seem necessary.

NATIONAL GALLERIES OF SCOTLAND, 83 Princes Street, Edinburgh EH2 2ER.
Chairman of Trustees: Robert Begg; Director: Timothy Clifford; Secretary and Accountant to the Board of Trustees: William Sinclair.
Consists of: National Gallery of Scotland, The Mound, Edinburgh. Keeper: post vacant. Also houses the Department of Prints and Drawings (Keeper: Hugh Macandrew). Scottish National Portrait Gallery, Queen Street, Edinburgh. Keeper: Duncan Thomson. Scottish National Gallery of Modern Art, Belford Road, Edinburgh. Keeper: post vacant.

NATIONAL GALLERY OF SCOTLAND. See National Galleries of Scotland.

NATIONAL LIBRARY OF SCOTLAND, George IV Bridge, Edinburgh EH1 1EW; T.-031-226 4531.
Founded: 1925.
Librarian: Prof E.F.D. Roberts.
A library of copyright deposit and therefore entitled to claim a copy of each new work published in Great Britain and Ireland. The largest library in Scotland with around 5,000,000 items. Concerns itself with the acquisition and preservation of Scottish books and manuscripts and has an unrivalled collection of these. Its map room houses the largest collection of maps in the United Kingdom north of Cambridge. The reading rooms are for reference and research that cannot readily be carried out elsewhere. Application forms for readers'

tickets are available from the Superinten-dent of Readers' Services.

NATIONAL MUSEUM OF ANTI-QUITIES OF SCOTLAND. See National Museums of Scotland.

NATIONAL MUSEUMS OF SCOT-LAND, (NMS), Royal Museum of Scotland, Chambers Street, Edin-burgh EH1 1JF; T.-031-225 7534.

Founded: 1985.
Chairman of Trustees: The Marquess of Bute; Director: Dr Robert Anderson; Research Director: Dr A. Fenton; Head of History and Applied Art: Miss D. Idiens; Head of Natural History: Dr M. Shaw; Head of Science, Technology and Working Life: Mr D. Storer; Head of Geology: Dr I Rolfe.
Combines Scotland's two long established national museums: the former National Museum of Antiquities of Scotland which traditionally concentrated on the nation's material heritage; and the former Royal Scottish Museum which was primarily con-cerned with worldwide collections of the decorative arts, technology and physical sciences, natural history and geology. In addition, the National Museums of Scotland includes a number of museums housing specialist collections: the Scottish United Services Museum at Edinburgh Castle, the Scottish Agricultural Museum at Ingliston, the Museum of Flight at East Fortune, East Lothian, Shambellie House Museum of Cos-tume near Dumfries, and Biggar Gasworks Museum in Lanarkshire.

NATIONAL PLAYING FIELDS ASSOCIATION (SCOTLAND), 12 Manor Place, Edinburgh EH3 7DD; T.-031-225 4307.

Founded: 1926.
President: Rt Hon Lord Clydesmuir, KT, CB, MBE, TD; Chairman: W.F.E. Forbes; Deputy Chairman: Brian M. Simmers; Director: M.R.S. Cunningham, MBE.
Encourages the provision and development of recreational and sporting facilities for the benefit of young people, assisting finan-cially by grants and loans.

NATIONAL SCHIZOPHRENIA FELLOWSHIP (SCOTLAND), 40 Shandwick Place, Edinburgh EH2 4RT; T.-031-226 2025.

Chairman: Mrs Freda Middleton; Vice-chairman: Dr G.H. Begbie; Legal Adviser: Mr A.H. Elder; Development Officer: Gilly

Peakman.
Established to: support sufferers from schizophrenia and their families; provide information and advice; spread a greater understanding of the special problems arising from the illness; secure the improve-ment of community care facilities of all kinds, particularly appropriately super-vised accommodation; encourage co-operation and communication between medical and social supervision and families caring for a relative; encourage the recogni-tion that it is the right of a mentally ill person to expect care and protection at a time when judgement is impaired.

NATIONAL TRUST FOR SCOT-LAND, (NTS), 5 Charlotte Square, Edinburgh EH3 1DU; T. 031-226 5922.

Founded: 1931.
President: The Earl of Wemyss and March, KT; Vice Presidents: The Duke of Atholl, Mrs Edward Denny, OBE, E.J. Ivory, A. Ken-nedy, A.S. Roger, MBE, JP, The Marquess of Bute; Chairman of Council: William M. Cuthbert; Deputy Chairman of Council: R.C. Tyrrell; Director: Lester Borley.
Formed to promote the preservation, for the benefit of the nation, of Scotland's heritage of architectural, scenic and historic treasures and to encourage public enjoy-ment of them. In its care are 100 properties covering 100,000 acres and including cas-tles and great houses, historic sites, gar-dens, islands, little houses, mountains, waterfalls, coastline and the birthplaces of some famous Scots. These attract over 1.5 million visitors annually. The trust is a charity dependent on legacies, donations and the subscriptions of its 145,000 members.

NATURE CONSERVANCY COUN-CIL, Headquarters for Scotland, 12 Hope Terrace, Edinburgh EH9 2AS; T.-031-447 4784.

Founded: 1973.
Director for Scotland: Dr J.M. Francis; Deputy Director for Scotland: J. McCarthy.
Government body responsible for nature conservation in Britain. Establishes nature reserves and carries out advisory and research work.

NESDA. See North East Scotland Develop-ment Authority.

NETWORK SCOTLAND, 74 Victoria Crescent Road, Glasgow G12 9JQ; T.-041-357 1774.

Founded: 1984.
Chairman: Alex Inglis, OBE; Executive Director: Michael W. Russell; Assistant Directors: Anne Docherty (Broadcasting), David Geer (Education and Training).
The broadcast support and educational information agency for Scotland. Formed by the IBA, BBC Scotland, the Scottish Community Education Council and the Scottish Council for Educational Technology to undertake information services in support of broadcasting and education. Handles over 150,000 enquiries each year, both for television and radio support materials and for referral to specialist agencies. In education, it both gives information on existing opportunities for adults and assists with the development and promotion of new opportunities. Has a growing involvement in information on training for industry and small business. The Scottish Health Education Group, the Manpower Services Commission and Scottish local authorities are also closely involved with its work.

NEWBATTLE ABBEY COLLEGE, Newbattle Road, Dalkeith, Midlothian EH22 3LL; T.-031-663 1921.
Founded: 1936.
Principal: Alexander D. Reid; College Secretary: Stuart W. Mair; Chairman of Board of Governors: Callan J. Anderson; Senior Tutor: David G.D. Turner; Short Course Organiser: Donald Mackay.
Scotland's only residential college for adult students. Set in a stately home, it offers one and two year courses in liberal studies, which can facilitate entry to university, and a programme of short courses catering for a wide range of interests. There is accommodation for 75 students, mostly in single rooms. Scottish Education Department grants are available for the long courses. For details of long courses, contact the Senior Tutor, for details of short courses, contact the Short Course Organiser.

NEW LANARK CONSERVATION TRUST, New Lanark, Lanark ML11 9DG; T.-0555 61345.
Founded: 1974.
Manager: J. Arnold; Chairman of Trust: H. Smith.
Objective is to revive the historic village of New Lanark. Various bodies are associated with the trust, including the New Lanark Association Ltd, the village housing association, Friends of New Lanark, and the Scottish Wildlife Trust who are responsible for the Falls of Clyde nature reserve. The plan is to bring the entire village back to life as part of an intergrated scheme.

NEW MUSIC GROUP OF SCOTLAND, (NMGS), Ainslie House, 11 St Colme Street, Edinburgh EH3 6AG; T.-031-225 4606.
Founded: 1973.
Director: Edward Harper; Chairman: Thomas Wilson; Administrator: Carol Main.
Exists for the advancement, promotion, encouragement and the fostering of public knowledge and appreciation of the arts, in particular contemporary chamber music, in Scotland and elsewhere. Promotes concerts, lectures, operas etc. and commissions new works.

NITHSDALE DISTRICT COUNCIL, Municipal Chambers, Dumfries DG1 2AD; T.-0387 53166.
Founded: 1974.
Provost: Kenneth Cameron, JP; Chief Executive: W.W. Japp; Director of Administration: I.W. Watson; Director of Finance: K.C. Brown; Director of Environmental Health: K.M. Stewart; Director of Technical Services and Housing: E.D. Denholm.
Political composition of council: Conservative 7, SNP 7, Labour 6, Independent 5, Non-affiliated 2, Independent Labour 1. Population of district: 57,149.

NORTH ATLANTIC SALMON CONSERVATION ORGANIZATION, (NASCO), 11 Rutland Square, Edinburgh EH1 2AS; T.-031-228 2551.
Secretariat established: 1984.
Secretary: Dr Malcolm Windsor; Assistant Secretary: Dr Peter Hutchinson; Personal Assistant to Secretary: Mrs Zila Clarke.
Inter-government organisation founded by a convention of which the parties are Canada, the EEC, Denmark (in respect of the Faroe Islands and Greenland), Iceland, Norway, Sweden, Finland, the USA and the USSR. Its aims are to promote the acquisition, analysis and dissemination of scientific information pertaining to salmon stocks in the North Atlantic ocean and the conservation, restoration, enhancement and rational management of these stocks through international co-operation.

NORTH COUNTRY CHEVIOT SHEEP SOCIETY, (NCCSS), The Cottage, Reay, Thurso, Caithness KW14 7RE; T.-084 781 202.

Founded: 1945.
President: Alistair Swanson; Senior Vice President: William Howat; Junior Vice President: John H. Borthwick.
Upholds and promotes the breed as one best fitted to meet modern day standards of carcase classification.

NORTH EAST FIFE DISTRICT COUNCIL, County Buildings, Cupar, Fife KY15 4TA; T.-0334 53722.

Founded: 1974.
Chairman: D.A. Barrie, JP; Chief Executive and Secretary and Legal Adviser: R.G. Brotherton; Director of Finance: M.C. Dyke; Director of Environmental Health: R.J. Vettraino; Director of Planning and Building Control: P.G. Hutchinson; Director of Housing: M. Stanley; Director of Technical Services: R.M. Hastie; Director of Recreation: A.C. Kydd.
Political composition of council: Liberal 11, Conservative 5, Independent 2. Population of district: 66,260.

NORTH EAST RIVER PURIFICATION BOARD, Woodside House, Mugiemoss Road, Persley, Aberdeen AB2 2UQ; T.-0224 696647.

River Inspector: F.J. Little.

NORTH EAST SCOTLAND DEVELOPMENT AUTHORITY, (NESDA), 8 Albyn Place, Aberdeen AB1 1YH; T.-0224 643322.

Director: David C. Ross; Depute Director: Ian R. Mackay; Assistant Director: James Knowles; Principal Development Officer: John Millar; Marketing: Sara Reid.
NESDA is the development department of Grampian Regional Council, and the business advice and information centre for the area. Its free and confidential advice and information service is offered on a broad range of business matters including business opportunities, incentives, marketing, joint ventures, contracts, agencies, licence agreements. A comprehensive file of available premises is maintained. Produces the *Grampian Directory* which lists over 2,000 companies in the region in a broad range of industries.

THE NORTH OF SCOTLAND COLLEGE OF AGRICULTURE, (NOSCA), School of Agriculture, 581 King Street, Aberdeen AB9 1UD; T.-0224 480291.

Founded: 1904.
Chairman: Mr N.S. Thornton-Kemsley; Vice-chairman: Mr W.J. Ferguson; Principal: Prof A.S. Jones; Secretary and Treasurer: Mrs S.S. Hannabuss.
Performs the three functions of advisory work, research and development, and education. Provides advice on all aspects of agriculture to the farming community throughout the North of Scotland. Provides courses at diploma, higher diploma and post diploma levels and, in association with Aberdeen University's Department of Agriculture, a degree in agriculture and postgraduate supervision. It is characteristic of its staff that most of them are engaged in two or three of its functions, providing an integrated approach to agriculture.

NORTH OF SCOTLAND GRASSLAND SOCIETY, c/o School of Agriculture, 581 King Street, Aberdeen AB9 1UD; T.-0224 480291.

Founded: 1961.
Secretary: Charles K. Mackie.
Aims to promote efficient production and utilisation of grass and forage crops and to encourage education and research into these crops. Activities include meetings, farm walks, demonstrations and competitions. A magazine is published annually reviewing the society's activities and current grassland information. The membership of 420 consists of farmers, trade representatives, agricultural advisers and research workers.

NORTH OF SCOTLAND HYDRO-ELECTRIC BOARD, 16 Rothesay Terrace, Edinburgh EH3 7SE; T.-031-225 1361.

Founded: 1943.
Chairman: M. Joughin, CBE; Deputy Chairman and Chief Executive: K.R. Vernon, CBE; Chief Engineer: A.T.L. Murray; Commercial Director: J.M. Chatwin; Financial Director: A.D. Stewart; Personnel Director: R.J. Jackson; Secretary: J.E.M. Watts; Computing and Services Controller: A.A. Robertson.
The board, an autonomous nationalised industry, is responsible to the Secretary of State for Scotland for the generation, transmission, distribution and retail sale of electricity in the North of Scotland. The board's district comprises Scotland to the north and west of a line roughly joining the Firths of Clyde and Tay, including all the island groups extending to the Outer Hebrides, Orkney and Shetland; it covers one quarter of the land area, and contains about 2% of the population of Great Britain.

Almost 100% of potential customers in the Board's district have been provided with a supply. The board was set up under the Hydro-Electric Development (Scotland) Act 1943 to exploit the water power resources of the Highlands. Operates hydro and pumped storage, steam, diesel, and gas turbine stations.

NORTH OF SCOTLAND MILK MARKETING BOARD, Claymore House, 29 Ardconnel Terrace, Inverness IV2 3AF; T.-0463 232611.
Founded: 1934.
Chairman: J. Clark; Vice-chairman: P.D. Cheyne; Managing Director: J.A. Anderson; Finance Director: W.L. Anderson; Production Manager: J. Matheson.
Responsible for the marketing of milk in Morayshire, Nairn, Inverness-shire, Caithness, Sutherland and Orkney. Collects all milk produced in the area and sells to buyers. Operates its own commercial division which processes and packages liquid milk and manufactures butter, cream and cheese.

NORTHSOUND RADIO, 45 King's Gate, Aberdeen AB2 6BL; T.-0224 632234.
Founded: 1981.
Chairman: A.D.F. Lewis; Managing Director: Paul Stevenson; Head of Finance: John Martin; Head of Sales: Gloria Taylor; Chief Engineer: Bob Barrow; News Editor: Rob Maclean; Head of Music: Graeme Moreland. Independent local radio station for Aberdeen and North East Scotland.

O

OATRIDGE AGRICULTURAL COLLEGE, Ecclesmachan, Broxburn, West Lothian EH52 6NH; T.-0506 854387.
Principal: Mr C.W. Nixon; Depute Principal: Mr I.J. Santer; Registrar: Mrs P.J. Skett.

OBAN, MULL AND DISTRICT TOURIST BOARD, Tourist Information Centre, Argyll Square, Oban; T.-Oban 63122.
Chairman: Ian Nicholson; Area Tourist Officer: Jane Johnson.
Promotes tourism in the area and provides information and accommodation booking services.

OMBUDSMAN. See Commissioner for Local Administration in Scotland.

THE OPEN UNIVERSITY IN SCOTLAND, 60 Melville Street, Edinburgh EH3 7HF; T.-031-226 3851.
Founded: 1969.
Scottish Director: George K.W. Arkieson, DFC; Deputy Scottish Director (Glasgow): Mrs Marion Jack, 2 Park Gardens, Glasgow G3 7YE, T.-041-332 4364.
Set up to provide higher education by distance teaching methods for adults in full-time employment or who work in the home. No academic qualifications are required for entry to the degree course. Continuing Education Programme offers a variety of single courses, both on academic subjects and vocational updating and professional training, as well as self-contained learning packages and short courses on matters of everyday concern.

ORDNANCE SURVEY, (OS), 160 Causewayside, Edinburgh EH9 1UX; T.-031-668 3281.
Founded: 1791.
Region Manager: Mr T.D. Shiell; Area Managers: Mr M.N. Gordon (North), Mr E. Pearson (South); Chief Surveyors: Mr P. Morrison (Planning), Mr E. Cameron (Technical).
Responsible for the official surveying and topographic mapping of Britain. Employs 126 staff in the Scottish Region, mainly surveyors and other technical staff who are dispersed throughout the area and operate from 14 local offices. Any OS office may be contacted for information on the latest available survey work, or for advice on cartographic or geodetic matters generally.

ORKNEY HEALTH BOARD, Health Centre, New Scapa Road, Kirkwall, Orkney; T.-0856 2763.
Founded: 1974.
Chairman: J.D.M. Robertson; Vice Chairman: A.H. Bevan; General Manager/Chief Administrative Medical Officer: Dr J.I. Cromarty; Chief Area Nursing Officer: H. Ferris; Chief Administrative Dental Officer: C.J. Booth; Chief Administrative Officer: J.A. Muir; Treasurer: A.F. Preen.
Health board.

ORKNEY ISLANDS COUNCIL, Council Offices, Kirkwall KW15 1NY; T.-0856 3535.
Founded: 1974.

Convener: E.R. Eunson; Chief Executive and Director of Finance: R.H. Gilbert; Director of Administration and Legal Services: R. McCallum; Director of Economic Development: J. Baster; Director of Education and Recreation Services: R.L. Henderson; Director of Engineering and Technical Services: H.L. Cross; Director of Environmental Health: A.E. Leslie; Director of Planning: T.W. Eggeling; Director of Social Work: H. MacGillivray; Director of Trading Standards and Consumer Protection: D.J. Macgruer; Director of Harbours: Capt H.A. Banks.
Non-political authority, 24 members. Population of area: 19,351.

ORKNEY TOURIST BOARD, Tourist Information Centre, 6 Broad Street, Kirkwall, Orkney KW15 1NX; T.-Kirkwall 2856.
Founded: 1969.
Chairman: Kenneth Anderson; Secretary: Josh Gourlay.
Promotes tourism in Orkney.

OUTER HEBRIDES TOURIST BOARD, 4 South Beach Street, Stornoway PA87 2XY; T.-0851 3088.
Promotes tourism in the Outer Hebrides.

P

THE PAISLEY CHAMBER OF COMMERCE AND INDUSTRY LTD, 51 Moss Street, Paisley PA1 1DS; T.-041-889 6244.
Founded: 1964.
President: William S. Burns; Vice President: J. Russell Cockburn; Treasurer: Angus Boyd; Secretary: J.R. McClymont.
Set up to provide for local industry and commerce a single voice in various discussions with the local and national authorities and to act on the members' behalf in representations to those bodies.

PAISLEY COLLEGE OF TECHNOLOGY, High Street, Paisley PA1 2BE; T.-041-887 1241.
Founded: 1897.
Principal: T.M. Howie; Vice Principal: R.W. Shaw; Secretary: J.M. Oswald; Chairman of Governors: A.E. Harper; Vice Chairman of Governors: J. McLaren.
Provides degree and postgraduate study for 3,000 students in engineering, science, management and social sciences. All courses have a strong vocational emphasis and in many the 'sandwich' structure

enables students to spend time working in their chosen field as part of their degree. Academic departments and specialised units maintain close collaboration with firms both large and small through Teaching Company Schemes, short course provision, consultancy and research.

PAISLEY/RENFREW ENTERPRISE TRUST, 5 Sandyford Road, Paisley; T.-041-889 0010.
Director: David Logan.

PARANTAN AIRSON FOGHLAM GAIDHLIG, (Parents for Gaelic-medium Education), 111 Academy Street, Inverness IV1 1LX; T.-0463 225469.
Chairman: Keith Scammell.
A charitable organisation encouraging the establishment of, and giving practical support to, Gaelic-medium primary school education.

PAROLE BOARD FOR SCOTLAND, St Margaret's House, London Road, Edinburgh EH8 7TQ; T.-031-661 6181.
Founded: 1968.
Chairman: Mrs J.D.O. Morris, MBE; Vice Chairman: Dr D. Chiswick; Secretary: I.C. Stewart.
Advises the Secretary of State for Scotland on the release of prisoners under licence, on the conditions of such licences, the revocation of such licences, and allied matters.

PENSION APPEALS TRIBUNALS FOR SCOTLAND, 20 Walker Street, Edinburgh EH3 7HS; T.-031-225 4734.
Founded: 1943.
President: J.A. Cameron; Secretary: Miss E. Wilson.
Hears and decides appeals against the rejection, by the DHSS, of War Pension claims.

PERTH COLLEGE OF FURTHER EDUCATION, Crieff Road, Perth; T.-0738 21171.
Founded: 1971.
Chairman, Marketing Committee: Roger J. Barnes.
Multi-disciplined body covering subjects from craft to Higher National Diploma level. Wide variety of open learning courses available from 'O' grades to management and technical studies. Approximately 180 staff and over 3,000 students. In response to

industry's needs, training and tutoring can be done in college or on an outreach basis.

PERTH AND KINROSS DISTRICT COUNCIL, Council Building, 2 High Street, Perth PH1 5PH; T.-0738 39911.

Founded: 1974.
Provost: John M. Mathieson, OBE; Chief Executive: J.E.D. Cormie; Director of Finance: H. Robertson; Director of Planning and Industry: David R. Penman; Director of Architectural Services: J.J. Turnbull; Director of Environmental Health: W.A. Dunlop, MBE; Director of Housing: G. Black; Director of Leisure and Recreation: Malcolm B. Wood; Director of Personnel: George Wallace.
Political composition of council: Conservative 14, Labour 6, Liberal/SDP Alliance 5, Independent 3, SNP 1. Population of district: 122,360.

PERTH MUSEUM AND ART GALLERY, George Street, Perth PH1 5LB; T.-0738 32488.

Founded: 1824.
Curator: James A. Blair.
Contains collections of fine art, ceramics, glass, silver, local history, archaeology and natural sciences. There are changing exhibitions on a wide range of subjects, and permanent exhibitions on Perth glass, Perth silver and the natural history of Perth and Kinross.

PERTH REPERTORY THEATRE LTD, 185 High Street, Perth PH1 5UW; T.-0738 21031/38123.

Founded: 1935.
Artistic Director: Joan Knight; General Manager: D.J. Bonnar; Secretary/ Treasurer: H. Robertson.
Scotland's oldest established repertory theatre. Presents a mixed season of drama and musicals, and plays host to occasional tours by other companies. Tours are also mounted by the company to other Scottish theatres. Art exhibitions take place in the theatre and there is a coffee bar and restaurant open daily.

THE PERTHSHIRE CHAMBER OF COMMERCE, 8 Charlotte Street, Perth PH1 5LL; T.-0738 37626.

Founded: 1871.
Chairman: Mr R.W. Dunbar; Vice Chairman: Mr J. Stewart; Secretary: Mr D.G. Elliot.
Represents the commercial and business interests of its 320 members. A member of the Association of Scottish Chambers of Commerce and the Association of British Chambers of Commerce. Provides an export service, certifying certificates of origin for member firms. An annual buyers' guide and trade directory is produced.

PERTHSHIRE TOURIST BOARD, PO Box 33, George Inn Lane, Perth; T.-0738 27958/9.

Founded: 1982.
Chairman, Management Committee: Norman T. Renfrew; Director of Tourism: John L. Granger.
Exists for the promotion and development of tourism throughout Perthshire.

PHAB SCOTLAND, Princes House, 5 Shandwick Place, Edinburgh EH2 4RG; T.-031-229 3559.

Founded: 1981.
Area Director: Isobel Munro; Chairman: R.P. Gibbs, OBE; Treasurer: A. Meldrum.
Main aim is to further the integration of the physically handicapped into the community by promoting opportunities for the physically handicapped (PH) and able bodied (AB) to come together on equal terms. This is done in a club setting, through holidays and training courses and through liaison with other agencies with similar interests. Recreational activities include sponsored walks, fun days, horseriding, swimming, arts and crafts. Although recreational and social activities are important to PHAB clubs, the HQ organisation is more concerned with increasing awareness of the need for integration and education.

PHARMACEUTICAL GENERAL COUNCIL (SCOTLAND), (PGC), 34 York Place, Edinburgh EH1 3HU; T.-031-556 2076/8351.

Chairman: Ian Mullen; Secretary: Dr Colin Virden.
The body recognised by the Secretary of State for Scotland as representing the interests of Scotland's 1,130 retail pharmacies in National Health Service matters. It is an elected body of 42 members drawn from the 15 health board areas. The Pharmaceutical Standing Committee, which has 15 members elected by the PGC, is the executive of the general council.

THE PIOBAIREACHD SOCIETY, 20 Otago Street, Glasgow G12 8JH; T.-041-334 3587.

Founded: 1902.
President: D.J.S. Murray; Honorary Secre-

tary: Seumas MacNeill; Honorary Treasurer: Tom Speirs.

Publishes a collection of piobaireachd (the classical music of the Highland bagpipe) in 14 parts, along with several other books relating to this kind of music. Sponsors competitions annually at Oban and Inverness. The annual conference, which is open to all, is held in April. Membership is in excess of 300. Similar societies, affiliated to this parent body, exist in Australia and New Zealand.

PITLOCHRY AND DISTRICT TOURIST ASSOCIATION, 22 Atholl Road, Pitlochry PH16 5BX; T.-0796 2215.
Founded: 1954.

Chairman: Erhart J. Penker; Tourist Officer and Secretary: James S. Todd; Treasurer: J. Wallace Crowe.

Promotes Pitlochry and district, operates its tourist information centre, markets the area and publicises its entertainments. It is the largest tourist association in Scotland.

PITLOCHRY FESTIVAL THEATRE, Port-na-Craig, Pitlochry PH16 5DR; T.-0796 3054.
Founded: 1951.

Artistic Director: Clive Perry; Administrator: Stephen Lawrence; General Manager and Licensee: Roy Wilson; Marketing Manager: Paul McLennan; Production Manager: Elaine Kyle.

Established in its famous 'tent' theatre for 30 years, it is now housed in a new building on the banks of the River Tummel. Presents drama, music, and art.

THE PLANNING EXCHANGE, 186 Bath Street, Glasgow G2 4HG; T.-041-332 8541.
Founded: 1972.

Chairman: William L. Taylor, CBE; Director: Anthony W. Burton.

An independent non-profit making organisation which acts as an information exchange and advice centre for all matters to do with planning, housing, economic development and public administration. Has the most comprehensive (computerised) library in Scotland on published and semi-published information on local government and related services. Membership provides access to a wide range of information, advice, research and training resources.

POLICE ADVISORY BOARD FOR SCOTLAND, (PABS), c/o Scottish Home and Health Department, St

Andrew's House, Edinburgh EH1 3DE; T.-031-556 8400.
Founded: 1965.

Exists to advise the Secretary of State for Scotland on non-negotiable matters affecting the police in Scotland (ie matters other than hours of duty, leave, pay and allowances, or issue, use and return of police clothing, personal equipment and accoutrements). Comprises representatives from the Association of Chief Police Officers (Scotland), the Association of Scottish Police Superintendents, the Scottish Police Federation, COSLA and five independent members. Meets at least once annually.

POLICE (SCOTLAND) EXAMINATIONS BOARD, (P(S)EB), c/o Scottish Home and Health Department, St Andrew's House, Edinburgh EH1 3DE; T.-031-556 8501.
Founded: 1922.

Chairman: J. Dunning; Vice-chairman: Dr W. Easton; Secretary: W.N. Cameron.

Conducts the qualifying examinations or such other examinations in connection with promotion or recruitment of constables, as designated by the Secretary of State. Determines the standard to be achieved by candidates in order to obtain a pass.

POST OFFICE USERS COUNCIL FOR SCOTLAND, (POUCS), Alhambra House, 45 Waterloo Street, Glasgow G2 6AT; T.-041-248 2855.
Founded: 1970.

Chairman: G.C.C. Duncan; Secretary: M. McNab.

Set up by Parliament to look after the interests of users of all Post Office services. The council is independent of the Post Office and consists of a chairman and up to 24 members. Members are appointed by the Secretary of State for Trade and Industry and are drawn from a wide variety of backgrounds. Receives and considers representations about services and deals with complaints from individuals.

PRESS & JOURNAL, Lang Stracht, Mastrick, Aberdeen AB9 8AF; T.-0224 690222.
Founded: 1748 (as Aberdeen Journal).

Editor: Harry Roulston.

Daily newspaper circulating in Aberdeen and the North of Scotland.

PRINCESS   LOUISE   SCOTTISH

HOSPITAL, Bishopton, Renfrewshire PA7 5PU; T.-041-812 1100.
Founded: 1916.
Chairman: Vice Adml Sir Thomas Baird, KCB; Commandant: Col W.K. Shepherd; Senior Medical Officer: Dr T. McFadyen; Matron: Mrs M.E. Lundie; Treasurer: Mr I.W. Grimmond; Secretary: Mr A.O. Robertson.
Founded by public subscription, initially to care for the limbless from the 1914-18 War. Subsequently accepted ex-servicemen and women from all three services (including the Merchant Navy) with all types of disability, illness and injury, whether caused in peace or war. More than 50,000 have been cared for since it opened. Provides long or short stay and convalescent hospital facilities and opportunities for rehabilitation, training and paid employment in sheltered workshops and a market garden. There are three self-catering holiday flats with nursing care for ex-service people and 53 cottages within the grounds for families. Largest ex-service hospital in the United Kingdom (300 beds), outwith the National Health Service and hence dependent on public financial support by legacy and donation.

PROCURATOR FISCAL SERVICE.
Glasgow and Strathkelvin Region, T.-041-204 2855. Regional Procurator Fiscal: J.M. Tudhope. *Lothian and Borders Region,* T.-031-226 4962. Regional Procurator Fiscal: J.D. Allan. *Grampian, Highlands and Islands Region,* T.-0224 645132. Regional Procurator Fiscal: A.S. Jessop. *Tayside, Central and Fife Region,* T.-0382 27535. Regional Procurator Fiscal: D.R. Smith. *North Strathclyde Region,* T.-041-887 5225. Regional Procurator Fiscal: J.B.R. Mackinnon. *South Strathclyde, Dumfries and Galloway Region,* T.-0698 284000. Regional Procurator Fiscal: S.W. Lockhart.
The Procurator Fiscal is the public prosecutor in the local Sheriff and District Courts and is subject to directions from the Lord Advocate. (See also Crown Office.)

PROCURATORS FISCAL SOCIETY, Sheriff Court, 149 Ingram Street, Glasgow; T.-041-552 3434.
Founded: 1930.
President of Council: N.G. O'Brien; Treasurer: W.G. Carmichael; Secretary: L.A. Higson.
Represents and promotes the career interests of members of the Procurator Fiscal Service, considers all subjects connected with the law of Scotland, the administration of justice, and the efficiency and conditions of the service.

PROFESSIONAL ASSOCIATION OF TEACHERS, (PAT), 22 Rutland Street, Edinburgh EH1 2AN; T.-031-229 7868.
Founded: 1970.
Secretary for Scotland: John A. Bell; Scottish Executive Chairman: 1986-87: Mrs J.R. Russell.
Recognised trade union with members in all sectors of the teaching profession throughout the United Kingdom. Has seats on negotiating bodies in Scotland and England. Positively opposes strikes, never involves children in its disputes. Provides a wide range of services to members, including free legal advice on non-professional matters. Scottish concerns are overseen by an elected executive committee. Scottish membership: 5,400.

PROPERTY SERVICES AGENCY, DEPARTMENT OF THE ENVIRONMENT, Directorate of Scottish Services, Argyle House, 3 Lady Lawson Street, Edinburgh EH3 9SD; T.-031-229 9191.
Founded: 1972.
Director: A.S. Gosling; Assistant Director: D.R. Smith.
Provides and maintains buildings and other installations for the Government and armed services.

Q

QUEEN MARGARET COLLEGE, (QMC), Clerwood Terrace, Edinburgh EH12 8TS; T.-031-339 8111.
Founded: 1875.
Principal: Mr Donald Leach; Vice-principal: Dr C.E.R. Maddox; Secretary: Mr A. Adams; Assistant Principal: Mr R.T.H. Smith.
A Scottish Central Institution providing mainly degree courses and professional diplomas for health care and consumer service professions. Also offers a growing range of post-registration courses for nursing and other health care professions. Research and consultancy facilities in all areas relative to undergraduate courses are available, as is registration for full and part-time CNAA research degrees. A Small Business Development Centre offers sup-

port for business start-up and expansion.

THE QUEEN'S COLLEGE, GLASGOW, 1 Park Drive, Glasgow G3 6LP; T.-041-334 8141.

Founded: 1875.
Principal: Dr G.A. Richardson; Vice Principal: Dr R.J. Chalmers; Secretary and Treasurer: Mr H.F.A. Rose.
A Scottish Central Institution providing vocationally orientated higher education in the fields of catering, home economics, health sciences, and social work to 838 students.

QUEEN'S HALL (EDINBURGH) LTD, 5 Hope Park Crescent, Edinburgh EH8 9NA; T.-031-668 3456.

Founded: 1979.
Chairman: Kenneth Newis, CB, CVO; Company Secretary: Jo Penney; Manager: David W.S. Todd.
The company has charitable status. Its principal activity is to own and manage the Queen's Hall which provides facilities for the performance of a wide range of music, principally by the Scottish Chamber Orchestra and the Scottish Ensemble, but also by others of both amateur and professional status. Provides facilities for meetings, conferences and private functions and operates a bar and restaurant open to the public during the week and to ticket holders before, during and after performances.

THE QUEEN'S NURSING INSTITUTE, (QNI), 31 Castle Terrace, Edinburgh EH1 2EL; T.-031-229 2333.

Founded: 1889.
Chairman of Council: The Hon Lord McDonald, MC; Honorary Secretary: Mrs George Russell; Honorary Treasurer: P.W. Simpson; Secretary and Treasurer: Charles C. McInroy.
Originally, the object was the training and provision of nurses for the sick poor in their own homes. Now, funds are applied to the promotion of district nursing interests in other areas. Current projects include night nursing services and a tutorship in the care of the terminally ill.

QUEEN'S OWN HIGHLANDERS (SEAFORTH AND CAMERONS), REGIMENTAL HEADQUARTERS, Cameron Barracks, Inverness; T.-Inverness 224380.

Colonel of the Regiment: Major General J.C.O.R. Hopkinson, CB; Regimental Secretary: Lt Col A.A. Fairrie; Assistant Regimental Secretary: Major A.F. Blincow, MBE.
Conducts regimental business on behalf of the Colonel of the Regiment, including running the Regimental Museum at Fort George, by Inverness.

R

RADIO CLYDE plc, Clydebank Business Park, Clydebank G81 2RX; T.-041-941 1111.

Founded: 1973.
Chairman: F.I. Chapman; Managing Director: James Gordon, CBE; Programme Controller: Alex Dickson; Finance Controller: John Bowman; Chief Engineer: G. Allan; Sales and Marketing Controller: Geoffrey Holliman.
Independent local radio station with weekly listenership of more than 1 million.

RADIO FORTH LTD, Forth House, Forth Street, Edinburgh EH1 3LF; T.-031-556 9255.

Founded: 1975.
Chairman: Sir Maxwell Harper Gow; Deputy Chairman and Chief Executive: Richard Findlay; Finance Director and Company Secretary: Alan Wilson; Programme Director: Thomas Steele; Sales Manager: George Wilson; Chief Engineer: Ian Wales.
The independent radio contractor for Edinburgh and East Central Scotland, broadcasting from its headquarters in Edinburgh and from a studio in Kirkcaldy. The programme mix is very much directed towards the local audience, and while it is popular in feel, a range of diverse programmes are produced including various music forms, news, sport, current affairs, documentaries, and advice and consumer topics.

RADIO TAY LTD, PO Box 123, Dundee DD1 9UF; T.-0382 29551.

Founded: 1980.
Managing Director and Chief Executive: Allen R. Mackenzie; Chairman: James B. Pow; Advertising Director: Ian M. Large.
The programme schedule comprises music of all kinds, local weather, travel round-ups, traffic reports, sports news, world news, local news, farming, quizzes and competitions, phone-ins and talk-ins. Has an on-air help line - the award winning Tay Action team. The Media Action Centre trains the public in how to use and understand the

media. Campus Radio is its on-air evening class.

RAMBLERS' ASSOCIATION (SCOTLAND), c/o Honorary Secretary, 12 Mosspark Road, Milngavie, Glasgow G62 8NJ.
Founded: 1965.
Honorary Secretary: Mr W.R. Forsyth.
Encourages rambling and mountaineering; fosters a greater knowledge, love, and care of the countryside; works for the preservation of natural beauty and for the provision of access to open country.

THE RED DEER COMMISSION, (RDC), Knowsley, 82 Fairfield Road, Inverness IV3 5LH; T.-0463 231751/2.
Founded: 1959.
Chairman: Ian K. Mackenzie; Vice-chairman: R.W.K. Stirling; Secretary: N.H. McCulloch; Assistant Secretary: G. Motion; Senior Deer Officer: L.A.H.K. Stewart, MBE; Deer Officer: R.W. Youngson.
Exists to further the conservation and control of red and sika deer in Scotland and to keep under review matters relating to all species of deer. Conducts an annual red deer census and advises on deer management, venison dealing and the prevention of the illegal taking and killing of deer.

REFORMED PRESBYTERIAN CHURCH OF SCOTLAND, 17 George IV Bridge, Edinburgh EH1 1EE; T.-031-225 1836.
Founded: 1743.
Synod Clerk: Rev A. Sinclair Horne.
Presbyterian church stemming directly from the Scottish covenanters. Has five congregations: Airdrie, Glasgow, Loanhead, Stranraer and Wishaw. Conservative in theology and maintaining the principle of exclusive psalmody in worship.

REGISTERS OF SCOTLAND, Meadowbank House, 153 London Road, Edinburgh EH8 7AU; T.-031-661 6111, Ext.533.
Keeper: W. Russell; Deputy Keeper: J. Robertson; Principal Establishment Officer: R.C. Brown; Staff Management and Finance Officer: R. Glen.
Responsible for compiling public registers provided for the registration of legal documents, in particular, those deeds relating to succession, trusts, family agreements, state appointments and others. In 1981, a new system of registration of title to land in Scotland was introduced and will eventually cover the whole of Scotland superseding the registration of deeds relating to rights in land.

REGULAR FORCES EMPLOYMENT ASSOCIATION, SCOTTISH SOCIETY, New Haig House, Logie Green Road, Edinburgh EH7 4HQ; T.-031-557 1747.
Founded: 1886.
Chairman: Col H.F.O. Bewsher, OBE; Secretary and Employment Officer: Flt Lt F. Roberts.
Helps find employment for ex-servicemen and women.

REID KERR COLLEGE, Renfrew Road, Paisley PA3 4DR; T.-041-889 4225.
Principal: Frederick Sharples; Depute Principal: William Morrison; Registrar: James A. Donnelly.
College of further education with 9,000 students.

RENFREW DISTRICT COUNCIL, Municipal Buildings, Cotton Street, Paisley PA1 1BU; T.-041-889 5400.
Founded: 1974.
Provost: W. McCready; Chief Executive and Director of Administration: W. McIntosh; Director of Finance: E. Goddard; Director of Housing: D. Johnston; Director of Cleansing: S.J. Dagg; Director of Personnel and Management Services: P.F. Waddell; Director of Leisure and Recreation: I.C. McAdam; Director of Physical Planning: C.D. Begg; Director of Technical Services: R.A.S. Rattray; Director of Environmental Health: B.J. Forteath.
Political composition of council: Labour 35, Conservative 5, SNP 3, Liberal/Alliance 1, SDP/Liberal Alliance 1. Population of district: 203,963.

ROBERT GORDON'S INSTITUTE OF TECHNOLOGY, (RGIT), Schoolhill, Aberdeen AB9 1FR; T.-0224 633611.
Founded: 1885.
Chairman of Governors: James T.C. Hay; Principal: Dr David A. Kennedy; Vice-principal: Gavin T.N. Ross; Secretary to the Institute: David C. Caldwell; Academic Registrar: Raymond A. Leslie.
An institution of higher education occupying six substantial teaching sites in Aberdeen, and providing vocational and professional courses at degree, diploma

and postgraduate levels to over 3,000 full-time and several hundred part-time students. More than 14,000 trainees each year attend short courses in offshore survival and in aspects of offshore health.

ROMAN CATHOLIC CHURCH.
Archdiocese of St Andrews and Edinburgh. Archbishop: Most Rev Keith O'Brien, St Bennet's, 42 Greenhill Gardens, Edinburgh EH10 4BJ; T.-031-447 3337. *Diocese of Aberdeen.* Bishop: Rt Rev Mario Conti, Bishop's House, 156 King's Gate, Aberdeen AB2 6BR; T.-0224 319154. *Diocese of Argyll and the Isles.* Bishop: Rt Rev Colin MacPherson, Bishop's House, Esplanade, Oban PA34 5AB; T.-0631 62010. *Diocese of Dunkeld.* Bishop: Rt Rev Vincent Logan, Bishop's House, 29 Roseangle, Dundee DD1 4LX; T.-0382 24327. *Diocese of Galloway.* Bishop: Rt Rev Maurice Taylor, Candida Casa, 8 Corsehill Road, Ayr KA7 2ST; T.-0292 266750. *Archdiocese of Glasgow.* Archbishop: Most Rev Thomas J. Winning, 40 Newlands Road, Glasgow G43 2JD; T.-(Diocesan Centre, 18 Park Circus, Glasgow G3 6BE) 041-332 9473. *Diocese of Motherwell.* Bishop: Rt Rev Joseph Devine, 17 Viewpark Road, Motherwell ML1 3ER; T.-Motherwell 63715. *Diocese of Paisley.* Bishop: Rt Rev Stephen McGill, Bishop's House, Porterfield Road, Kilmacolm, Renfrewshire PA13 4PD; T.-041-549 2494.
Scotland's estimated Catholic population is 808,000. There are two archdioceses, six dioceses and a total of 477 parishes.

ROSS AND CROMARTY DISTRICT COUNCIL, County Buildings, Dingwall IV15 9QN; T.-0349 63381.
Founded: 1974.
Convener: George Finlayson; Chief Officer: Douglas Sinclair; Director of Legal Services: David Neill; Director of Finance: John Glashan; Director of Architectural Services: George Smith; Director of Environmental Services: George Lemmon; Director of Housing: William Gillies; Director of Leisure and Recreation: John Watt.
Political composition of council: Others 19, Labour 2, Conservative 1. Population of district: 47,478.

ROSS AND CROMARTY TOURIST BOARD, Tourist Office, North Kessock, Ross-shire IV1 1XB; T.-0463 73 505.
Tourist Officer: Mrs E.A. Allan; Chairman: Mr I. McCrae.
Exists for the promotion of tourism.

ROTHESAY AND ISLE OF BUTE TOURIST BOARD, The Pier, Rothesay, Isle of Bute PA20 9AQ; T.-0700 2151.
Founded: 1978.
Chairman: George F. Wilson; Vice-chairman: Mrs Jean McIntosh; Honorary Treasurer: James Gracie; Secretary: James S. McMillan.
The board is a partnership between the tourist industry on the island, the Highlands and Islands Development Board and Argyll and Bute District Council. Membership is open to all carrying on business on the island. Main functions: the provision of a comprehensive tourist information service; the promotion of tourism; maintaining liaison with all organisations related in any way to tourism on the island.

ROWETT RESEARCH INSTITUTE, Greenburn Road, Bucksburn, Aberdeen AB2 9SB; T.-0224 712751.
Founded: 1913.
Chairman, Governing Body: Principal G.P. McNicol; Vice Chairman: Prof H.M. Keir; Director: Prof W.P.T. James; Secretary: J.M. Kelty; Senior Staff: Dr P.J. Reeds (Biochemistry), Dr A. Chesson (Nutrition), Dr J.C. MacRae (Physiology), Dr A. Smith (Services).
Funded almost entirely by the Department of Agriculture and Fisheries for Scotland. Considered to be the prime nutrition institute in the agricultural research service, and while the emphasis has been on animal nutrition in recent years, there is now a renewed interest in human nutrition. The total staff is 300, of whom 200 are in the science category.

ROXBURGH DISTRICT COUNCIL, District Council Offices, High Street, Hawick TD9 9EF; T.-0450 75991.
Founded: 1974.
Chairman: J.R. Irvine, JP; Chief Executive: Kenneth W. Cramond; Director of Administrative and Legal Services: William R. Millan; Director of Finance: Eric Gibson; Director of Housing and Development: Robert M. Johnson; Director of Technical Services: John J. McLaren.
Political composition of council: Independent 8, Conservative 5, Non-political/Non-party 2, Liberal 1. Population of district: 35,210.

ROYAL AND ANCIENT GOLF CLUB, St Andrews, Fife KY16 9JD; T.-0334 72112.

Founded: 1754.
Chairman, General Committee: D.L. Hayes; Chairman, Championship Committee: A.J. Low; Secretary: M.F. Bonallack; Deputy Secretary: W.G. Wilson; Rules Secretary: J. Glover; Championship Secretary: D. Hill.
A private members' club, but also, except in the USA and Mexico, the world wide governing authority for the rules of golf and the conditions for amateur status. Organises the Open Championship.

THE ROYAL BANK OF SCOTLAND plc, 42 St Andrew Square, Edinburgh EH2 2YE; T.-031-556 8555.

Founded: 1727.
Chairman: Sir Michael Herries; Group Chief Executive: Mr C.M. Winter; Chief General Manager: Mr H.E. Farley.
Transacts all customary banking business and operates over 800 branches in Scotland, England and overseas. Has correspondents throughout the world.

ROYAL BOTANIC GARDEN, Inverleith Row, Edinburgh EH3 5LR; T.-031-552 7171.

Founded: 1670.
Regius Keeper: Prof D.M. Henderson, CBE; Deputy Keeper: Dr J. Cullen; Curator: Mr R. Shaw; Education/PR Officer: Dr I.D. Edwards; Horticultural Training Officer: Mr G. Anderson; Librarian: M.V. Mathew.
Main aim is to carry out research on plant taxonomy. Also has an important educational function. Scientific work relies on a large herbarium with two million specimens, a library of 100,000 volumes and a living collection of 14,000 plants. Educational work includes a diploma in horticulture course, Interlink programme for schools and adult education evening classes. There are three outstations: Logan; Younger Botanic Garden, Benmore; and Dawyck. Visitors in 1985 exceeded 800,000.

ROYAL BRITISH LEGION SCOTLAND, (RBLS), New Haig House, Logie Green Road, Edinburgh EH7 4HR; T.-031-557 2782.

Founded: 1921.
President: General Sir Michael Gow, GCB; Chairman: Major General Sir John Swinton, KCVO, OBE; General Secretary: Brigadier R.W. Riddle, OBE.
A democratic, non sectarian and non political organisation open to all serving and ex-servicemen and women in Scotland. Has 240 branches, 100 of which have social clubs. Aims: remembrance, comradeship, assistance to ex-servicemen and women in need.

ROYAL CALEDONIAN CURLING CLUB, (RCCC), 2 Coates Crescent, Edinburgh EH3 7AN; T.-031-225 7083.

Founded: 1838.
President: Alec Torrance; President-elect: Robin Brechin; Past-president: Bill Muirhead; Secretary: Brian Alderman; President, Ladies' Branch: Mary Tyre; Ladies' President-elect: Elizabeth Paterson-Brown.
The governing body of the sport in Scotland. Over 30,000 regular members take part, playing on 23 ice rinks. Oversees national competition organisation for men, ladies and juniors, leading to world finals. Has representatives on the International Curling Federation. When cold weather prevails, it organises the 'Grand Match' - an outdoor bonspeil in which over 2,000 curlers take part.

THE ROYAL CELTIC SOCIETY, 23 Rutland Street, Edinburgh EH1 2RN; T.-031-228 6449.

Founded: 1820.
President: Sir Donald H. Cameron of Lochiel, KT, CVO, TD; Vice Presidents: Dr Kenneth A. Mackay, A.I.S. Macpherson, Iain Noble; Chairman of Council: Kenneth M. Hay, BEM; Honorary Secretary and Treasurer: J.G.S. Cameron.
Maintains and promotes interest in the history, traditions, language and arts of the Highlands and western islands of Scotland and encourages the general and proper use of the Highland dress. Holds social meetings, assists in the publication of suitable material, gives prizes for compositions in Gaelic and for skill in music and proficiency in the arts and industries of the Highlands and western islands.

THE ROYAL COLLEGE OF MIDWIVES SCOTTISH BOARD, (RCM), 37 Frederick Street, Edinburgh EH2 1EP; T.-031-225 1633.

Founded: 1881.
Chairman: Mrs Margaret Brown; Secretary/ Treasurer: Mrs Sheila Davidson; Education/ Professional Officer: Miss E. Creighton.
The only professional organisation and trade union specifically for midwives. It is a voluntary organisation supported entirely by members' subscriptions and donations and by fees for post certificate courses. Has its headquarters in London and is governed

by a national council consisting of representatives nominated by the four RCM boards in England, Northern Ireland, Wales and Scotland and 11 members nominated and elected by the branches throughout the United Kingdom.

ROYAL COLLEGE OF NURSING OF THE UNITED KINGDOM, SCOTTISH BOARD, 44 Heriot Row, Edinburgh EH3 6EY; T.-031-225 7231.

Chairman: John Kelly; Secretary: Elizabeth McLaren.

ROYAL COLLEGE OF PHYSICIANS OF EDINBURGH, (RCPE), 9 Queen Street, Edinburgh EH2 1JQ; T.-031-225 7324.

Founded: 1681.
President: Prof M.F. Oliver, CBE; Secretary: Dr T.M. Chalmers; Treasurer: Dr A.J. Keay; Registrar: Dr J.L. Anderton; Honorary Librarian: Dr B. Ashworth; Librarian: Miss J.P.S. Ferguson.
Exists to maintain specialist standards amongst physicians in the United Kingdom and overseas. Awards basic registrable qualifications and postgraduate diplomas in medicine, pharmaceutical medicine, and community child health. Disseminates medical knowledge by meetings and publications.

ROYAL COLLEGE OF PHYSICIANS AND SURGEONS OF GLASGOW, 234-242 St Vincent Street, Glasgow G2 5RJ; T.-041-221 6072.

Founded: 1599.
President: Prof A.C. Kennedy; Visitor: James McArthur; Honorary Secretary: Dr A.D. Beattie; Honorary Treasurer: Douglas Gilmore; Honorary Librarian: Prof R.N.M. MacSween; Registrar: John W. Robb.
A college of international standing in the field of postgraduate medical education. Maintains standards of practice in all specialities and conducts training courses and examinations leading to higher qualifications in medicine. Has 5,600 members resident in many countries.

THE ROYAL COLLEGE OF SURGEONS OF EDINBURGH, (RCSEd), Nicolson Street, Edinburgh EH8 9DW; T.-031-556 6206.

Founded: 1505.
President: Mr T.J. McNair; Vice-presidents: Mr W.A.T. Robb, OBE, Mr A.C.B. Dean; Honorary Secretary: Peter Edmond, CBE;

Honorary Treasurer: Mr A.B. MacGregor; Clerk to the College: Miss Margaret Bean.
Promotes and maintains standards in surgical training and practice.

ROYAL COMMISSION ON THE ANCIENT AND HISTORICAL MONUMENTS OF SCOTLAND, (RCAHM(S)), 54 Melville Street, Edinburgh EH3 7HF; T.-031-225 5994.

Founded: 1908.
Chairman: The Rt Hon The Earl of Crawford and Balcarres, PC; Secretary: J.G. Dunbar; Curator, National Monuments Record of Scotland: Miss C.H. Cruft.
Appointed to make an inventory of the ancient and historical monuments of Scotland and to specify those that seem most worthy of preservation. Also has a responsibility to record monuments threatened with destruction, including a statutory duty to record historic buildings for which listed building consent for demolition has been granted. The National Monuments Record of Scotland, a branch of the commission, contains an extensive collection of pictorial and documentary material relating to Scottish ancient monuments and historic buildings and is open daily for public reference. Also supplies archaeological information to the Ordnance Survey for mapping purposes.

ROYAL ENVIRONMENTAL HEALTH INSTITUTE OF SCOTLAND, Virginia House, 62 Virginia Street, Glasgow G1 1TX; T.-041-552 1533.

Founded: 1983.
President: W.A. Dunlop; Secretary: Anne B. McKenzie.
Professional body promoting the advancement of all aspects of health and hygiene.

ROYAL FACULTY OF PROCURATORS IN GLASGOW, 12 Nelson Mandela Place, Glasgow G2; T.-041-637 9324.

Founded: 1796.
Dean: James Kevin Maguire; Clerk, Treasurer, and Fiscal: J.H. Sinclair.
Represents the interests of solicitors practising in the Glasgow area.

ROYAL FINE ART COMMISSION FOR SCOTLAND, 9 Atholl Crescent, Edinburgh EH3 8HA; T.-031-229 1109.

Founded: 1927.
Chairman: Prof Alexander J. Youngson;

Secretary: Charles Prosser; Assistant Secretary: Mrs M. Tierney; Investigator: Tom Watson.

Consists of 12 members, appointed by The Queen on the advice of the Secretary of State for Scotland. Advises on the quality of the built environment insofar as this affects the public interest (including considerations of urban environmental planning design, architecture and conservation) and also on works of art in relation to building exteriors and interiors. Reports are made about every three years, and are published by HMSO as command papers. Exhibitions on aspects of the commission's work are held annually during the Edinburgh International Festival.

THE ROYAL GLASGOW INSTITUTE OF THE FINE ARTS, 12 Sandyford Place, Glasgow G3 7NE; T.-041-248 7411.

Founded: 1861.

President: Sir Norman Macfarlane; Honorary Treasurer: Robert W. Begg, CBE; Honorary Secretary: Danny Ferguson; Secretary: R.C. Liddle.

Promotes an open annual exhibition of oils, water-colours, drawings, prints, sculpture etc in the McLellan Galleries in Glasgow in October. Also operates the John D. Kelly Gallery at 118 Douglas Street, Glasgow, which is rented to artists for their own exhibitions. Membership totals around 1,350.

THE ROYAL HIGHLAND AND AGRICULTURAL SOCIETY OF SCOTLAND, (RHASS), Ingliston, Edinburgh EH28 8NF; T.-031-333 2444.

Founded: 1784.

Chairman: D. Goldie; Past Chairman: J.T. Wood; Honorary Secretary: J.A. Barron; Honorary Treasurer: R.J. Forrest; Chief Executive: J.D.G. Davidson; Secretary: J.R. Good.

Scotland's national agricultural society, with a membership of 17,000. An educational charity incorporated by Royal Charter with the main objects of agricultural promotion and education. Organises the annual Royal Highland Show in June, the largest single venue public event in Scotland, and is involved in other events, award schemes and educational projects.

THE ROYAL HIGHLAND FUSILIERS REGIMENTAL HEADQUARTERS, (Princess Margaret's Own Glasgow

and Ayrshire Regiment), 518 Sauchiehall Street, Glasgow G2 3LW; T.-041-332 5639/0961.

Founded: 1959.

Regimental Secretary: Lt Col J.M.R. Fleming; Assistant Regimental Secretary: Major D.I.A. Mack.

The permanent HQ of the regiment, located within the regimental area. Includes the regimental museum which is open to the public.

ROYAL INCORPORATION OF ARCHITECTS IN SCOTLAND, (RIAS), 15 Rutland Square, Edinburgh EH1 2BE; T.-031-229 7205.

Founded: 1916.

President: John Lane; Secretary and President: Charles McKean.

The professional organisation for chartered architects in Scotland. Concerned with the promotion of Scottish architecture, exhibitions, the RIAS bookshop, the RIAS/Landmark architectural guides to Scotland. Has two quarterly journals: *Prospect* (founded in 1920) and *Practice Information.* Membership: 2,800.

THE ROYAL INSTITUTION OF CHARTERED SURVEYORS, SCOTTISH BRANCH, (RICS), 9 Manor Place, Edinburgh EH3 7DN; T.-031-225 7078.

Founded: 1897.

Chairman: I.C. Stanners; Senior Vice-chairman: D.J. Hughes Hallett; Vice-chairmen: C.D. Burgess, A.L. Peter, D.C. Russell; Honorary Secretary: S.M. Smith; Scottish Secretary: J.M. Ritchie.

Members are involved in the valuation, measurement, management and development of land and buildings. They work in private practice, business and commerce, local authorities, Government service, and statutory bodies. RICS has a worldwide membership of 77,000, including 6,500 in Scotland. Entry to the profession is either through the institution's own examination system, or increasingly through degree and diploma courses supplemented by a period of practical training.

ROYAL LYCEUM THEATRE COMPANY, Grindlay Street, Edinburgh EH3 9AX; T.-031-229 7404.

Founded: 1965.

Chairman: W. Menzies Campbell, QC; Artistic Director: Ian Wooldridge; General Manager: Roger Spence.

Aims to present major dramatic works from the whole spectrum of world theatre at the highest possible international standards to as large and varied an audience as possible.

ROYAL MEDICO-CHIRURGICAL SOCIETY OF GLASGOW, c/o John W. Turner, Institute of Neurological Sciences, Southern General Hospital, Glasgow G51 4TF; T.-041-445 2466, Ext. 3743.

Founded: 1814.
Exists to advance knowledge of, and promote research in, medicine, surgery, and allied sciences.

ROYAL OBSERVATORY, Blackford Hill, Edinburgh EH9 3HJ; T.-031-667 3321.

Founded: 1818.
Director: Prof M.S. Longair; Secretary: Mr J.B. McInnes.
A national observatory. The Director is the Astronomer Royal for Scotland and the Regius Professor of Astronomy in the University of Edinburgh. Since 1965, the observatory has been one of the establishments of the Science and Engineering Research Council, whose primary purpose is to support postgraduate education and research. In addition to providing computing and other facilities at Edinburgh, it is responsible for the operation of the UK Infrared Telescope and the James Clerk Maxwell Telescope in Hawaii and the UK Schmidt Telescope in Australia. Has 115 staff.

THE ROYAL SCOTS REGIMENTAL MUSEUM AND REGIMENTAL HEADQUARTERS, The Castle, Edinburgh EH1 2YT; T.-031-336 1761, Ext. 4267.

Founded: 1951.
Regimental Secretary: Lt Col J.L. Wilson Smith, OBE; Assistant Regimental Secretary: Lt Col S.W. McBain; Museum Curator: Mr A. Clarke.
The Royal Scots is the oldest regular regiment in the British army. The museum shows uniforms and regimental insignia from 1633 to the present day. There is a large display of campaign relics, medals and decorations, colours, pipe banners, silver, weapons, paintings, drawings and photographs.

ROYAL SCOTTISH ACADEMY, (RSA), The Mound, Edinburgh EH2 2EL; T.-031-225 6671.

Founded: 1826.
President: H. Anthony Wheeler, OBE; Secretary: Robert R. Steedman; Treasurer: William J.L. Baillie.
Founded after many efforts had been made to arrange exhibitions of contemporary painting, and in order to establish some form of society of fine art. Received a Royal Charter in 1838. Has some 60 members elected from the disciplines of painting, sculpture and architecture.

ROYAL SCOTTISH ACADEMY OF MUSIC AND DRAMA, (RSAMD), St George's Place, Glasgow G2 1BS; T.-041-332 4101.

Founded: 1847.
Principal: Philip Ledger, CBE; Director of Drama: Edward Argent; Director of Music: Dr Rita MacAllister; Registrar: Thomas Gourdie; Treasurer: A. Isobel Fowler.
Scotland's only specialist conservatoire of the performing arts. Degree and diploma courses are offered in music and drama and activities are centred around the Athenaeum Theatre, the Stevenson Hall and the television studio. Former students include: Hannah Gordon, Ian Richardson, Tom Conti, James Loughran, Margaret Marshall, Isobel Buchanan and Sir Alexander Gibson. In 1987, it will move to its new purpose-built home designed by Sir Leslie Martin.

ROYAL SCOTTISH AGRICULTURAL BENEVOLENT INSTITUTION, (RSABI), Ingliston, Newbridge, Midlothian EH28 8NB; T.-031-333 1023.

Founded: 1897.
President: The Duke of Buccleuch and Queensberry, KT, VRD; Chairman, Board of Directors: David C. Marshall, VRD; Vice-chairman, Board of Directors: John M. Stevenson; Secretary: Kenneth M. Campbell.
Founded to commemorate Queen Victoria's Diamond Jubilee. The only national organisation in Scotland which assists aged or infirm farmers or their dependants who are in needy circumstances. In 1986, the total expended in payments and grants was over £79,000. Income is solely derived from voluntary contributions and bequests.

THE ROYAL SCOTTISH AUTOMOBILE CLUB, (RSAC), 11 Blythswood Square, Glasgow G2

4AG; T.-041-221 3850.
Founded: 1899.
Chairman: Eric M. Hagman; Vice-chairmen: Douglas S. Thomson, A.C. McNicol; Chief Executive: Hugh Dewar; Assistant Secretary: Jonathan C. Lord.
Formed to promote, encourage and develop automobilism. Now one of Scotland's leading social clubs with premises which contain restaurants, bars, bedrooms and function facilities as well as a fully equipped leisure centre. Plays an active part in defending the interests of the motorist by reviewing impending legislation and other transport matters. Acts as the agent of the Secretary of State for Scotland in authorising motor events on the public highway, and organises Scotland's only international motor sport event, the Scottish Rally, a round of the European Championship held each June.

THE ROYAL SCOTTISH COUNTRY DANCE SOCIETY, (RSCDS), 12 Coates Crescent, Edinburgh EH3 7AF; T.-031-225 3854.
Founded: 1923.
Chairman: Dr A. MacFadyen; Vice Chairman: Mr A.S. Aitkenhead; Organising Secretary: Miss M. Muriel Gibson; Treasurer: Mrs M.A. Jeffcoat.
Objects: to preserve and further the practice of traditional Scottish country dances, and to provide education and instruction to this end; to promote and encourage the formation of branches; to publish descriptions of dances with music and diagrams; to collect books, manuscripts and illustrations relating to Scottish country dances. Has 150 branches throughout the world and some 500 affiliated groups. Membership: over 26,000.

ROYAL SCOTTISH FORESTRY SOCIETY, (RSFS), 11 Atholl Crescent, Edinburgh EH3 8HE; T.-031-229 8851/8180.
Founded: 1854.
President: James Henderson; Vice President: Andrew Little; Honorary Secretary: Neil Findlay.
Represents the interests of forestry in Scotland. Supported wholly by members' voluntary subscriptions and aims to encourage all forms of interest in forestry in Scotland. Regular meetings are organised both on a national and regional basis and an annual conference or excursion held over three days takes place each May. Publishes a quarterly journal *Scottish Forestry* which is distributed to members and others worldwide. Membership: around 2,000.

ROYAL SCOTTISH GEOGRAPHICAL SOCIETY, 10 Randolph Crescent, Edinburgh EH3 7TU; T.-031-225 3330.
Founded: 1884.
Secretary: A.B. Cruickshank; Honorary Treasurer: W.R. Ballantyne.

ROYAL SCOTTISH MUSEUM. See National Museums of Scotland.

ROYAL SCOTTISH PIPE BAND ASSOCIATION, 45 Washington Street, Glasgow G3 8AZ; T.-041-221 5414.
Founded: 1930.
President: William Sinclair; Chairman: John W. Smith; Executive Officer: Robert Nichol.
Aims to promote fellowship among all pipebandsmen; organises and promotes the Pipe Band College and organises pipe band competitions.

ROYAL SCOTTISH PIPERS' SOCIETY, (RSPS), 127 Rose Street Lane South, Edinburgh.
Founded: 1881.
Honorary Pipe Major: Mr D.D. Watson; Honorary Pipe Corporal: Mr B.G. Douglas; Honorary Secretary: Mr J.J. Burnet.
Private club established to encourage the playing of bagpipes among amateurs. Awards prizes at the leading professional competitions and from time to time promotes recitals of bagpipe music by the most prominent solo professional players. Membership, totalling around 330, is by election.

THE ROYAL SCOTTISH SOCIETY OF PAINTERS IN WATER-COLOURS, (RSW), 29 Waterloo Street, Glasgow G2 6BZ; T.-041-226 3838.
Founded: 1878.
President: William J.L. Baillie; Secretary: Roger C.C. Frame.
Has around 100 members, all of whom have been proposed and seconded by existing members and have submitted works for consideration to the annual general assembly before being elected. Promotes an open annual exhibition in the Royal Scottish Academy galleries.

ROYAL SCOTTISH SOCIETY FOR THE PREVENTION OF CRUELTY

TO CHILDREN, (RSSPCC), 41 Polwarth Terrace, Edinburgh; T.-031-337 8539.
Founded: 1884.
President: Princess Margaret; General Secretary: Arthur M.M. Wood, OBE; Chairman: Rev H.M. Ricketts.
Objectives: to protect and promote the rights and interests of children; to offer help to children and their parents where abuse and/or neglect is thought to have occured; to develop programmes designed to prevent child abuse and/or neglect before it occurs. The society responds to referrals and assesses the child and his or her circumstances, offers support and advice to families with children, develops educational programmes of prevention, engages in research, critically examines local and central Government policy to do with children and families, and lobbies Government on behalf of children and families.

ROYAL SOCIETY OF EDINBURGH, 22-24 George Street, Edinburgh EH2 2PQ; T.-031-225 6057.
Founded: 1783.
President: Sir Alwyn Williams; Vice Presidents: D.H. Pringle, Prof V.B. Proudfoot, Prof D.M. Walker; General Secretary: C.D. Waterston; Treasurer: C. Blake; Curator of the Library and Museum: Prof D.M. Henderson; Fellowship Secretary: Prof M.M. Yeoman; Programme Convener: J.C. Gould; Executive Secretary: W. Duncan.
Established by Royal Charter granted by George III. Its origins can be traced to a number of scientific, medical, philosophical, and literary societies that were active in Edinburgh during the period of the Scottish Enlightenment. The principal functions of the society have been the promotion of all branches of scholarship through the organisation of meetings, the publication of journals, and the maintenance of its library, now held in the National Library of Scotland. Although the society was founded and is based in Edinburgh, its Fellows, from the earliest days, have been drawn from all parts of Scotland and beyond, and have included scholars of all disciplines.

ROYAL SOCIETY FOR THE PREVENTION OF ACCIDENTS, (RoSPA), Slateford House, 53 Lanark Road, Edinburgh EH14 1TL; T.-031-444 1155.
Founded: 1924.
Director for Scotland: A. Fraser Dryburgh.
Europe's largest and most comprehensive safety organisation. Completely independent professional body drawing on a wealth of voluntary expertise available to it through its national committees. Much of its work is educational, teaching people how to avoid accidents in all environments. Specialist training to combat accidents at work is available at the society's training centre in Birmingham or at venues throughout the country.

THE ROYAL SOCIETY FOR THE PROTECTION OF BIRDS, (RSPB), 17 Regent Terrace, Edinburgh EH7 5BN; T.-031-557 3136.
Founded: 1889.
Chairman: Sir John Lister-Kaye, Bt; Director (Scotland): Frank Hamilton.
Acquires and manages nature reserves (106 in the United Kingdom, including 41 in Scotland covering some 140,000 acres). Carries out practical research, particularly on problems of land-use practices, which are monitored wherever possible. Concerned with planning matters and land-use practices such as forestry and agriculture, pollution as it affects birds and protects and assists in the enforcement of the law relating to birds. Conducts an extensive programme of formal education in schools and colleges and in informal activity through the 90,000 members of the Young Ornithologists Club. Produces and distributes its own bird films and has an extensive publications department. United Kingdom membership is 410,000, with 21,000 in Scotland. At all times it endeavours to work with statutory and non-governmental organisations involved in the countryside.

ROYAL TOWN PLANNING INSTITUTE, SCOTTISH BRANCH, 15 Rutland Square, Edinburgh EH1 2BE.
Founded: 1914.
Honorary Secretary: William Amcotts, T.-031-337 3423.
National organisation for planners. The branch publishes *Scottish Planner* and runs a programme of topical conferences and seminars, as well as supporting environmental education projects and four planning aid groups.

ROYAL YACHTING ASSOCIATION, SCOTLAND, 18 Ainslie Place, Edinburgh EH3 6AU; T.-031-226 4401.
Chairman: I.M.A. Mackay; Honorary Treasurer/Secretary: M.H.G. Pollett; Scottish National Coach: John Jameson.
Looks after the interests of craft from the

greatest ocean racers to the smallest funboards. As ombudsman it assists members in disputes and difficulties in anything to do with pleasure craft. As publisher, it produces many technical publications useful to all boat owners. As negotiator, it covers international and national conferences. As innovator it starts new schemes. It organises speed records and cruising seminars, gives grants for Olympic yachting and runs a training scheme for each type of craft.

THE ROYAL ZOOLOGICAL SOCIETY OF SCOTLAND, (RZSS), Edinburgh Zoo, Murrayfield, Edinburgh EH12 6TS; T.-031-334 9171.
Founded: 1909.
President: The Rt Hon The Viscount of Arbuthnott; Vice-president: Prof Sir Alexander Robertson; Vice-president and Honorary Treasurer: F. Wilson Horne; Society Director: R.J. Wheater.
A charitable, non-profit-making organisation devoted to the study and conservation of wildlife. National in scope and much of its effort is concerned with developing the Scottish National Zoological Collection located at Edinburgh Zoo and the Highland Wildlife Park. Membership is open to all and stands at 9,000.

RURAL FORUM (SCOTLAND), The Gateway, North Methven Street, Perth PH1 5PP; T.-Perth 34565.
Founded: 1982.
Chairman: Col William Swan, CBE; Vice Chairman: Barbara Kelly; Treasurer: Eric Todd.
Umbrella organisation of all the interests operating in the Scottish countryside. Aims to improve the quality of life of the inhabitants of rural Scotland. Twelve sponsoring organisations.

RUTHERFORD HOUSE, 17 Claremont Park, Edinburgh EH6 7PJ; T.-031-554 1206.
Founded: 1982.
Warden: Rev Dr Nigel M. de S. Cameron; Treasurer: Duncan Martin; Administrative Secretary: Mrs Ruth Mitchell; House Manager: Miss Janella Glover; Librarian: Mrs N.F.W. Downie.
Residential theological research library and publisher, established on a conservative evangelical doctrinal basis. Sponsors research and co-ordinates study projects, publishes several journals in the fields of theology and medical ethics as well as books and pamphlets. Arranges lecture tours and provides reading accommodation for students, academics and ministers in its library. The house is inter-denominational although it maintains a special interest in the Church of Scotland.

S

SABHAL MOR OSTAIG, (SMO), Teanga, An t-Eilean Sgitheanach IV44 8RQ; T.-04714 280.
Founded: 1973.
Chairman: Rev Jack MacArthur; Principal: Dr Colin MacLeod; Finance Committee Chairman: Alasdair MacDonald; Academic Council Chairman: Dr Colin MacLeod; Appeal Committee Chairman: Iain Noble; College Secretary: Norman N. Gillies.
Registered educational charity offering a unique Scottish Higher National Diploma course in Business and Gaeltachd Studies, taught in Gaelic and specifically designed for people wishing to make their livelihood in the Highlands and Islands. Features of the course are: the setting up of real companies by the students, field trips abroad, guest speakers and integrated computer training. Short courses are offered in Gaelic language and culture, piping, computing, accountancy and management.

ST ANDREW'S AMBULANCE ASSOCIATION, St Andrew's House, 48 Milton Street, Glasgow G4 0HR; T.-041-332 4031.
Founded: 1882.
President: The Duke of Buccleuch and Queensberry, KT, VRD; Chairman of Council: Dr H.R.F. Macdonald, OBE; Director General and Secretary: J.W.R. Cunningham; Director (Administration): A. Wilkie; Director (Training): G.A. Watt.
Provides training and qualifications in first aid and home nursing, and equipment in these fields. Through a corps of trained volunteers, the association also provides first aiders to assist at public occasions and events as a community service.

ST ANDREW'S COLLEGE OF EDUCATION, Bearsden, Glasgow G61 4QA; T.-041-943 1424.
Founded: 1981.
Chairman, Board of Governors: Rt Rev Joseph Devine; Principal: Bartholomew J. McGettrick; Vice Principal: Sister Dorothea M.E. Sweeney; Assistant Principal: Arthur

Naylor.

Formed as a result of a merger between Notre Dame and Craiglockhart Colleges of Education, to become Scotland's national Catholic college for the training of teachers.

ST ANDREWS FESTIVAL (1987) SOCIETY LTD, Festival Office, 66 South Street, St. Andrews KY16 9JT.

Founded: 1971.

Programme Controller: James Mallet; Programme Co-ordinator: Nicholas Watkins.

As the only professional arts festival run on student initiative, the biennial St Andrews Festival is unique in Europe. The programmes are drawn up by the student controllers, although overall financial responsibility is retained by the directors of the Festival Society Ltd. Artistes in the past have included: John Williams, Scottish Opera, The Alexander Roy Ballet, Polish Chamber Orchestra, Sir David Wilkie and Richard Stilgoe.

ST ANDREWS AND NORTH EAST FIFE AREA TOURIST BOARD, 78 South Street, St Andrews KY16 9TE; T.-0334 74671.

Founded: 1983.

Chairman: Cllr W.R.S. MacKenzie; Tourism Manager: Kyle N. MacKay.

Exists for the promotion of tourism in St Andrews and North East Fife.

THE ST ANDREW SOCIETY, PO Box 84, Edinburgh; T.-031-228 1902.

Founded: 1907.

President: Cecil G. McGregor; Vice-president: Gordon M. Hector, CMG, CBE; Chairman: T. Graham Salmon, JP; Vice-chairman: Alister W. Mackintosh; Secretary: Lt Col M.M. Gibson; Treasurer: Miss E.A. Wark.

Exists to uphold the rights and privileges of Scotland and the Scottish people, encourage the celebration of St Andrew's Day and the study of Scottish literature, arts, music, and customs, and maintain connections with affiliated societies abroad.

ST ANDREWS, UNIVERSITY OF, College Gate, St Andrews, Fife KY16 9AJ; T.-0334 76161.

Founded: 1410.

Chancellor: Sir Kenneth J. Dover; Rector: Stanley Adams; Principal and Vice-chancellor: Prof Struther Arnott; Vice-principal: Prof P.H. Grinyer; Master of the United College: Dr Kathleen M. MacIver; Principal of St Mary's College: Prof William McKane; Pro-vost of St Leonard's College: Prof R.M.M. Crawford; Dean of Faculty of Arts: Prof D.A. Bullough; Dean of Faculty of Divinity: Prof D.W.D. Shaw; Dean of Faculty of Science: Prof A. Serafini-Fracassini; Secretary and Registrar: Dr M.J.B. Lowe.

The university was inaugurated in 1410, incorporated in 1412, and granted the full privileges of a university in 1413. It comprises the United College of St Salvator and St Leonard, and St Mary's College. There are over 3,700 students in three faculties: Arts, Divinity, and Science.

ST ANDREWS, UNIVERSITY OF, DEPARTMENT OF ADULT EDUCATION AND EXTRA-MURAL STUDIES, 3 St Mary's Place, St Andrews KY16 9UY; T.-0334 73429.

Founded: 1967.

Director: Clarke Geddes; Assistant Director: Dr John C. Horobin.

Responsible for the university's extra-mural provision and for the more specialised post-experience vocational provision for adults in continuing education. Runs summer schools, residential holiday programmes and special interest courses, conferences, and extra-mural provision in association with Fife Regional Council.

ST MARGARET OF SCOTLAND ADOPTION SOCIETY LTD, 274 Bath Street, Glasgow G2 4JR; T.-041-332 8371.

Founded: 1955.

Chairman: Rev William Mone; Vice-chairperson: Mrs Margaret Duffy; Secretary: Philip Rooney; Treasurer: Brian Hay.

A Catholic voluntary agency serving the west coast area of Scotland. Provides a comprehensive adoption service in relation to babies. Offers counselling and support to natural parents, prospective adopters, adoptees and adoptive parents. Works closely with other agencies, particularly Strathclyde Regional Council in seeking to find permanent alternative family placement for Catholic children in their care who have some degree of special need, for example older and handicapped children.

THE SALTIRE SOCIETY, Saltire House, 13 Atholl Crescent, Edinburgh EH3 8HA; T.-031-228 6621.

Founded: 1936.

President: Prof David Daiches; Chairman: Ian Barr; Honorary Treasurer: Miss M.A. Matheson; Honorary Secretary: Dr F.W. Freeman; Administrator: Miss Kathleen

Austin.
Promotes all things Scottish. By mounting award competitions, it encourages excellence in housing design, civil engineering design, environmental planning, arts, music, education and literature. Membership is open to all. Has its own list of publications, available on request. Membership: 1,100.

SALVATION ARMY IN SCOTLAND, Houldsworth Street, Glasgow G3 8DU; T.-041-221 3378.
Founded: 1879.
Territorial Commander: Col Dinsdale Pender; General Secretary: Lt Col W. Bramwell Baird; Field Secretary: Lt Col S. Pallant; Financial Secretary: Major John Flett; Territorial Youth Secretary: Major Mrs Audrey Neal.
Objects are the advancement of the Christian religion by the advancement of education, the relief of poverty, and other charitable objects beneficial to society or the community of mankind. It has 147 centres in Scotland, including 22 social service establishments, more than 200 full-time officers, 400 employees, and some 5,000 voluntary paying members.

SARGENT CANCER FUND FOR SCOTLAND, MALCOLM. See Malcolm Sargent Cancer Fund for Children.

SCOTCH QUALITY BEEF AND LAMB ASSOCIATION LTD, (SQBLA), 17 Grosvenor Crescent, Edinburgh EH12 0PQ; T.-031-226 3797.
Founded 1974.
Chairman: John E. McNaughton, OBE, JP; Vice-chairman: James G. Ewing; Director and Secretary: Ian Brown.
Created to promote the sale and image of quality Scotch beef and lamb wherever markets can be developed profitably. Members include the National Famers' Union of Scotland, the Institute of Auctioneers and Appraisers in Scotland, the National Association of Wholesale Meat Salesmen of Scotland and the Scottish Federation of Meat Traders' Associations.

SCOTLAND-USSR SOCIETY, 8 Belmont Crescent, Glasgow G12 8ET; T.-041-339 3008.
Founded: 1945.
President: Lady Ritchie Calder; Vice-president: William Taylor, CBE; Chairman: Robert Brown; General Secretary: George McAlister.
A non-governmental wholly Scottish-based organisation whose constitutional aim is to 'promote peace and mutual understanding between the peoples of Scotland and the USSR'. The practical implementation of this aim extends from promoting the teaching of Russian, arranging scholarships, and educational, trade union, technical and professional exchanges of people between the two countries. The society produces its own publications and organises film shows, lectures and exhibitions both independently and in association with other broad-ranging organisations and public authorities.

SCOTLAND'S CAMPAIGN AGAINST IRRESPONSIBLE DRIVERS, (SCID), Deskford, Cullen AB5 2YU; T.-0542 40119.
Founded: 1985.
Aims to help victim families of road crashes; deter irresponsible drivers by the imposition of more relevant sentences; seek to re-structure the law on criminal traffic offences which cause death or disablement; encourage drivers through education to adopt safer standards.

SCOTLAND'S GARDENS SCHEME, 31 Castle Terrace, Edinburgh EH1 2EL; T.-031-229 1870.
Founded: 1931.
Chairman: The Hon Mrs Macnab of Macnab; Deputy Chairman: Mrs S. Luczyc-Wyhowska; General Organiser: Mr R.S. St. Clair-Ford; Secretary: Mrs I.R. Rodger.
An independent charity with more than 200 gardens throughout Scotland open each year to the public on specific days for the benefit of two main beneficiaries: the Queen's Nursing Institute (Scotland) and the Gardens Fund of the National Trust for Scotland. Each garden owner may also select his own charity to which 40% of his gross takings are allocated. Two or three six day tours to houses and gardens are run each year. Details of all garden openings are given in the annual handbook *Scotland's Gardens,* available in mid-March each year.

SCOTS ANCESTRY RESEARCH SOCIETY, 3 Albany Street, Edinburgh EH1 3PY; T.-031-556 4220.
Founded: 1945.
Honorary Presidents: Rt Hon The Earl of Elgin, KT, Rt Hon The Earl of Wemyss, KT, Sir John Clerk of Penicuik, Bt, CBE, VRD, JP; Chief Executive: Dr John Imrie, CBE; Secretary: Mrs Beatrix L. Walker.

Non-profit-making organisation with a council representing Scottish historians, and central and local archives and libraries. Established by the late Thomas Johnston when he was Secretary of State for Scotland, to assist people of Scottish blood to trace facts about their ancestors in Scotland. Over the years, it has investigated more than 55,000 postal and personal enquiries from people of Scottish descent both at home and overseas.

THE SCOTSMAN, 20 North Bridge, Edinburgh EH1 1YT; T.-031-225 2468.
Founded: 1817.
Editor: Chris Baur.
Daily newspaper circulating throughout Scotland.

SCOTTISH ACCIDENT PREVENTION COUNCIL, (SAPC), Slateford House, 53 Lanark Road, Edinburgh EH14 1TL; T.-031-444 1155.
Founded: 1930.
Secretary: A. Fraser Dryburgh.
Exists to co-ordinate and stimulate the work of accident prevention by the constituent local authorities and by all other organisations with an interest in accident prevention in Scotland. Its objectives are achieved through three main standing committees: road safety, home safety and water safety. The secretariat for the council is provided by the Royal Society for the Prevention of Accidents.

SCOTTISH ADOPTION ASSOCIATION, 69 Dublin Street, Edinburgh EH3 6NS; T.-031-556 2070.
Founded: 1923.
Chairman: Lady Cowie; Treasurer: Mrs E.M. Campbell; Medical Adviser: Dr N. Johnston; Fund Raising Chairman: Mrs A. Crow; Director of Adoption Services: Mrs E.M. Thornton.
A voluntary organisation whose aim is to find loving and secure adoptive homes for young children unable to remain with their natural parents. Provides: counselling for unmarried or separated parents to enable them to decide whether or not to place their child for adoption; fostering for a few weeks before placement when requested by the natural mother; support for mothers who decide to keep their babies; counselling for childless couples; and information and preparation for prospective adopters. Co-operates with local authority social work departments.

SCOTTISH AEROMODELLERS ASSOCIATION, (SAA), c/o The Secretary, 6 Crookston Path, Glasgow G52 3LN; T.-041-883 2655.
Founded: 1944.
Chairman: Mr J.P. Speirs; Vice-chairman: Mr D. McIntyre; Secretary: Mr T. Gray; Assistant Secretary: Mr K. Whyte.
Holds national championships for model aircraft annually, and various smaller competitions. Enters Scottish teams in the various disciplines in international competitions. Membership: around 1,200 in 40 clubs throughout Scotland.

SCOTTISH AGRICULTURAL ARBITERS ASSOCIATION, 10 Dublin Street, Edinburgh EH1 3PR; T.-031-556 2993.
Founded: 1925.
President: G.K. Robertson; Vice-president: Adam Gray; Secretary: K.M. Campbell.
The association's members are people engaged in agricultural arbitration or valuation in Scotland. Its purposes are: to protect the interests of agricultural arbiters; to afford arbiters opportunities to discuss practical problems; to endeavour to ensure uniformity of practice in arbitration procedures; to provide advice on practical and legal problems; to make available to members reports of decisions, arbitrations and changes in legislation.

SCOTTISH AGRICULTURAL CONSULTATIVE PANEL, c/o Department of Agriculture and Fisheries for Scotland, Chesser House, 500 Gorgie Road, Edinburgh EH11 3AW; T.-031-443 4020.
Established as the Winter Keep Consultative Panel. Advises on certain cases of dispute between the Department of Agriculture and Fisheries for Scotland and farmers, and expresses views on other agricultural matters.

SCOTTISH AGRICULTURAL INDUSTRIES PLC, 25 Ravelston Terrace, Edinburgh EH4 3ET; T.-031-332 2481.
Founded: 1928.
Chairman: B. Appleton; Managing Director: Q. Brown.
Manufacturers and suppliers of fertilisers and seeds and suppliers of agrochemicals and feeding stuffs to agriculture. Has an oil subsidiary which services offshore oil activities, a horticultural subsidiary, and an agricultural computer firm. Turnover: £115

million.

SCOTTISH AGRICULTURAL ORGANISATION SOCIETY LTD, (SAOS), Claremont House, 19 Claremont Crescent, Edinburgh EH7 4JW; T.-031-556 6574.

Founded: 1905.
President: Alec R. Manson; Vice President: Douglas Cargill; Chief Executive: Edward Rainy Brown.
The central body in Scotland for farmers' co-operatives. Has over 100 members with sales in Scotland of an annual value of over £400 million. SAOS provides representation at Scottish, United Kingdom and European levels, acts as a co-ordinating influence and provides management services to smaller co-operatives. A development service provides advice and assistance to projects which use co-operation as a means by which farmers can increase their returns from the marketplace as well as control costs.

SCOTTISH AGRICULTURAL WAGES BOARD, (SAWB), Chesser House, 500 Gorgie Road, Edinburgh EH11 3AW; T.-031-443 4020.

Founded: 1949.
Chairman: R.A. Bennett, CBE, QC; Secretary: Mr J. Nimmo.
Determines minimum wage rates and certain other conditions of employment for agricultural workers in Scotland. Employers and workers are represented on the board. The chairman and independent members are appointed by the Secretary of State for Scotland.

SCOTTISH AIRPORTS LTD, St Andrews Drive, Glasgow Airport, Paisley PA3 2SW; T.-041-887 1111.

Founded: 1966.
Managing Director - Dr W. Gordon Watson.
Scottish Airports is a subsidiary holding company of BAA plc, responsible for the operation of the four major Scottish airports: Glasgow, Edinburgh, Prestwick and Aberdeen. Glasgow and Edinburgh handle domestic and short-haul international services. Prestwick is Scotland's long-haul intercontinental gateway airport, principally used by transatlantic services. Aberdeen is Europe's premier oil airport and the world's busiest heliport, in addition to handling domestic and short-haul international flights. In 1985-86, the Scottish airports handled 6.2 million passengers.

SCOTTISH AMATEUR ATHLETIC ASSOCIATION, (SWAA), 18 Ainslie Place, Edinburgh EH3 6AU; T.-031-226 4401.

President: J.E. Clifton; Honorary General Secretary: R.W. Greenoak; Honorary Treasurer: J. Brown.
The governing body for male amateur athletics in Scotland. Promotes national championships for all age groups from senior boys to senior men. Responsible for the encouragement and training of athletes up to international level where they compete in individual and team competitions. Clubs are affiliated to the association through the Eastern, Western and Northern districts and through the Border association, making a total of 150 clubs catering for many thousands of athletes.

SCOTTISH AMATEUR BALLROOM DANCERS' ASSOCIATION, (SABDA), 37 Tanzieknowe Drive, Cambuslang, Glasgow G72 8RG; T.-041-641 5073.

Founded: 1945.
Chairman: Peter McLaughlan; Vice Chairman: Archie McColl; General Secretary: Helen Bradley; Treasurer: May Donaldson; Secretary: Ella Hill.
The governing body in Scotland for amateur ballroom dancing. The objectives are the support and encouragement of amateur ballroom dancing in Scotland. Promotes modern, Latin American and disco competitions each year for adult and junior competitors. Provides scrutineers and stewards at professional events. Represents the Scottish amateur dancer on the British Council of Ballroom Dancing and represents Scotland on the International Council of Amateur Dancers.

SCOTTISH AMATEUR BOXING ASSOCIATION, (SABA), c/o Honorary General Secretary, 96 High Street, Lochee, Dundee; T.-0382 611412.

Founded: 1909.
Honorary General Secretary: Frank Hendry; National Coach: Mr R. McTaggart.
Governs amateur boxing in Scotland. Stages senior and junior annual championships. Has 120 fully affiliated clubs and 80 subsidiary clubs. Selects and enters teams for the European and Commonwealth Championships and supplies referees and judges to officiate at all club promotions of amateur boxing tournaments. Maintains strict medical control of all registered boxers.

SCOTTISH AMATEUR FENCING UNION, c/o Honorary Secretary, Breastmill House, Kirkliston EH29 9EA; T.-031-333 3016.
Honorary Secretary: Prof H.T. Bracewell.

SCOTTISH AMATEUR FOOTBALL ASSOCIATION, (SAFA), Beechwood, Gateside Road, Barrhead, Glasgow G78 1EP; T.-041-881 4025.
Founded: 1909.
President: Thomas A. Wilkie; Vice President: Robert Hay; Secretary and Treasurer: Iain McTweed; Match Secretary: Andrew S. Laird; Assistant Match Secretary: James Robertson.
Exists to promote football played by amateurs. Membership: 2,800 clubs in 150 associations or leagues. Organises competitions for its members. The main competition is the Scottish Amateur Cup, currently sponsored by Tennent Caledonian Breweries Ltd, and eight district amateur cup competitions. In addition, it holds six Scottish amateur under age cup competitions, one senior inter-league competition and four inter-league age limit competitions. While in membership of the Scottish Football Association Ltd, the council of the SAFA is the controlling governing body for all the associations and leagues.

SCOTTISH AMATEUR GYMNASTICS ASSOCIATION, (SAGA), 18 Ainslie Place, Edinburgh EH3 6AU; T.-031-226 4401.
President: Alex G. Strachan; Honorary Secretary: Mrs L.L. Martin; National Coach: Gordon Forster; Administrator: Pam Scott.
Encourages, promotes and controls the sport and practice of gymnastics. Aims to improve the standard of gymnastics in Scotland.

SCOTTISH AMATEUR MUSIC ASSOCIATION, (SAMA), 7 Randolph Crescent, Edinburgh EH3 7TH; T.-031-225 7592.
Founded: 1956.
Honorary President: Philip Ledger, CBE; President: David G. Robertson, CBE; Chairman: George C. McVicar; Honorary Secretary: E.J. Bradley Catto.
Provides a common meeting place for discussion of the promotion and stimulation of local music effort; encourages such effort; assists in the formulation of policy for the promotion of musical activity and for the furtherance of new and extended advisory services. Promotes and administers the National Youth Brass Band of Scotland, its reserve band and training school; the National Youth String Orchestra of Scotland and its preparatory school orchestras; the National Wind Band of Scotland and its reserve band; a Scots fiddle and piping summer school; an organists' summer school; a recorder school.

SCOTTISH AMATEUR ROWING ASSOCIATION, (SARA), c/o The Honorary Secretary, 46 Churchill Drive, Bridge of Allan, Stirling FK9 4TJ; T.-0786 833029.
Founded: 1881.
President: W. Brian Snowden; Honorary Secretary: Peter G. Morrison; Honorary Treasurer: John H. McKinney.
Exists to promote rowing and sculling in Scotland. Has 24 fully affiliated clubs with a larger number of indirectly affiliated clubs. There are several thousand participants of both sexes in the main rowing areas of Aberdeen (River Dee), Edinburgh (canal at Craiglockhart), Stirling (River Forth), Loch Lomond (Balloch), Glasgow (River Clyde at Glasgow Green), Dumfries (River Nith), Greenock and Loch Winnoch.

SCOTTISH AMATEUR SWIMMING ASSOCIATION, Airthrey Castle Annexe, University of Stirling, Stirling FK9 4LA; T.-Stirling 70544.
Administrator: Mrs Rita Hallam; Director of Swimming: H. Hamilton Smith.

SCOTTISH AMATEUR WEIGHT-LIFTERS' ASSOCIATION, c/o Secretary, 86 Saughton Road North, Edinburgh EH12 7JU; T.-031-334 6402.
Secretary: Mr I.T. Thomson.

SCOTTISH AMATEUR WRESTLING ASSOCIATION, (SAWA), 16 Royal Crescent, Glasgow G3 7SL; T.-041-332 4624.
Founded: 1930.
National Organiser: Sandy McNeil.
Exists to develop Olympic and Cumberland wrestling in Scotland. Main Scottish national and district championships are held at all levels.

SCOTTISH AMBULANCE SERVICE, Maitland Street, Glasgow G4 0HX; T.-041-332 6001.
Director: John M. Wilby.

Administered from headquarters in Glasgow, the service handles 2 million patients a year, of whom about 300,000 are emergencies and urgent cases. The service has 2,200 staff operating more than 900 vehicles out of 138 ambulance stations. It is believed to be the largest ambulance service in the world.

SCOTTISH ANGLERS' NATIONAL ASSOCIATION, (SANA), 307 West George Street, Glasgow G2 4LB; T.-041-221 7206.

President: John Reid; Vice President: Michael McKinnell; Honorary Secretary/ Treasurer: David A. Biggart.
The governing body for the sport of game fishing in Scotland. Formed as a result of a merger between the Scottish Anglers National Association (founded 1880) and the Scottish Anglers' Association (founded 1911). Responsible for running the Scottish National Fly Fishing Championship which forms the basis of the international fly fishing team. Membership: 400 clubs and 70 life and individual members.

SCOTTISH ANTI-COMMON MARKET COUNCIL, (SACC), 9 South Gray Street, Newington, Edinburgh EH9 1TE; T.-031-668 1358.

Founded: 1976.
President: Lord MacLeod of Fuinary; Chairman: T. Graham Salmon; Secretary: Iain McGregor.
Pressure group seeking complete withdrawal from the EEC and European Parliament.

SCOTTISH ANTI-VIVISECTION SOCIETY, (SAVS), 121 West Regent Street, Glasgow G2 2SD; T.-041-221 2300.

Founded 1876.
Organising Secretary: John F. Robins.
Pressure group working for the abolition of experiments on living animals and the promotion of animal rights. Publishes *SAVS News*, four times per year, plus an annual report and various leaflets. Member of Mobilisation for Animals.

SCOTTISH ARCHERY ASSOCIATION, c/o The Secretary, 35 Laburnum Grove, Stirling FK8 2PR; T.-0786 65333.

Secretary: A.M. Bowman.

SCOTTISH ARTS CLUB, (SAC), 24 Rutland Square, Edinburgh EH1 2BW; T.-031-229 8157.

Founded: 1874.
Honorary Secretary: W.B. Logan.
Objects are to promote the interests of the arts in general, and social contact among members. Governed by a council of 17 members. Membership: 450, around half being professional and the other half being lay members.

SCOTTISH ARTS COUNCIL, (SAC), 19 Charlotte Square, Edinburgh EH2 4DF; T.-031-226 6051.

Founded: 1947.
Director: Timothy Mason; Deputy Director: Harry McCann; Literature Director: Walter Cairns; Music Director: Christie Duncan; Combined Arts Director: John Murphy; Art Director: Lindsay Gordon; Drama and Dance Director: Robert Palmer.
One of the principal channels for Government funding of the arts in Scotland. Forms part of the Arts Council of Great Britain, a registered charity incorporated by Royal Charter in 1946. The Government grant to ACGB for 1986/87 was £135.6 million, of which the SAC's share was £13.5 million. The council's primary role is to help make the arts available to the public and to assist artists of all kinds, giving priority to professional arts activities. The bulk of its funds is used to support over 1,000 organisations and individuals. In addition, some 120 arts and music clubs and guilds, serving towns and villages throughout Scotland, are subsidised by the council.

SCOTTISH ASIAN ACTION COMMITTEE, (SAAC), 537 Sauchiehall Street, Glasgow G3 7PQ; T.-041-248 5033.

Founded: 1982.
President: Mr K.P. Rahim; Vice President (Senior): Mr G.S. Bhopal; Vice President (Junior): Mrs B. Gandhi; Secretary: Mr P.K. Bhaumik.
Federation of many Asian organisations in the Strathclyde area. Main objective is to safeguard the interests of the Asian communities. Makes representations to public and private bodies, runs a day-care centre for the elderly and provides advice and assistance to Asians with problems. Scottish Asian Youth is the youth wing of SAAC, and is involved in sporting, cultural, and educational activities and in uniting and raising social awareness of the youth. Scottish Asian Women's Association is the women's wing and is involved in making women

socially aware and organising activities beneficial to women.

THE SCOTTISH ASSESSORS ASSOCIATION, c/o Ian M. Rogers, Secretary, 30-31 Queen Street, Edinburgh EH2 1LZ; T.-031-225 1399.
Founded: 1975.
President: James Thomson; Vice President: Jack W. Wood.
Objects are to encourage amongst its members, the exchange of ideas regarding their statutory duties; to promote uniformity in operating the provisions of the Valuation and Registration Acts; to act as a consultative and advisory body; and to represent the collective interest of assessors. Membership: 32, 10 of whom are regional assessors and 22 are deputies.

SCOTTISH ASSOCIATION OF BOYS' CLUBS, 53 George Street, Edinburgh EH2 2HT; T.-031-226 7255.
Secretary: Mr C. Adams, MBE.

SCOTTISH ASSOCIATION FOR THE CARE AND RESETTLEMENT OF OFFENDERS, 53 George Street, Edinburgh EH2 2EH; T.-031-226 4222.
Director: John Phillips.
Regional schemes: Lothian, T.-031-668 1091; Strathclyde, T.-041-332 1763; Tayside, T.-0382 23445; Central, T.-0324 474876; Fife, T.-0333 21215.

SCOTTISH ASSOCIATION OF CHILDREN'S PANELS, (SACP), Woodlands, Wellbank, by Dundee DD5 3QF.
Founded: 1977.
Chairman: Dr John Dalrymple; Vice Chairman: Duncan Shaw; Honorary Secretary: Mrs Alice Allen; Honorary Treasurer: Terry Hartery.
Acts as a corporate voice for the views of members of children's panels throughout Scotland, and provides a means of communication between the panels and other bodies.

SCOTTISH ASSOCIATION OF CITIZENS ADVICE BUREAUX, 82 Nicolson Street, Edinburgh EH8 9EW; T.-031-667 0156.
Founded: 1975.
Chairwoman: Esme Walker; Vice Chairman: Mary Sherrard; Honorary Treasurer: John Fergusson; Chief Executive Officer: John Palmer.

Represents a network of 61 Citizens Advice Bureaux throughout Scotland. The association provides resources of information, training, field staff, and legal consultancy through a staff of 14 professionals. The organisation provides free, confidential, and impartial advice, information and assistance to all enquirers.

THE SCOTTISH ASSOCIATION OF COMPANY AND COMMERCIAL ACCOUNTANTS, 190 St Vincent Street, Glasgow G2 5SP; T.-041-204 2833.
President: John Mather; Vice President: Madan Kapoor; Secretary and Treasurer: David I. Strachan.
Professional body of accountants, primarily in commerce and industry.

SCOTTISH ASSOCIATION FOR COUNSELLING, 26 Frederick Street, Edinburgh EH2 2JR; T.-031-225 5006.
Founded: 1977.
Honorary President: Rt Rev Michael Hare Duke; Honorary Vice Presidents: Sheriff Nigel Thomson, Rev Prof James Whyte; Executive Secretary: Margaret E. Clement.
Promotes and provides education and training for counsellors, provides support and supervision and promotes the use of counselling as a valuable aid to the well-being of the community.

THE SCOTTISH ASSOCIATION FOR THE DEAF, (SAD), Moray House, Holyrood Road, Edinburgh EH8 8AQ; T.-031-556 8137.
Founded: 1927.
Honorary Director: Miss S. Morag Turner; President: Dr J. Fulton Christie; Vice-president: Mr T. McLaren; Chairman: Dr Arnold M. Grier; Vice-chairman: Rev G. Smith; Honorary Treasurer: Alan Macdonald.
Established as a voluntary body to co-ordinate the work of all organisations, voluntary or statutory, working for and with deaf people of all ages in Scotland. Membership includes representatives of all such organisations and individuals, and for the past 50 years it has been recognised as the body responsible for co-ordinating all their activities, thereby ensuring the well-being of all deaf people in Scotland, especially in their dealings with statutory and other bodies. The word 'deaf' is used in its widest sense as applying to all people whose hearing impairment is such as to constitute a handicap.

SCOTTISH ASSOCIATION OF GEOGRAPHY TEACHERS, (SAGT), c/o Jordanhill College of Education, 76 Southbrae Drive, Glasgow G13 1PP; T.-041-959 1232.
Founded: 1970.
President: Alastair Robinson; Vice-president: Philip Galbraith; Secretary: Jack Bairner; Treasurer: John Vannet; Editor: Norman Thomson.
Association for teachers of geography at all levels of education. Involved in United Kingdom and European associations of geography teachers. Membership: 750.

SCOTTISH ASSOCIATION OF LOCAL SPORTS COUNCILS, c/o Carnegie Centre, Pilmuir Street, Dunfermline, Fife; T.-0383 723211.
Secretary: Mr N. Grimshaw.

SCOTTISH ASSOCIATION OF MASTER BAKERS, 4 Torphichen Street, Edinburgh; T.-031-229 1401.
Founded: 1891.
President: John K. Young; Director: John Lefley.
Trade association representing and promoting the interests of its members, who cover the vast majority of firms in the bakery and allied trades in Scotland.

SCOTTISH ASSOCIATION FOR MENTAL HEALTH, 40 Shandwick Place, Edinburgh EH2 4RT; T.-031-225 3062.
Chairman: Rt Rev M.G. Hare Duke; Vice Chairman: Dr R.A.Y. Stewart; Director: Peter J. Clarke.
Independent organisation concerned with people who experience mental illness. Seeks to develop voluntary action and influence policy.

SCOTTISH ASSOCIATION FOR PUBLIC TRANSPORT, (SAPT), c/o GCVS, 11 Queen's Crescent, Glasgow G4 9AS.
Founded: 1972.
Chairman: J. Pinkerton; Secretary: M. Foreman; Treasurer: D.S. Brown.
Voluntary body which seeks to publicise the economic, social and environmental value to Scotland of an integrated transport system for public use. SAPT policy is based on the scope which effective public transport offers for energy conservation, for the safer movement of goods and passengers, for environmental gains and for good access to employment, leisure and other facilities for all sections of the population. Policies include support for co-ordinated air, rail, ship, bus and taxi services with high-quality interchange and marketing, through ticketing, family fares and attractive zonal fares. Membership: 200 (both corporate and individual available).

SCOTTISH ASSOCIATION FOR THE SPEAKING OF VERSE, 38 Dovecot Road, Edinburgh EH12 7LE; T.-031-334 5241.
Founded: 1924.
President: Norman MacCaig; Chairman: Peter France; Secretary: Robin Bell.
Promotes Scottish poetry in all its forms. One of the leading organisers of readings by poets, not only from Scotland, but from elsewhere in the United Kingdom and overseas.

SCOTTISH ASSOCIATION OF TRACK STATISTICIANS, c/o Honorary Secretary, 27 St Ninian's Terrace, Edinburgh EH10 5PW.
Honorary Secretary: Mr J. Carter.
Recording of athletics statistics.

THE SCOTTISH ASSOCIATION OF WRITERS, (SAW), 1D Vicarland Place, Kirkhill, Cambuslang, Glasgow G72 8QE; T.-041-641 7203.
Founded: 1969.
President: Mrs Margaret Ryan; Honorary Secretary: Mrs Beth Thomson; Treasurer: Mrs Kathleen Ross-Hale.
An association of writers' groups and clubs throughout Scotland. Exists to promote and encourage the art and craft of writing in all its forms. These aims embrace writers at any level of experience, including beginners. Organises conferences, competitions and weekend schools for its members. Membership is approaching 500.

SCOTTISH ASSOCIATION OF YOUNG FARMERS' CLUBS, (SAYFC), Young Farmers' Centre, Ingliston, Newbridge, Midlothian EH28 8NE; T.-031-333 2445.
Founded: 1938.
Director: John Kerr; National Field Officer: Margaret R. Whiteford; Proficiency Testing and Training Officer: Elaine J. Kilgour; President: Malcolm Logan; Chairman: Bobby A. Lennox; Vice-chairman: Arthur Lawrie.
A national voluntary youth organisation with 125 clubs providing activities for 6,000 mem-

bers in all parts of Scotland. Offers members an extensive range of educational, recreational and social activities, the competitive age range being 14 to 25 years. Lays great stress on training and personal development and all the clubs elect their own office bearers and leaders. Membership is open to any young people with an interest in the countryside. Activities include speechmaking, drama, handicrafts, sport, educational visits, international exchanges; agricultural skills competitions, craft training, skills testing and fun.

SCOTTISH ASSOCIATION OF YOUTH CLUBS, Balfour House, 17 Bonnington Grove, Edinburgh EH6 4DP; T.-031-554 2561.

Founded: 1933.
Chairman: The Hon E.D. Bruce; Vice Chairman (designate): W. McFarlane; Treasurer: Ian C. Lewis; Director: Audrey W. Milan; Youth Work Manager: Zander Jack.
Aims to give young people opportunities for enjoyable and constructive leisure time activities. Supports voluntary adult helpers, clubs, and area associations, carries out a programme of competitive and non-competitive sport, trains senior members and leaders, and arranges conferences for young people. Membership: 113,000 young people in 1,088 clubs, and 7,500 adults, mainly voluntary workers.

SCOTTISH AUTO CYCLE UNION, c/o The Secretary, Kippilaw, Longridge Road, Whitburn, West Lothian EH47 0LG; T.-0501 42663.

Secretary: T. Arnott Moffat.

SCOTTISH BADMINTON UNION, (SBU), Cockburn Centre, 40 Bogmoor Place, Glasgow G51 4TQ; T.-041-445 1218.

Founded: 1901.
President: Tom W. Pettigrew; Honorary Secretary: David R. McIntyre; Honorary Treasurer: Macdonald Henderson; Executive Administrator: Miss Anne Smillie.
Objectives are: to foster and encourage the game of badminton in Scotland; to hold annually a Scottish championship tournament, and Scottish national championships and group competitions for senior and junior players; to select Scottish international teams and make arrangements for international matches; to do all other things considered necessary or desirable for the promotion of the game in Scotland and in the interests of the members of the union. Has 550 affiliated clubs and over 11,000 affiliated members.

THE SCOTTISH BALLET, 261 West Princes Street, Glasgow G4 9EE; T.-041-331 2931.

Founded: 1969.
General Administrator: Robin Anderson; Artistic Director: Peter Darrell; Assistant Artistic Director: Gordon Aitken; Director of Touring: Douglas Pringle; Director of Planning: Ann Baird; Marketing and Publicity: Judy Aitken.
Scotland's national dance company. Consists of 42 dancers with supporting administrative, technical and design staff. The main company presents an average of 90 full scale performances each year with full orchestra in major theatres. It also undertakes smaller scale touring when the company is split into two groups to present single performances in theatres and town halls from Wick in the north to Dumfries in the south. Maintains a permanent educational group of five dancers and a musician whose work is exclusively in education and the community.

SCOTTISH BASKETBALL ASSOCIATION, (SBA), 8 Frederick Street, Edinburgh EH2 2HB; T.-031-225 7143.

Founded: 1947.
Chairman: W.B. McGuinness; Vice-chairman: W.D. McInnes; Secretary: Ms E. Dudgeon; Treasurer: M.J. Gilbert; Technical Director: K.D.A. Johnston.
Object is to develop, promote and control the playing of basketball, and to encourage interest in the game in Scotland.

SCOTTISH BILLIARDS ASSOCIATION AND CONTROL COUNCIL, c/o Honorary Secretary, 12 Station Road, Bardowie, Milngavie, Glasgow G62 6ET; T.-041-212 0249.

Honorary Secretary: Stuart Ramsden.

SCOTTISH BOARD SAILING ASSOCIATION, c/o Secretary, Beinn Bhan, Kilmory Road, Lochgilphead, Argyll.

Secretary: Mr F.A. Johnston.

SCOTTISH BOAT BUILDERS ASSOCIATION, (SBBA), 36 Renfield Street, Glasgow G2 1BD; T.-041-248 6161.

Secretary: A. Ferrie.

SCOTTISH BOOK MARKETING GROUP, 25A South West Thistle Street Lane, Edinburgh EH2 1EW; T.-031-225 5795.
Founded: 1986.
Chairman: Bill Campbell; Publicist: Alison Harley.
Joint venture formed by the Scottish branch of the Booksellers' Association and the Scottish Publishers Association to promote books published in Scotland through Scottish bookshops.

SCOTTISH BORDERS TOURIST BOARD, (SBTB), Municipal Buildings, High Street, Selkirk TD7 4JX; T.-0750 20555.
Founded: 1982.
Director of Tourism: Michael Ambrose; Assistant Director: Riddell Graham.
A partnership organisation linking the trade and local authorities in the Scottish borders, and seeking to promote the district as a holiday area as well as providing information services for visitors once they arrive. Has a membership of almost 700 businesses, representing hotels, bed and breakfast, self-catering accommodation, retailers, historic homes etc. Produces a wide range of publicity material. Operates nine tourist information centres, all of which are open from Easter until the end of October.

SCOTTISH BOWLING ASSOCIATION, 50 Wellington Street, Glasgow G2 6EF; T.-041-221 8999.
Founded: 1892.
Secretary and Treasurer: Peter Smith.
Fosters, safeguards and controls the game of bowls. Responsible for organising the Scottish championships and selecting international teams.

SCOTTISH BUILDING CONTRACT COMMITTEE, 39 Castle Street, Edinburgh EH2 3BH; T.-031-225 1200.
Founded: 1965.
Secretary: G.W. Burnet.
The committee's constituent bodies are: Royal Incorporation of Architects in Scotland; Scottish Building Employers' Federation; Scottish Branch, Royal Institution of Chartered Surveyors; Committee of Associations of Specialist Engineering Contractors; COSLA; Federation of Associations of Specialists and Sub-Contractors, Scottish Branch; Association of Consulting Engineers, Scottish Group; CBI; Association of Scottish Chambers of Commerce. The remit of the committee from its constituent bodies is to prepare forms of contract for building work in Scotland and to amend or revise these from time to time, as may be required; and generally to consider and advise upon other matters relating to building contracts in Scotland.

SCOTTISH BUILDING EMPLOYERS' FEDERATION, (SBEF), 13 Woodside Crescent, Glasgow G3 7UP; T.-041-332 7144.
Founded: 1895.
President: W.G. Robertson; Senior Vice President: S.A. Howard.
The employers' organisation for the building industry in Scotland. Recognised as such by central and local Government, the trades unions and the professions. The federation is affiliated to the Building Employers' Confederation which performs the same task in England and Wales. In order to cover the whole of Scotland, there are 28 local building and trade associations, all of which are in membership of the federation. The 1,600 individual firms in membership of the local associations are corporate members of the federation. In addition to the HQ office, the federation has four area offices: Aberdeen, Edinburgh, Glasgow and Inverness.

SCOTTISH BUSINESS ACHIEVEMENT AWARD TRUST LTD, PO Box 25, Edinburgh EH3 6UD; T.-031-556 3521.
Founded: 1981.
Chairman: Sandy Irvine Robertson.
The aim of the award is to select a young business person in Scotland (under 35) who has shown outstanding achievement in business. It is believed that by identifying and praising such achievement, there will also be created a wider recognition of the importance of excellence and effort by younger people in Scotland.

SCOTTISH BUSINESS IN THE COMMUNITY, (ScotBIC), Eagle Star House, 25 St Andrew Square, Edinburgh EH2 1AF; T.-031-556 9761.
Founded: 1982.
President: The Prince of Wales; Chairman, Governing Council: Sir Hector Laing; Chairman, Executive Council: William Stevenson; Director: Graham T. Ross; Company Secretary and Treasurer: M. Robert Wilson.
Aims to encourage industry and commerce to become more involved in meeting the

needs of local communities, and encourage the concept of local partnerships of business, local authorities and other organisations working together for the benefit of the community. Has played a major role in the creation of a network of over 30 local enterprise trusts which seek to stimulate local economies through the provision of free advice to new and existing businesses.

SCOTTISH BUSINESS SCHOOL, 79 West George Street, Glasgow G2 1EU; T.-041-221 3124.

Founded: 1970.
Chairman of Council: Sir Monty Finniston; Dean: Prof A.W.J. Thomson.
Consortium of the management education departments of five universities: Glasgow, Edinburgh, Strathclyde, Stirling and Heriot-Watt. Provides a range of educational and consultancy services in the management field to both the private and public sectors of Scottish industry, commmerce and administration.

SCOTTISH CAMPAIGN FOR NUCLEAR DISARMAMENT, 420 Sauchiehall Street, Glasgow G2; T.-041-331 2878.

Chairperson: Nancy Dangerfield; Administrators: Liz Anderson, Kay Caldwell.
Pressure group campaiging for nuclear disarmament.

SCOTTISH CAMPAIGN TO RESIST THE ATOMIC MENACE, (SCRAM), 11 Forth Street, Edinburgh EH1 3LE; T.-031-557 4283.

Founded: 1975.
Aims and objectives: to inform the public on energy issues; to oppose all nuclear developments in Scotland and the United Kingdom; to promote safe, renewable energy systems. Publishes SCRAM, a bi-monthly energy journal, and publishes a number of books, pamphlets and information sheets on energy issues.

SCOTTISH CANOE ASSOCIATION, (SCA), 18 Ainslie Place, Edinburgh EH3 6AU; T.-031-226 4401.

Founded: 1939.
President: P.F. Nelson; Vice President: A.J. Cook; General Secretary: J. Mooney; Treasurer: A.J. Warrender; Administrator: Mrs M. Winter.
Governing body for the sport of canoeing in

Scotland. Has eight technical sub-committees: slalom, white water racing, sprint racing, marathon racing, canoe polo, touring, coaching, surf. Membership: 1,500 individuals, 60 clubs.

SCOTTISH CARAVAN CLUB, c/o Honorary Secretary, 52 Windmill Knowe, Crossgates, Cowdenbeath, Fife KY4 8AT.

Chairman: T.R. Christie; Honorary Secretary: D. Rushin.
Scottish division of the Caravan Club. Provides full range of services for the touring caravanner including caravan sites, certificated locations, foreign touring service etc. Membership: over 250,000.

SCOTTISH CATHOLIC ARCHIVES, (SCA), Columba House, 16 Drummond Place, Edinburgh EH3 6PL; T.-031-556 3661.

Keeper: Rev G. Mark Dilworth, OSB.
Primary purpose is to make available to scholars the records of the post-reformation Roman Catholic Church in Scotland. Involves: cataloguing the documents surviving from the past; summarising the catalogue in a widely available handlist; allowing bona-fide researchers free access to catalogue, documents and reference library.

SCOTTISH CATHOLIC INTERNATIONAL AID FUND, (SCIAF), 43 Greenhill Road, Rutherglen, Glasgow G73 2SW; T.-041-647 2113/9434.

Founded: 1965.
President: Bishop John Mone; Chairman: Father Ian Murray; Secretary: John McKee; Executive Director: Duncan MacLaren.
Aims: to support the poor in the Third World in their efforts to liberate themselves from poverty, underdevelopment and oppression; to educate Scots, and in particular the Scottish Catholic community, about the basic injustice between the rich and the poor in the world and their role in changing the structures which cause the injustice. Funds self-help development projects, mostly in sub-Saharan Africa, Latin America, the Indian sub-continent and South East Asia. Most projects are small, should arise from a basic need of the people, should benefit everyone and should be concerned with the causes as well as the conditions of poverty.

SCOTTISH CENTRAL FILM AND VIDEO LIBRARY, (SCFVL), Dowanhill, 74 Victoria Crescent Road, Glasgow G12 9JN; T.-041-334 9314.
Founded: 1934.
Assistant Director: J.F. Murray.
Holds more than 7,000 titles of films and videotapes covering virtually all subjects at all levels.

SCOTTISH CENTRAL FIRE BRIGADES ADVISORY COUNCIL, (SCFBAC), Room 274, St Andrew's House, Edinburgh EH1 3DE; T.-031-556 8501, Ext. 2860.
Founded: 1947.
Chairman: W.K. Reid; Secretary: R.A. McFarlane.
Advises the Secretary of State for Scotland on fire service matters.

SCOTTISH CENTRE FOR AGRICULTURAL ENGINEERING, (SCAE), Bush Estate, Penicuik, Midlothian EH26 OPH; T.-031-445 2147.
Founded: 1987 (1946, as Scottish Institute of Agricultural Engineering).
Liaison Officer: Mr B.W. Sheppard.
From 1 April 1987, the centre will consist of the Agricultural Engineering Department of the East of Scotland College of Agriculture, which will also incorporate part of the Scottish Institute of Agricultural Enginering after this disbands on 31 March 1987. The centre has the responsibility for co-ordinating R & D in agricultural engineering for all three Scottish colleges of agriculture, while undertaking a major part of this work itself. In addition, it provides specialist advice on agricultural engineering in its own 'college area' and provides teaching facilities and staff for the Edinburgh School of Agriculture.

SCOTTISH CENTRE FOR THE TUITION OF THE DISABLED, (SCTD), Queen Margaret College, Clerwood Terrace, Edinburgh EH12 8TS; T.-031-339 5408.
Founded: 1979.
Chairman: Mr I.S. Flett, CBE; Secretary and Scottish Organiser: Ms E. Sutherland; Strathclyde Co-ordinator: Mrs M. Graham; Administrative Assistant: Miss A. Durie; Honorary Treasurer: Mr S. Fullerton.
A voluntary organisation which provides information and advice about educational opportunities to adults with disabilities. Also provides a home teaching service using volunteers. Its aim is to encourage and enable the integration of adults with disabilities into existing educational provision. When this is not possible or appropriate, the centre's volunteer organisers, based in the regions, find voluntary tutors to work on a one to one basis, usually in the student's home. Help is given free in a wide variety of activities, from academic studies to arts and crafts. Students who are following a course of study at an educational institution can receive additional support from a voluntary tutor if they need it.

SCOTTISH CHAMBER ORCHESTRA, 12-18 Howden Street, Edinburgh EH8 9HL; T.-031-667 7354.
Chairman: A. Donald M. MacDonald; General Manager: Ian Ritchie.
Gives concert series in major Scottish towns; plays in smaller towns where facilities are not large enough to support a full symphony orchestra; tours extensively abroad.

SCOTTISH CHESS ASSOCIATION, 44 Stewart Clark Avenue, South Queensferry EH30 9QH; T.-031-331 1751.
President: Bill Smerdon; General Administrator: Mrs L. Morrison.

SCOTTISH CHILD AND FAMILY ALLIANCE, (SCAFA), 56 Albany Street, Edinburgh EH1 3QR; T.-031-557 2780.
Founded: 1983.
Chairman: Lord Mackay of Clashfern, PC; Vice-chairman: John Rea; Deputy Chairman: Prof Ross Mitchell; Director and Company Secretary: Rachel Jenkins; Training Officer: Stephanie Tristam.
A voluntary organisation which represents the interests of children and families. Has a wide-ranging membership of organisations from health, education, social welfare, child law and special needs. There is increasing representation from statutory bodies and individuals. Aims to foster communication and co-operation between professionals, voluntary bodies and the voluntary and statutory sectors; to provide a forum for discussion on policy issues; to evaluate and respond to policy proposals. Organises regular conferences, seminars and open meetings. Services include training, information and publications.

SCOTTISH CHURCHES ARCHI-

TECTURAL HERITAGE TRUST, (SCAHT), 15 North Bank Street, Edinburgh EH1 2LP; T.-031-225 8644.
Founded: 1978.
Chairman: The Viscount of Arbuthnott; Founder Chairman: Magnus Magnusson; Director: Mrs Florence MacKenzie; Treasurer: T.A. Turnbull.
Established to care for Scottish church buildings in use, principally by raising funds for their repair and restoration and by acting as a source of technical advice and assistance on maintenance and repair. Entirely dependent on support from private individuals, business organisations and all those concerned with maintaining Scotland's invaluable architectural and historic heritage.

SCOTTISH CHURCHES' COUNCIL, (SCC), Scottish Churches House, Kirk Street, Dunblane FK15 0AJ; T.-0786 823588.
Founded: 1964.
Chairman: Very Rev Dr William B. Johnston; Vice-chairmen: Rev Dr Derek B. Murray, Rev Raymond J. Bade, Mrs Maidie Hart; General Secretary: Rev Canon Kenyon E. Wright; Administrative Secretary: Miss Christine M. Hoskings; Honorary Treasurer: Tom Turnbull.
Consists of directly elected representatives of nine Protestant churches and five interdenominational Christian organisaions in Scotland. The Roman Catholic Church is represented as a participant observer. The aim of the council is to promote greater unity, renewal, and mission among the Scottish churches. Two main committees, Mission and Unity, and Community, Justice and Peace, try to co ordinate church activities in these fields. Scottish Churches House is a 50-bed centre for conferences, consultations and retreats.

SCOTTISH CHURCH HISTORY SOCIETY, (SCHS), Grange Manse, 51 Portland Road, Kilmarnock KA1 2EQ; T.-Kilmarnock 25311.
Founded: 1922.
Honorary President: Rev A. Ian Dunlop, TD; President: Rev Prof Alex C. Cheyne; Honorary Secretary and Treasurer: Rev Colin G.F. Brockie; Editor: James Kirk.
Seeks to promote the study of the history of all branches of the Church in Scotland. Since its inception, scholars have given papers on every aspect of ecclesiastical history and most of these have been published in the records of the society which are distributed annually to all members. Membership: 181 and 79 libraries.

THE SCOTTISH CIVIC TRUST, 24 George Square, Glasgow G2 1EF; T.-041-221 1466.
Founded: 1967.
Chairman: Rt Hon Viscount Muirshiel, KT, CH, CMG; Chairman, Management Committee: James W. Wilson, OBE; Administrative Director: Mrs Sadie Douglas; Technical Director: John Gerrard; Consultant: Dr Maurice Lindsay, CBE, TD.
Aims to encourage public interest in the good appearance of towns and countryside and to inspire generally a sense of civic pride and desire for high quality in Scottish architecture and planning. It is particularly concerned with the conservation of buildings of architectural distinction or historic interest, the elimination and prevention of ugliness, whether from bad design or neglect, and the encouragement of informed and constructive participation in planning matters. Operates locally through civic or amenity societies registered with the trust, and is able to give advice on, and help with, environmental problems.

SCOTTISH COLLEGE OF TEXTILES, (SCOT), Netherdale, Galashiels, Selkirkshire TD1 3HF; T.-0896 3351.
Founded: 1883.
Chairman: J. Walker; Principal: J.C. Furniss; Secretary and Treasurer: E. Wood; Vice-principal: Dr R.H. Harwood.
A Central Institution of Higher Education. Offers full-time and sandwich courses at degree level in subjects related to the textile and clothing industries. Postgraduate diploma courses and research are available for MPhil and PhD. Business related courses are also available at Higher National Diploma and Post Degree/Diploma levels. Operates the Scottish Borders Management Centre for short courses and consultancy for industry and commerce, and is involved in the Scottish Textile and Technical Centre providing services for industry. Activity holiday courses offered each summer.

SCOTTISH COLPORTAGE SOCIETY, (SCS), 11 Newton Place, Glasgow G3 7PR; T.-041-333 0546.
Founded: 1793.
Chairman: Basil Mackenzie; Vice Chairman: John Dodds; Colporteur: Mary McBain.
'A Bible in every home in Scotland' is the aim of the society. Full-time and voluntary colporteurs are engaged in door-to-door work

and are readily available to speak or give illustrated lectures on the society's work.

SCOTTISH COMMERCIAL TRAVELLERS' ASSOCIATION, (SCTA), 20 Anderson Street, Airdrie ML6 0AA; T.-023 64 56161.

National President: J. Monteith; National Vice-president: J. Dougall; General Secretary and Treasurer: R.M. Wood.

Exists to organise, promote and protect the interests of the commercial traveller; to further the objects of the association by propaganda; to raise funds by means of subscriptions or otherwise; to obtain for its members transport concessions, special insurance rates, legal advice and other advantages which can be more readily obtained by united action. Membership: 500.

SCOTTISH COMMITTEE OF THE COUNCIL ON TRIBUNALS, (SCCT), 20 Walker Street, Edinburgh EH3 7HR; T.-031-225 3236.

Founded: 1958.

Chairman: R.N.M. MacLean, QC; Secretary: Mrs E.M. Chalmers; Assistant Secretary: Miss A. Hunter.

The council was established by the Tribunals and Inquiries Act 1958. The main statute now governing its operations is the Tribunals and Inquiries Act 1971. Its main function is to keep under review the constitution and working of the tribunals specified in Schedule I to the Act to ensure that the conduct of hearings is characterised by openness, fairness and impartiality. The council has largely delegated its functions in Scotland to the Scottish Committee and it has long been accepted practice for departments to approach the Scottish Committee directly with proposals relating to tribunals or inquiries in Scotland. The committee also acts as the council's agents in relation to Scottish aspects of British tribunals.

SCOTTISH COMMITTEE ON OPEN LEARNING, (SCOL), Scottish Council for Educational Technology, Dowanhill, 74 Victoria Crescent Road, Glasgow G12 9JN; T.-041-334 9314.

Founded: 1983.

Chairman: Ian Collie; Secretary: Nigel Paine.

Exists to encourage the development of open learning in Scotland. Identifies priorities in the development of open learning and implements them. Identifies the educational needs of the post-16 sector best met through open learning schemes and recommends suitable provision. Encourages research and pilot ventures in open learning. Liaises with other Scottish and United Kingdom bodies interested in open learning.

SCOTTISH COMMITTEE OF OPHTHALMIC OPTICIANS, c/o A.M. Thomson, Secretary and Treasurer, Savoy Tower, 77 Renfrew Street, Glasgow G2 3BY; T.-041-333 9770.

Founded: 1934.

Represents ophthamlic opticians in all matters affecting them.

SCOTTISH COMMUNITY DRAMA ASSOCIATION, (SCDA), Saltire House, 13 Atholl Crescent, Edinburgh EH3 8HA; T.-031-332 3980.

Founded: 1926.

Chairman: Peter Stevens; Administrator: Alan Nicol.

Exists for the development of amateur drama in Scotland, particularly on a community basis. Binds together amateur dramatic societies throughout the country, and offers them advice, encouragement, and practical help in the furtherance of their aims.

SCOTTISH COMMUNITY EDUCATION COUNCIL, (SCEC), Atholl House, 2 Canning Street, Edinburgh EH3 8EG; T.-031-229 2433.

Founded: 1972.

Chairman: The Baroness Carnegy of Lour; Director: Dorothy Dalton; Assistant Director: Marcus Liddle; Assistant Director: Allen Mercer.

Advises the Secretary of State for Scotland on the development of community education in Scotland and promotes its development. SCEC is an information, resource and development centre for those involved in community education and active in their communities.

SCOTTISH CONSERVATION PROJECTS TRUST, Balallan House, 24 Allan Park, Stirling FK8 2QG; T.-0786 79697.

Founded: 1984.

President: Sir James Stormonth-Darling, CBE, MC, TD; Chairman: Alistair Campbell, OBE; Vice Chairman: Colin Taylor; Honor-

ary Treasurer: Dr Alan Mowle; Director: Nicholas Cooke; Trust Administrator: Catherine Smith.
Charitable voluntary body which promotes outdoor conservation work throughout Scotland, involving voluntary groups, schools, the unemployed and students. Projects such as drystane dyking, fencing, tree planting and path construction are carried out to enhance the wildlife or scenic amenity value of the urban and rural environment for the benefit of the public at large. The trust currently supports a network of 40 affiliated local groups; runs over 50 residential projects and 30 weekend skills training courses a year; sponsors MSC funded school and community schemes; and involves over 4,000 volunteers of all ages in its work. In 1986, 30,000 conservation work days will be completed through the trust's activities.

SCOTTISH CONSERVATIVE PARTY, 3 Chester Street, Edinburgh EH3 7RF; T.-031-226 4426.
Chairman: Sir James Goold; Deputy Chairman: Sir Donald Maclean; Vice- Chairman: Ian Lang, MP; Director: William R. Henderson, TD; Deputy Directors: Robert M. Balfour, Walter M. Ross.
Central organisational offices of the Scottish Conservative Party.

SCOTTISH CONSERVATIVE AND UNIONIST ASSOCIATION, 3 Chester Street, Edinburgh EH3 7RF; T.-031-226 4426.
President: Iain A. McCrone; Vice Presidents: Councillor Kenneth G. Ferguson, James B. Highgate, CBE; Honorary Treasurer: Matthew D. Goodwin, CBE; Secretary: Ann C. Hay.

SCOTTISH CONSUMER COUNCIL, (SCC), 314 St Vincent Street, Glasgow G3 8XW; T.-041-226 5261.
Founded: 1975.
Chairman: Mrs Barbara Kelly; Vice-chairman: Mrs Helen Millar; Director: Peter Gibson.
The Scottish Consumer Council, a committee of the National Consumer Council, was established by Government to identify and represent the interests of Scottish consumers, particularly the disadvantaged. Keeps a watching brief on the goods and services provided by central and local Government, and other public bodies as well as by commercial firms and professions. Research is carried out into areas of consumer concern, and the council then presses for whatever changes are required in the law and in the provision of services to meet the needs of consumers. The council consists of 13 members plus a chairman, appointed by the Minister for Consumer Affairs in the Department of Trade. There are 10 permanent staff.

SCOTTISH CO-OPERATIVE EDUCATION ASSOCIATION, 95 Morrison Street, Glasgow G5 8LP; T.-041-429 2556.
Chairman: R.S. Stewart; Secretary: R. Bluer.
Promotes adult education for co-operative employees and members, promotes new co-operatives and runs courses in establishing new co-operatives.

SCOTTISH CO-OPERATIVES DEVELOPMENT COMMITTEE LTD, (SCDC), Templeton Business Centre, Templeton Street, Glasgow G40 1DA; T.-041-554 3797.
Founded: 1977.
Director: Alexander Smith; Deputy Director: John Whyte; Training Officer: Patrick Boase; Company Secretary: Ishbel Johnstone; Development Officers: Fiona Weir, John Cummins, Alan McGregor, Brian Travers.
Objective is to promote the concept of workers' co-operatives throughout Scotland. SCDC has consultancy agreements with Strathclyde Regional Council and the Scottish Development Agency to set up and maintain co-operative businesses. Funding has also been obtained from Glasgow District Council, the HIDB, Aberdeen District Council and the regional and district councils in Fife to maintain locally based development officers.

SCOTTISH CO-OPERATIVE WOMEN'S GUILD, 95 Morrison Street, Glasgow G5 8LP; T.-041-429 1457.
Founded: 1892.
General Secretary: Mrs M. Marsden.
Exists for the study and practice of the best means of strengthening and extending the co-operative movement; stimulates thought on all questions of social and political reform.

SCOTTISH CORN TRADE ASSOCIATION LTD, (SCTA), c/o Touche Ross & Co, 15 Melville Street, Edinburgh EH3 7PQ; T.-031-225 6834.
Founded: 1936.

President: A.C. Brown; Vice-president: C.W.L. Reid; Secretaries: Touche Ross & Co. Membership consists of 90 companies and firms connected with the grain trade. Represents members' interests in Scotland. Has representation on the Grain and Feed Trade Association's council to cover EEC and worldwide trade matters of interest to Scottish traders. Has its own trading conditions and rules for use in trading grain in Scotland.

THE SCOTTISH COT DEATH TRUST, Royal Hospital for Sick Children, Yorkhill, Glasgow G3 8SJ; T.-041-357 3946.

Founded: 1985.
Chairman: Prof G.C. Arneil; Trust Co-ordinator: Mrs Hazel Brooke.
Three main aims: to raise funds to support and promote research into the cause, epidemiology and prevention of cot death of which a baby dies every second day in Scotland; to extend and improve support to the bereaved families; to educate the public concerning cot death by using information leaflets and publicity. Has helped organise two major cot death conferences and published an information leaflet for bereaved parents. Various Cot Death Support Groups throughout Scotland have been brought together. Monitoring of at risk babies is being encouraged and two major research projects into the cause of cot deaths are underway.

SCOTTISH COUNCIL ON ALCOHOL, (SCA), 147 Blythswood Street, Glasgow G2 4EN; T.-041-333 9677.

Founded: 1973.
Chairman: The Rt Hon The Earl of Minto; Treasurer: John D.M. Urquhart; Director: Douglas T. Allsop.
The national body in Scotland dealing with all aspects of alcohol use and abuse, offering services, help and advice to both people experiencing problems with alcohol and their families, through a national network of 25 affiliated local councils.

SCOTTISH COUNCIL FOR CIVIL LIBERTIES, (SCCL), 146 Holland Street, Glasgow G2 4NG; T.-041-332 5960.

Founded: 1969.
Chairman: Richard Kinsey; Vice-chairperson: Ruth Forbes; General Secretary: David Godwin; Treasurer: Susan Watson.
A democratic, non-party membership organisation, the objectives of which are the protection and promotion of civil liberties in Scotland. Membership is open to individuals and organisations. While primarily a campaigning organisation, advice and referral services are provided and an archive resource is maintained. A publications list and membership information are available on request.

SCOTTISH COUNCIL FOR DANCE, c/o Honorary Secretary, PO Box 410, WDO, Edinburgh EH12 6AR.

Honorary Secretary: Miss P. Woodeson.

THE SCOTTISH COUNCIL DEVELOPMENT AND INDUSTRY, (SCDI), 23 Chester Street, Edinburgh EH3 7ET; T.-031-225 7911.

Founded: 1946.
President: Rt Hon Lord Clydesmuir, KT, CB, MBE; Chairman: D.M. McCallum, CBE; Chief Executive: H.R. Morrison; Operations Director: A. Wilson; Policy Director: R.C. Campbell; Secretary: H.H. Hunter.
Formed by the merger of the Scottish Development Council and the Scottish Council on Industry. Financed voluntarily by companies, local authorities, banks, chambers of commerce, trade unions and other corporate bodies, as well as by private individuals, all of whom are represented on the executive which is the governing body. The broad aim is to promote the industrial and economic development of Scotland. Within this general framework, the specific objectives of the council are chosen according to their value in advancing the prosperity and well-being of Scotland.

SCOTTISH COUNCIL ON DISABILITY, (SCD), Princes House, 5 Shandwick Place, Edinburgh EH2 4RG; T.-031-229 8632.

Founded: 1982.
Chairman: Drummond Hunter; Director: David Dunsmuir; Assistant Director: Robin Law.
The national voluntary organisation for all of Scotland's disabled people. Services are provided which are not otherwise available, but which are essential to disabled people and their families. Promotes change and improvements in areas such as housing, education, employment, access to buildings, transport, health and social services, state benefits and training to offer a better quality of life to people in Scotland who have a disability. The council's activities are sup-

ported by a wide range of services, for example, committees on access, mobility, the arts, benefits, an information department, a mobile advice centre, a reference library and a clothing advisory service.

SCOTTISH COUNCIL FOR EDUCATIONAL TECHNOLOGY, (SCET), Dowanhill, 74 Victoria Crescent Road, Glasgow G12 9JN; T.-031-334 9314.

Founded: 1975.
Director: George Paton.
Autonomous body supported by the Scottish Education Department and the regional authorities in Scotland. Its objects are: 'to promote and encourage the understanding and application of educational technology in its widest sense throughout education both formal and informal and in commercial and industrial training'. Concerned with research and development, software development, communications and publications, learning systems, media resources, and a microelectronics programme (SCAMP), enabling schools to carry out administration on computer.

SCOTTISH COUNCIL OF LAW REPORTING, 26 Drumsheugh Gardens, Edinburgh; T.-031-226 7411.

Founded: 1957.
Secretary: Kenneth W. Pritchard.
Company limited by guarantee to prepare and publish reports of civil and criminal cases in the High Court of Scotland and the House of Lords in regard to Scottish cases.

SCOTTISH COUNCIL FOR OPPORTUNITIES IN PLAY EXPERIENCE, (SCOPE), 16 Sandyford Place, Glasgow G3 7NB; T.-041-221 4149.

Founded: 1983.
Chairman: Prof Edward McGirr; Executive Officer and Company Secretary: Mrs Frances Love.
An organisation born out of the need to provide a structure within which Scottish Pre-school Play Association, Play in Scottish Hospitals and Scottish Stepping Stones projects grow and develop in their own special ways yet remain linked by a common philosophy and a co-operative sharing of knowledge and expertise. SCOPE offers the opportunity for individuals and organisations who identify with its philosophy to have an overall view of the work and activities of all the constituent parts.

SCOTTISH COUNCIL OF PHYSICAL EDUCATION, c/o Honorary Secretary, Regional Council Office, Newtown St Boswells TD6 0SA; T.-08352 3301.

Honorary Secretary: G.M. Donald.

SCOTTISH COUNCIL FOR POST-GRADUATE MEDICAL EDUCATION, 8 Queen Street, Edinburgh EH2 1JE; T.-031-225 4365.

Founded: 1970.
Chairman: Prof Donald Campbell; Secretary: Dr K.M. Parry; Deputy Secretary: Dr R.G. Cairncross.
An independent body whose terms of reference are: to co-ordinate and stimulate the organisation and development of postgraduate medical and dental education and training in Scotland; to provide a national forum for discussion of postgraduate medical and dental education and training; and to provide the Government with an authoritative source of advice on these matters. Has 30 members and a chairman.

SCOTTISH COUNCIL FOR RESEARCH IN EDUCATION, 15 St John Street, Edinburgh EH8 8JR; T.-031-557 2944.

Founded: 1928.
Chairman: Gordon Kirk; Director: Dr S. Brown.
Semi-autonomous body funded by grants from the Scottish Education Department, local authorities, and teachers' associations, and through commissioned projects. In addition to undertaking research, and assisting others involved in research, it publishes reports and organises workshops and conferences. Also provides information in response to inquiries about educational issues.

SCOTTISH COUNCIL OF THE ROYAL COLLEGE OF GENERAL PRACTITIONERS, 2 Hill Square, Edinburgh EH8 9DR; T.-031-667 3115.

Founded: 1953.
Chairman: D.W. MacLean; Vice-chairman: A.D. Milne; Honorary Secretary and Treasurer: P.G. Gaskell.
Exists to help its members to maintain and to raise the quality of their work as general practitioners, individually and collectively. Throughout the United Kingdom, it is organised on a geographical basis by faculties, of which there are five in Scotland, with a total of around 1,750 members. The

Scottish council facilitates the intentions of the United Kingdom council in Scotland, administers certain matters confined to Scotland, co-ordinates some of the work of the faculties and represents the college in Scotland to numerous outside bodies. The council's 25 members meet three times a year, alternately with its executive committee.

SCOTTISH COUNCIL FOR SINGLE HOMELESS, (SCSH), 4 Old Assembly Close, Edinburgh EH1 1QX; T.-031-226 4382.
Founded: 1974.
Convener: Pam Gallagher; Vice-convener: Sheila Campbell; Honorary Treasurer: John Evans; Director: Laurie M. Naumann; Administrative Secretary: Allison Bertram.
Offers advice and information to organisations and individuals on the range of issues relating to single homelessness and its prevention in Scotland. Publishes papers, organises study days, comments on legislation and campaigns for the rights of single homeless people as well as concerning itself with the promotion of single person housing.

SCOTTISH COUNCIL FOR SINGLE PARENTS, (SCSP), 13 Gayfield Square, Edinburgh EH1 3NX; T.-031-556 3899.
Founded: 1945.
Convener: Mrs Audrey M. Lowe; Director: Miss Julie-Ann Macqueen; Honorary Treasurer: Mrs Marilyn A. Jeffcoat.
Works for the preservation and protection of the good health, welfare, education and the alleviation of poverty and distress of single parent families in Scotland, be they separated, divorced, unmarried or bereaved. Brings together all appropriate organisations, keeps them informed of changing needs, stimulates new ventures, undertakes research, publishes informative booklets and audio-visual material, organises study days and acts as a consultative body. Offers individual clients a limited casework service, acts as a referral agency and provides a specialist advisory service to professionals on all matters regarding single parents. It has pioneered a flat let scheme, a sitter service and single parent community action projects in Strathclyde and Tayside.

SCOTTISH COUNCIL FOR SPASTICS, 'Rhuemore', 22 Corstorphine Road, Edinburgh EH12 6HP; T.-031-

337 9876.
Founded: 1946.
Chairman: Mr G.D. Holmes, CB; Director: Mr I.G. McBain; Finance Officer: Mr R.I.H. Scott.
Gives direct help and care to spastic men, women and children throughout Scotland, in their schools, adult work centres and residential homes. Also acts as a body of information relating to Cerebral Palsy.

SCOTTISH COUNCIL FOR VOLUNTARY ORGANISATIONS, (SCVO), 18-19 Claremont Crescent, Edinburgh EH7 4QD; T.-031-556 3882.
Founded: 1943.
Director: Ross Flockhart; Assistant Director, Communications: Dr Alistair Grimes; Assistant Director, Operations: James Jackson.
Exists to promote and support voluntary action in Scotland; provide services for the voluntary sector; promote action on housing, unemployment and poverty in Scotland; extend the range of voluntary activity. Membership is open to voluntary, community and other organisations (more than 230), and there is a category for individual members.

SCOTTISH COUNTIES EVANGELICAL MOVEMENT, (SCEM), 342 Argyle Street, Glasgow G2 8LY; T.-041-248 5359.
Founded: 1965.
Chairman, Council of Reference: Mr W. McInnes; Chairman, Strategy Group: Mr G. Russell; Chairman, Training and Prayer: Dr A. McIntosh; Chairman, Publicity: Mr H. Hill; Treasurer: Mr J. Allan; Chairman, Outreach, and Secretary: Mr P. Sunderland.
Established to assist evangelical churches in rural areas which were declining in numbers and whose existence was threatened, and also to establish evangelical churches where none existed. Between six and eight summer mission teams of approximately 20 young people have gone out each summer since 1965. Over 150 towns have been visited from Lerwick in the north to Annan in the south.

SCOTTISH COUNTRY LIFE MUSEUMS TRUST, (SCLMT), c/o Royal Museum of Scotland, Queen Street, Edinburgh EH2 1JD; T.-031-557 3550.
Founded: 1970.
Chairman: Prof Noel Robertson; Secretary: Dr Alexander Fenton; Assistant Secretary: Gavin Sprott.

Founded to promote the development of museums of country life in Scotland, both at national and local level, and to promote education about country life in the past. The first major objective was achieved with the opening of the Scottish Agricultural Museum at Ingliston in Midlothian, in 1983.

SCOTTISH COUNTRYSIDE ACTIVITIES COUNCIL, (SCAC), 39 Clepington Road, Dundee DD4 7EL; T.-0382 41095.

Founded: 1968.
Chairman: Dr Robert Aitken; Vice-chairman: Matthew Smith; Honorary Secretary: Dr Kathleen M. Watson, MBE; Honorary Treasurer: Miss D. Vivien Wilson.
Objectives: to gather information affecting the use of the countryside for leisure activities; to spread knowledge about the countryside; to reconcile conflicting interests in its use and to represent agreed interests to persons and authorities having responsibility for the countryside. Members are, primarily, the Scottish organisations that are concerned with leisure-time activities in the countryside. Membership is also open to organisations outwith Scotland if their field of recreation includes Scotland. Associate membership is open to individuals. Members seek through the council to preserve and develop access to and through the countryside and to conserve the land, its wildlife, and natural beauty.

SCOTTISH COUNTRYSIDE RANGERS ASSOCIATION, (SCRA), c/o Lochore Meadows Country Park, Crosshill, Lochgelly, Fife KY5 8BA; T.-0592 860086.

Founded: 1975.
Chairman: Bob Reid; Vice-chairman: Nic Bullivant; Secretary: Mrs Susan Manson; Treasurer: David Warnock; Honorary President: Sir Robert Grieve; Honorary Vice-president: Keith Graham.
The professional organisation for countryside rangers in Scotland. Aims to promote and encourage a high standard of professionalism among members; to advise on matters related to the structure, organisation and training of ranger services in Scotland; to assist the development of communication and exchange of ideas amongst members and between the association and other bodies. Membership is open to serving countryside rangers in Scotland. Other interested parties may become associate members. Annual train-

ing course. Vacancy notification scheme. Quarterly publication: 'Scramble'. Membership 70-80.

SCOTTISH COURTS ADMINISTRATION, (SCA), 26-27 Royal Terrace, Edinburgh EH7 5AH; T.-031-556 0755.

Founded: 1972.
Director: Mr G. Murray.
Responsible for the organisation and staffing of courts and for other matters relating to the administration of justice in Scotland.

SCOTTISH COVENANTER MEMORIALS ASSOCIATION, (SCMA), c/o Honorary Secretary, 3 Richmond Terrace, Cumnock KA18 1DN; T.-0290 20295.

Founded: 1966.
President: Bryan Nutter; Honorary Secretary: George Scott; Honorary Treasurer: James Brackenridge; Vice-chairman: Rev J. Loudon Melrose.
Exists for the restoration, repair and preservation of the graves and memorials of the covenanters. Non-sectarian, non-political organisation. The work on the memorials is carried out mainly by volunteer workers drawn from the membership. The more difficult renovations are carried out by professionals commissioned by the association.

SCOTTISH CRAFT CENTRE, 140 Canongate, Edinburgh EH8 8DD; T.-031-556 8136.

Chairman of Council: Barbara Davidson; Administrator and Secretary: Freda Spencer.
Exists to encourage the highest standards of craft work by providing a showcase of members' products.

SCOTTISH CRICKET UNION, 18 Ainslie Place, Edinburgh EH3 6AU; T.-031-226 4401.

Honorary Secretary: R.W. Barclay; Administrator: Robin Prentice; National Coach: D. Wilson.

SCOTTISH CROFTERS UNION, Old Mill, Broadford, Isle of Skye IV49 9AQ; T.-047 12 529.

President: Frank Rennie; Vice President: Ronald Campbell; Director: James Hunter.
Represents crofting interests and negotiates on behalf of crofters with Government agencies. Services offered include legal advice and insurance. Has 55 branches and 3,300 members.

SCOTTISH CROP RESEARCH INSTITUTE, (SCRI), Errol Road, Invergowrie, Dundee DD2 5DA; T.-Invergowrie 731.
Founded: 1981.
Director: Prof J.R. Hillman; Secretary: Mr N.D. Anderson.
Financed by the Department of Agriculture and Fisheries for Scotland. Has around 300 members of staff. The scientists are organised into the divisions of crop protection, crop science, plant breeding and virology. The work of the institute is to improve the productivity and quality of crops by studying their breeding, culture and protection from diseases and pests. Fundamental research is also done which contributes to the establishment of scientific principles. Potato, barley (especially for malting), forage brassica (especially swede, rape and kale), raspberry and black currant are the major crops in the research programme.

SCOTTISH CROQUET ASSOCIATION, (SCA), c/o The Secretary, 17 Greygoran, Sauchie, Clackmannanshire FK10 3ET; T.-0259 213515.
Founded: 1974.
Chairman: A.H.M. Adam; Secretary/Treasurer: I. Howard Wright.
Exists to encourage, promote and develop the sport of croquet in Scotland; to promote and manage individual and inter-club competition; and to encourage the coaching of players and the training of referees, handicappers and tournament managers. Membership is open to individuals as well as clubs. There are 12 affiliated clubs, with about 250 members, and about 50 associate members. Clubs are mainly found in the central belt of Scotland and in Ayrshire.

SCOTTISH CROSS COUNTRY UNION, (SCCU), 18 Ainslie Place, Edinburgh EH3 6AU; T.-031-226 4401.
Founded: 1890.
President: W.M. Robertson; Secretary: J.E. Clifton; Treasurer: R.L. McSwein.
Objects are: to foster, control and promote cross country running in Scotland.

SCOTTISH CYCLISTS' UNION, c/o General Secretary, 13 Broom Terrace, Johnstone, Renfrewshire; T.-0505 21251.
General Secretary: Len M. Rankin.

SCOTTISH DAIRY COUNCIL, 266 Clyde Street, Glasgow G1 4JH; T.-041-221 4838.
Founded: 1957.
Chairman: J.A. Brown; Secretary: J. Russell.
Promotes and extends the sale of milk and milk products in the United Kingdom and elsewhere. Promotes and undertakes investigation, research, and education in matters affecting the processing, manufacture, or sale of milk and milk products.

SCOTTISH DAIRY TRADE FEDERATION, 24 Blythswood Square, Glasgow G2 4QS; T.-041-226 3766.
Founded: 1980.
Secretaries and Treasurers: K.M.G. Thomson McLintock.
Promotes the interests of the Scottish dairy industry in all its branches, particularly the processing and distribution of liquid milk and the manufacture of milk products.

SCOTTISH DANCE TEACHERS ALLIANCE, (SDTA), 339 North Woodside Road, Glasgow G20 6ND; T.-041-339 8944.
Founded: 1935.
President: John Stewart; General Secretary: Miss Joyce Molyneaux.
The Scottish dance teaching association. Amateur and professional syllabus in tap, ballet, modern, Highland, Latin American, ballroom, rock 'n' roll, disco and majorette. Promotions include competitions and medal test in these.

SCOTTISH DARTS ASSOCIATION, (SDA), 83 East Way, Hillend Industrial Estate, Dunfermline KY11 5JF; T.-0383 824724.
Founded: 1971.
General Secretary: Tom Frost; Chairman: Peter Forbes; Financial Director: Iain Tweedie.
The governing body of darts in Scotland. Instigates and controls national championships for members and on an open basis, and co-operates with the British Darts Organisation for British and international events. Also operates on behalf of any individual company favouring a darts promotion, and assists with the supply of equipment. Membership is by affiliation to the leagues who register with the association. Has 16 area associations who administer their own region. Membership: 181 leagues, comprising 2,909 club teams, amounting to approximately 40,000 players (75% men and 25% women).

SCOTTISH DECORATORS FEDERATION, (SDF), 249 West George Street, Glasgow G2 4RB; T.-041-221 7090.

Founded: 1878.
President: Charles W. Aitken; Senior Vice President: Kenneth R. Wallace; Junior Vice President: Brian Smith; General Secretary: J. Cameron Henderson.
Formed to co-ordinate and speak for master painters and decorators in Scotland. Negotiates wage rates, organises training, liaises with CITB and similar bodies and with sister organisations such as the British Decorators Association, the Scottish Building Employers' Federation, and similar bodies in the Republic of Ireland and Ulster. Also collaborates with paint and wallpaper manufacturers.

SCOTTISH DEVELOPMENT AGENCY, 120 Bothwell Street, Glasgow G2 7JP; T.-041-248 2700.

Founded: 1975.
Chairman: Robin Duthie, CBE; Deputy Chairman: Douglas Hardie, CBE; Chief Executive: George Mathewson; Director (Finance): Robert McEwan; Director (Small Business and Electronics): Peter Carmichael, CBE; Director (Planning and Projects): Edward Cunningham; Director (Area Development): Richard Colwell; Director (Property Development and Environment): Alan Dale; Director (Investment): Donald Patience; Director (North East Scotland): John Condliffe; Director (Locate in Scotland): Iain Robertson; Head of Marketing: Lloyd Fraser; Secretary: David A. Lyle.
Formed with the objectives of furthering economic development, promoting industrial efficiency and international competitiveness, and improving the environment. Current priorities identified in the agency's corporate plan are: small business development, support for technology, encouragement of investment and area development. The agency aims to act as a catalyst to encourage commitment to and investment in Scotland's future growth. Emphasis is on partnership, working alongside the public and private sector.

SCOTTISH DEVELOPMENT DEPARTMENT, New St Andrew's House, Edinburgh EH1 3TD; T.-031-556 8400.

Secretary: T.R.H. Godden, CB; Private Secretary: P.J. Smith.
The department's responsibilities cover policy and functions affecting the physical development of Scotland, including town and country planning, housing, urban renewal, roads and transport, water supplies and sewerage, control of air and river pollution and building control, conservation, historic buildings and ancient monuments. The department is also responsible in Scotland for general policy on local government administration.

SCOTTISH DOWN'S SYNDROME ASSOCIATION, (SDSA), 54 Shandwick Place, Edinburgh EH2 4RT; T.-031-226 2420.

Founded: 1982.
Chairman: Mrs Janet Hessing; Vice-chairman: Mrs T. Stewart; Treasurer: Mrs S. Peterson; Executive Director: Graham Kelly.
Affiliated to the Down's Children's Association in London. Aim is to provide help and advice to parents and foster parents of those with Down's Syndrome living in Scotland. Has established seven branches in Scotland: Strathclyde, Lothian, Tayside, Central, Grampian, Highland, and Dumfries and Galloway. Also encourages groups to be formed in different areas within the branches. Sends out newsletters to all members every two months, and holds two conferences each year with speakers. Membership: 560 members and 500 professionals (doctors, hospitals etc.).

SCOTTISH ECONOMIC SOCIETY, c/o Department of Political Economy, University of Aberdeen, Aberdeen AB9 2TY.

President: Prof I.G. Stewart; Secretary: Mr R.F. Elliott.
Publishes a quarterly journal, Scottish Journal of Political Economy and holds occasional conferences and seminars to promote study and research into theoretical and applied economic problems and policies.

SCOTTISH EDUCATION AND ACTION FOR DEVELOPMENT, 29 Nicolson Square, Edinburgh EH8 9BX; T.-031-667 0120.

Founded: 1978.
Organisers: Stephen Maxwell, Paul Baker, Susan Moffat, Mark Lazarowicz; Administrator: Anne Chisholm.
Exists to develop Scottish awareness of the challenge and problems of world development. Produces publicity material, organises meetings and conferences, handles media enquiries, and liaises with other world development groups. It is the only body of its kind in Scotland.

SCOTTISH EDUCATION DEPART-MENT, New St Andrew's House, Edinburgh EH1 3DU; T.-031-556 8400.

Secretary: J.A. Scott, MVO; Private Secretary: T.W. Lodge.

Responsible for the administration of public education in Scotland (except universities), youth and community services, social work services, the arts, libraries, museums, galleries and sport.

SCOTTISH ENGINEERING EMPLOYERS' ASSOCIATION, 105 West George Street, Glasgow G2 1QL; T.-041-221 3181.

Founded: 1865.

President: P.R. Prenter, JP; Director: Lt Col H.A.J. Jordan, MBE.

Largest employers' association in Scotland, with a membership of 350 engineering companies covering all disciplines from traditional heavy mechanical to microelectronics. Provides comprehensive support on all matters involving labour force, including industrial relations, negotiation with trade unions, employment legislation, industrial tribunals, training, health and safety. Fulfils a representational role to Government and European Commission in matters affecting the engineering industry's working and economic environment. The association is a constituent association of the Engineering Employers' Federation.

SCOTTISH ENGINEERING TRAIN-ING SCHEME, 127 St. Vincent Street, Glasgow; T.-041-221 6420.

Founded: 1957.

Chairman: K.A. Shaw; Chief Executive: John K. McIntyre; Secretary: Mrs I.K. Liddell; Senior Administrative Officer: Miss R. Dempsey.

Exists for the industrial training of graduate and undergraduate engineers within a framework established with the relevant professional institutions and Engineering Industry Training Board.

SCOTTISH ENSEMBLE, (SE), 34-40 South Clerk Street, Edinburgh EH8 9PS; T.-031-667 3828.

Founded: 1969.

Chairman: Lt Gen Sir Derek Lang, KCB, DSO, MC; Administrator: Michael Chibbett; Artistic Director: Leonard Friedman.

Originally formed by the violinist Leonard Friedman and called the Scottish Baroque Ensemble. Recognised as one of the five main national music bodies in Scotland. Has a normal playing strength of 13, including harpsichord, and plays without conductor under the guidance of the artistic director. Repertoire ranges from classical baroque music to specially commissioned contemporary works. Promotes concerts and accepts engagements throughout Scotland and has toured extensively abroad.

SCOTTISH EPISCOPAL CHURCH, 21 Grosvenor Crescent, Edinburgh EH12 5EE; T.-031-225 6357.

President: Most Rev Lawrence Edward Luscombe, Primus, Bishop of Brechin; Secretary General and Treasurer: J.G. Davies; Deputy Treasurer: D. Logan Smith; Deputy Secretary General: Martin D. Patterson; Bishops: Rt Rev Frederick Charles Darwent (Aberdeen and Orkney), Rt Rev George Kennedy Buchanan Henderson, MBE (Argyll and the Isles), Most Rev Lawrence Edward Luscombe (Brechin), Rt Rev Richard Frederick Holloway (Edinburgh), Rt Rev Derek Alec Rawcliffe, OBE (Glasgow and Galloway), Rt Rev George Minshull Sessford (Moray, Ross and Caithness), Rt Rev Michael Geoffrey Hare Duke (St Andrews, Dunkeld and Dunblane); Convener, Standing Committee: A.A.R. Carleton.

Has a membership of 68,000 with churches situated throughout Scotland. Governed by a General Synod with 163 members divided between lay and clerical. Has boards and committees which deal with education, social responsibility, overseas and home mission affairs, as well as a full range of the usual pastoral, financial and administrative concerns.

SCOTTISH ESPERANTO FEDERA-TION, (SEF), 92 Liberton Brae, Edinburgh EH16 6LB; T.-031-664 1060.

Founded: 1905.

President: Peter Harvey; Secretary: Mr R.D.M. Calder; Treasurer: Mr D. Gilmour; Magazine Editor: Dr A. Goodheir.

Exists to promote the practice, teaching and dissemination in Scotland of the international language of Esperanto. Publishes a magazine and holds an annual congress. Membership: 100.

SCOTTISH EVANGELISTIC COUN-CIL, (SEC), 11 Newton Place, Glasgow G3 7PR; T.-041-333 0546.

Founded: 1929.

Honorary President: Ernest Fischbacher; President: Rev Alexander M. Roger; Vice President: Tom Dunn; Honorary Secretary:

John Dodds; Treasurer: Neil J. Robertson. Work consists of spreading the Christian message throughout Scotland by means of Bible Witness Rallies. Works with children through caravan missioners and by summer missions in the country or at the seaside.

SCOTTISH EXAMINATION BOARD, (SEB), Ironmills Road, Dalkeith, Midlothian EH22 1LE; T.-031-663 6601.

Founded: 1964.
Director: Dr J.H. Walker; Depute Director: M.R.M. Hendry; Assistant Directors: J.N. Gillam, H.A. Long, H. Charleson.
Makes arrangements for, and conducts, examinations each year, for the award of the Scottish Certificate of Education and the Certificate of Sixth Year Studies.

SCOTTISH EXHIBITION & CONFERENCE CENTRE, Glasgow G3 8YW; T.-041-248 3000.

Chief Executive: Chris P. Garrett.
Comprises five interlinked halls and a seminar suite, grouped round a central glass concourse which houses a bank, shops, travel and accommodation bureau, offices and an administration centre. There is parking for 3,500 vehicles. The centre houses exhibitions, conferences and events. A luxury hotel will be completed in 1988.

SCOTTISH FAMILY CONCILIATION SERVICE (LOTHIAN), 127 Rose Street South Lane, Edinburgh EH2 5BB; T.-031-226 4507.

Founded: 1983.
Chairman: Hugh Donald, WS; Co-ordinator: Julia Ross.
Objectives are: to assist divorcing and separating couples to reach agreements amicably, especially over the arrangements for their children; to reduce the levels of hostility and anger between the couple who are separating in order that amicable arrangements can be made for the future; to help children keep a loving relationship with both their parents. Appointments are offered to divorcing couples and their families and advice and information is given on conciliation and divorce. Publications: explanatory leaflets on conciliation and custody and access; annual report.

SCOTTISH FEDERATION FOR COARSE ANGLING, c/o Honorary Secretary, 4 Porton Place, Bishopton,

Renfrewshire PA7 5LT; T.-0505 862460.
Honorary Secretary: John McMenemy.

SCOTTISH FEDERATION OF FISHERMEN'S CO-OPERATIVES LTD, (SFFC), 86 Dickson Street, Dunfermline KY12 7SA; T.-0383 738830.

Founded: 1973.
President: W. Hughes; Vice-president: R. Fraser; Secretary/Manager: J.A.H. Wallace.
Comprises 34 member societies in Scotland, Northern Ireland and the Isle of Man. The main objectives are to protect and promote the interests of fishermen's co-operatives in Scotland and elsewhere and to represent their interests and to encourage, assist and promote the adoption of co-operative principles and the formation of co-operative organisations amongst fishermen.

SCOTTISH FEDERATION OF HOUSING ASSOCIATIONS, 40 Castle Street North, Edinburgh EH2 3BN; T.-031-226 6777.

Director: Donald R. MacLennan; Research and Development Officer: Deborah Miller.
Representative body for housing associations in Scotland. Organises training courses and seminars for members and provides model rules for registration of new societies.

THE SCOTTISH FEDERATION OF MEAT TRADERS' ASSOCIATIONS, (SFMTA), 3 Kinnoull Street, Perth PH1 5EN; T.-0738 37785.

Founded: 1918.
President: Adam McLay; Secretary: Mrs Moira Brady.
An advisory organisation to private, independent butchers. Membership is through local associations, of which there are 19 spread throughout Scotland. Objective: effective representation of affiliated associations and associate members to Government bodies.

SCOTTISH FEDERATION OF SEA ANGLERS, (SFSA), 18 Ainslie Place, Edinburgh EH3 6AU; T.-031-225 7611.

Founded: 1960.
President: Martin L. Rowlands; Vice Presidents: Stanley Thompson, Robert Walker; Vice President and PRO: Duncan Mackay; Honorary Treasurer: James K. Crawford; Secretary/Administrator: Mrs Cath Watson.
The governing body for the sport of sea

angling in Scotland. Accepted as the advisory body on sea angling by the Scottish Sports Council, the Scottish Tourist Board and the Highlands and Islands Development Board. Consists of clubs or district associations in Scotland and individual members throughout the world.

SCOTTISH FIELD ARCHERY ASSOCIATION, c/o Secretary, 26 Kilmory Gardens, Carluke ML8 5SB.
Secretary: Miss Sheena McDowall.

SCOTTISH FIELD STUDIES ASSOCIATION, (SFSA), Kindrogan Field Centre, Enochdhu, Blairgowrie PH10 7PG; T.-025 081 286.
Founded: 1945.
Chairman: Prof Joy Tivy; Vice-chairman: Dr A.W. Pike; Honorary Secretary: Prof J.B. Caird; Executive Secretary: Mr D. Pearson; Director, Kindrogan Field Centre: Dr A.H. Lavery.
A non-profit seeking company with charitable status created to promote the development, within Scotland, of field studies, both academic and recreational. Strives to create among young people and adults a greater awareness and understanding of the Scottish countryside. Kindrogan Field Centre is operated by the association to provide facilities for residential courses in a wide range of subjects including all aspects of natural history. Trained staff at the centre lead courses in environmental education for students of all ages. The association is directed by an executive committee drawn from a range of academic and business backgrounds. Membership: approximately 200.

SCOTTISH FILM COUNCIL, (SFC), Dowanhill, 74 Victoria Crescent Road, Glasgow G12 9JN; T.-041-334 9314.
Founded: 1934.
Director: David Bruce; Chairman: John Donachy.
Has developed a wide range of activities over the years, particularly in promoting the use of film in education. Its promotion of film culture covers four main areas of activity: education, exhibition, production and archives. The promotion of film-making activities is carried out through support for the Scottish Film Production Fund and the Scottish Film Training Trust, both of which are administered by the council.

SCOTTISH FISHERIES MUSEUM, St

Ayles, Harbourhead, Anstruther, Fife KY10 3AB; T.-0333 310628.
Curator: Richard Wemyss.

SCOTTISH FISHERMEN'S FEDERATION, (SFF), 35 Albert Street, Aberdeen AB1 1XU; T.-0224 641981.
Founded: 1973.
President: William F. Hay, CBE; Vice-president: Cecil T. Finn; Chief Executive/Secretary: Robert Allan.
A trade protection organisation constituted by seven associations of fishermen and two associations of fish salesman for the purpose of representing the interests of over 1,000 fishing vessels in Scotland and in the Shetland Islands. Primary responsibilities include the formulation of policies on the Scottish fishing industry and the transmission of such policies to Government departments and officials, to the European community at large as well as its institutions, and to Members of Parliament in Westminster and in Europe. Also responsible for promoting the policies of its members to the news media and to the public at large, as well as for general liaison with all other groups and interests.

SCOTTISH FISHERMEN'S ORGANISATION LTD, (SFO), 601 Queensferry Road, Edinburgh EH4 6EA; T.-031-339 7972.
Founded: 1973.
Chief Executive and Secretary: Iain M. MacSween.
Producers' organisation as defined by relevant EEC legislation. Has 600 member vessels with a turnover of £90 million.

THE SCOTTISH FLAG FUND, PO Box 84, Edinburgh; T.-031-228 1902.
Founded: 1984.
Chairman of Trustees: C.G. McGregor; Treasurer: Elizabeth A. Wark; Auditor: T.M. Walker; Clerk: J. McIntosh.
Objectives are to seek and provide financial support for the upkeep of the Saltire Memorial at Athelstaneford in East Lothian and to encourage the proper use of the national flag elsewhere.

THE SCOTTISH FOOTBALL ASSOCIATION, (SFA), 6 Park Gardens, Glasgow G3 7YF; T.-041-332 6372.
Founded: 1873.
President: D.H. Will; 1st Vice-president: P. Gardiner; 2nd Vice-president: I.R.G.

Gellatly; Treasurer: W.H. Dickie; Secretary: E. Walker.
Promotes the game of association football and organises Scottish international matches at all levels, the Scottish Qualifying Cup (North and South) competitions and the Scottish Cup competition.

THE SCOTTISH FOOTBALL LEAGUE, (SFL), 188 West Regent Street, Glasgow G2 4RY; T.-041-248 3844.

Founded: 1890.
President: I.R.G. Gellatly; Vice-president: Dr J. Crorie; Treasurer: J.Y. Craig; Secretary: J. Farry.
Objects are to promote and extend the game of association football and: to provide league championships and league cup competitions and to promote and guard the interests of the clubs comprising the league; to conclude commercial contracts relative to sponsorship and the transmission of recording by television, radio or other means of fixtures provided by the league.

SCOTTISH FURTHER EDUCATION ASSOCIATION, Gordon Chambers, 90 Mitchell Street, Glasgow G1 3NQ; T.-041-221 0018.

Founded: 1964.
President: E. Bouchard; General Secretary: Graham Alison; Assistant General Secretary: Maureen Mitchell.
Professional association and trade union representing lecturers in colleges of further education throughout Scotland.

SCOTTISH GAMES ASSOCIATION, (SGA), 'Craigview', 19 Abbot Street, Perth PH2 0EE; T.-0738 39617.

Founded: 1946.
President and Treasurer: Mrs Margaret Mitchell; Vice President: Mr J.N. Brown; Secretary: Mr A. Rettie.
Concerned with the management of Highland and Border games. Encourages high standards of ethics and performance, and enforces rules and regulations covering professional athletics.

THE SCOTTISH GENEALOGY SOCIETY, (SGS), c/o 21 Howard Place, Edinburgh EH3 5JY; T.-031-556 3844 (after 6pm).

Founded: 1953.
Honorary President: Emeritus Prof Gordon Donaldson; Honorary Secretary: Miss J.P.S. Ferguson; Honorary Treasurer: Dr R. R.

MacAndrew; Honorary Editor: Ivor R. Guild; Honorary Librarian: R.M. Strathdee; Chairman of Council: Dr A. MacKie.
Exists to promote research into Scottish family history and undertake the collection, exchange and publication of material relating to genealogy. Academic and consultative body only. World-wide membership. Lectures are held monthly from September until April. Publishes a quarterly journal *The Scottish Genealogist.*

SCOTTISH GIRLS' VENTURE CORPS, c/o Administrative Assistant, 6 Glen Afton Drive, New Cumnock, Ayrshire.

Administrative Assistant: Mrs H.C. Hill.

SCOTTISH GLASS MERCHANTS AND GLAZIERS ASSOCIATION, 13 Woodside Crescent, Glasgow G3 7UP; T.-041-332 7144.

President: W. Brooks.
A member of the Scottish Building Employers' Federation, which is the umbrella organisation for the whole of the building industry in Scotland. Represented on various committees within the SBEF and plays a constructive and active part in all matters affecting the industry. There are around 70 members of the association, which has a vetting procedure to ensure that members are all bona fide firms with glass and glazing experience. Wages and conditions are negotiated at a national level and the membership has a firm commitment to apprenticeship training within the industry.

SCOTTISH GLIDING ASSOCIATION, c/o Secretary, 5 Gamekeepers Court, Kinnesswood, Kinross KY13 7LZ; T.-059284 275.

Secretary: Colin J. Hamilton.

SCOTTISH GLIDING UNION LTD, (SGU), Portmoak, Scotlandwell, by Kinross KY13 7JJ; T.-Scotlandwell 543.

Founded: 1934.
President: Andrew Thorburn; Chairman: John Goudie; Secretary: David Bruce.
The SGU, Scotland's oldest established gliding club, operates from a site near the shores of Loch Leven. Offers air experience flights to visitors and, in the summer months, conducts courses for beginners and experienced pilots. Accommodation for courses is provided. The club owns eight gliders and launches are by winch or

aerotow.

SCOTTISH GOLF UNION, (SGU), The Cottage, 181a Whitehouse Road, Barnton, Edinburgh EH4 6BY; T.-031-339 7546.

Founded: 1920.
President: Denis J. Miller; Vice-presidents: A.V. Plant, R.W. McLaren; Secretary: Ian Hume.
The governing body for amateur golf in Scotland. Directly affiliated to the European Golf Association and the Council of National Golf Unions, the co-ordinating body for the United Kingdom. The objects and functions are to foster and maintain a high standard of amateur golf in Scotland and to administer and organise, and generally act as the governing body of, amateur golf in Scotland.

SCOTTISH GROCERS' FEDERATION, 3 Loaning Road, Restalrig, Edinburgh EH7 6JU; T.-031-652 2482.

Founded: 1918.
Honorary President: J.P. Irving; President: D. Edgar; Senior Vice-president: T. Wilson; Junior Vice-president: A. Nicol; Chairman, Scottish Grocery Trade Training Association: J. Dwyer; Chief Executive: L. Dewar; Chairman, PGMA (Scotland) Ltd: J. McGuire.
Representative of retail grocers and provision merchants in Scotland; promotes the formation of local associations and the interests of the retail grocery and provision trade; confers with local and national authorities on matters affecting the trade; seeks to maintain the status of the trade.

SCOTTISH HANG GLIDING FEDERATION, c/o Secretary, 20 Glencorse, Penicuik EH26 ONN.

Secretary: Colin Hood.

SCOTTISH HEALTH EDUCATION GROUP, (SHEG), Woodburn House, Canaan Lane, Edinburgh EH10 4SG; T.-031-447 8044.

Director: Stanley Mitchell.
Applies a vigorous health education policy across Scotland. The objective is to improve the lifestyle of the population in relation to health. Programme includes advice on alcohol, smoking, immunisation, dental health, mental health, the elderly etc. Aims to help each person make the best possible choice for optimum health and well being ...
'Be All You Can Be'.

SCOTTISH HEALTH SERVICE PLANNING COUNCIL, St Andrew's House, Edinburgh EH1 3DE; T.-031-244 2348.

Chairman: Dr W. Keith Davidson, CBE; Secretary: W.J. Farquhar.
Keeps under review the development of the Health Service in Scotland and is the main advisory body to the Secretary of State on the exercise of his functions under the Health Service Acts.

SCOTTISH HELLENIC SOCIETY, c/o Department of Greek, University of Glasgow, Glasgow G12; T.-041-339 8855, Ext. 4155/4157.

Founded: 1959.
Honorary President: Dr H.S. MacKintosh; Honorary Vice-presidents: Prof D.M. Mac-Dowell, Mr G. Tombazis; Chairman: Mrs M.K.A. Smith; Honorary Secretary: Dr R.A. Knox; Honorary Treasurer: Mr J. Karkalas.
Exists to promote, among Scots and Greeks in Scotland, mutual interest in Greek and Scottish culture, both past and present, and to provide opportunities for social contact between Scots and Greeks. Meetings are held monthly from October to April. No knowledge of the Greek language is required. Lectures cover a wide range of topics, ancient, Byzantine and modern, relating to Greek literature, history, archaeology and life. At least one Scottish topic is covered each year. Social events offer Greek food and wine and Greek dancing. Membership: 117.

SCOTTISH HILL RUNNERS ASSOCIATION, c/o Secretary, 33 Morningside Road, Edinburgh EH10 4DR; T.-031-447 8846.

Secretary: Mr R.L. Morris.

SCOTTISH HISTORIC BUILDINGS TRUST, (SHBT), c/o The Secretary, Vennel Cottage, Goose Green, Gullane, East Lothian EH31 2BA; T.-0620 842086.

Founded: 1985.
Chairman: The Hon Lord Jauncey; Secretary: John A. Clare; Architectural Adviser: James Simpson.
Charitable company limited by guarantee whose objectives are the acquisition, restoration and sale, for appropriate long-term use, of architecturally or historically important buildings throughout Scotland.

SCOTTISH HISTORY SOCIETY,

(SHS), c/o Dr Annette M. Smith, Department of Modern History, University of Dundee DD1 4HN; T.-0382 23181.
Founded: 1886.
President: Prof T.C. Smout; Chairman: Mr S. Maxwell; Honorary Secretary: Dr A.M. Smith; Honorary Treasurer: Prof I.B. Cowan; Honorary Editor: Dr T.I. Rae.
Publishes manuscript sources relating to the history of Scotland, covering all periods and a wide range of topics. Usually publishes one volume each year. The AGM is held in Edinburgh in December.

SCOTTISH HOCKEY ASSOCIATION, (SHA), 18 Ainslie Place, Edinburgh EH3 6AU; T.-031-226 4401.
Founded: 1901.
President: T.I. Morrison; Chairman: Dr A.B. Tramschek; Vice-chairman: A.W. Gray; Treasurer: G. Toner; Administrator: A.R.J. Scoular.
Aims are: to maintain and improve levels of participation in European and world events, both indoor and outdoor; to raise the standard of play in all domestic competitions; to act as an umbrella under which a strong and vigorous club structure can flourish; to encourage children to take up the sport; to promote development in the provision of coaches and umpires for all levels and ages.

SCOTTISH HOME AND HEALTH DEPARTMENT, St Andrew's House, Edinburgh; T.-031-556 8400.
Secretary: W.K. Reid, CB; Private Secretary: I.D. Williamson.
Responsible for (a) the central administration of functions relating to law and order; and (b) the administration of the National Health Service in Scotland. Under (a) the department is concerned with the police, criminal justice and legal aid, and is responsible for the administration of penal institutions. The department is also the central authority in Scotland for the fire service and civil defence, and has responsibility for legislation concerning shops, theatres, cinemas, licensed premises, land tenure matters and electoral and private legislation procedures, and general constitutional matters affecting Scotland.

SCOTTISH HOMING UNION, Bank of Scotland Buildings, Hopetoun Street, Bathgate, West Lothian; T.-Bathgate 52943.
President: G. Thomson; Secretary: Mrs J. Gauld.
Organises the sport of homing pigeons.

SCOTTISH HOMOSEXUAL RIGHTS GROUP, (SHRG), Lesbian and Gay Community Centre, 58A Broughton Street, Edinburgh EH1 3SA; T.-031-557 3620.
Founded: 1969.
Convenor: Gordon G. Gosnell; Secretary: James G. McManus; Treasurer: Marion McK. McLauchlin.
Scots law makes young homosexual men criminals if they have sex before they are 21. SHRG wishes to change that and many other things. It supports all political groups who support total equality for homosexuals. Runs the newly renovated Lesbian and Gay Community Centre in Edinburgh and from there, *Gay Scotland* magazine (Editor: Ian Dunn) is published every two months.

SCOTTISH HOSPITAL ADVISORY SERVICE, (SHAS), 21 Hill Street, Edinburgh EH2 3JP; T.-031-225 3108.
Founded: 1970.
Administrative Secretary: David Duff.
Provides information and advice to the Secretary of State and to health boards regarding the general management of, and patient care within, hospitals for the mentally ill, mentally handicapped, geriatric and young physically disabled patients.

SCOTTISH HOSPITAL ENDOWMENTS RESEARCH TRUST, 16 Hope Street, Charlotte Square, Edinburgh EH2 4DD; T.-031-226 2561.
Founded: 1954.
Chairman: Sir Andrew Watt Kay; Secretariat: W. & J. Burness, WS.
Has been supporting medical research in Scotland for over 30 years, acting on a broad policy of promoting health through research into the causation, treatment and prevention of common and disabling conditions. In future, the trust aims primarily to support the research of promising young doctors and scientists, and to provide them with the opportunity to gain a sound research training.

SCOTTISH HOTEL SCHOOL, University of Strathclyde, Curran Building, 94 Cathedral Street, Glasgow G4 0LG; T.-041-552 4400, Ext. 3941.
Founded: 1946.
Acting Head of Department: Dr C.L. Jenkins; Tutor for Postgraduate Courses in Tourism:

Dr C.L. Jenkins; Director, Hotel and Catering Classes and Tutor for Postgraduate Courses in Hotel Administration: Dr J. Steel; Undergraduate Admissions: David A.C. Gee.

A department of the Strathclyde Business School offering undergraduate classes to pass and honours degree level in hotel and catering management, and postgraduate courses in tourism and hotel administration. Many graduates now hold senior management positions in the hotel and catering industry, in tourism and in industries linked with leisure and recreation, and are found throughout the world. Attracts students from the Caribbean, Africa, the Middle East, the Far East and Europe as well as the United Kingdom.

SCOTTISH HOUSE-BUILDERS ASSOCIATION, (SHBA), 13 Woodside Crescent, Glasgow G3 7UP; T.-041-332 7144.

Founded: 1965.
President: K. Ross.
The SHBA is the private housebuilding section of the Scottish Building Employers' Federation which, in turn, is the employers' organisation for the building industry in Scotland. It is accepted by central and local Government that the association represents the private housebuilding sector in Scotland.

SCOTTISH ICE FIGURE SKATING ASSOCIATION, c/o Honorary Secretary, Murrayfield Ice Rink, Riversdale Crescent, Edinburgh EH12 5XN.

Honorary Secretary: Mr J. Kerr.

SCOTTISH ICE HOCKEY ASSOCIATION, c/o President and Administrator, 16 Glencairn Road, Ayr KA7 3HL; T.-0292 266203.

Secretary: Mr F. Dempster.

SCOTTISH INDOOR BOWLING ASSOCIATION, (SIBA), c/o 41 Montfode Court, Ardrossan; T.-0294 68372.

Founded: 1936.
President: Peter Watson; Vice-president: Hugh Spence; Junior Vice-president: L.G. Ross; Immediate Past President: John Breakenridge; Secretary: James Barclay; Treasurer: Hugh Phillips.
The administrative body in Scotland for indoor bowling played on flat greens.

Objects are: to promote and foster indoor bowling in Scotland; to act in the best interests of its member clubs; to enforce the laws of the game as produced and approved by the World Indoor Bowls Council, subject to amendment by the British Isles Indoor Bowls Council, and the SIBA, and to resolve any disputes; to conduct and control all national competitions and to licence all open competitions conducted by clubs; to approve bye laws to suit special local conditions. Has 35 member clubs with a total of approximately 20,000 male members.

SCOTTISH INDUSTRIAL HERITAGE SOCIETY, (SIHS), c/o Mr E. Watt, 129 Fotheringay Road, Glasgow G41 4LG.

Founded: 1984.
Chairman: J.E. Arnold; Vice Chairman: C. McNab; Secretary: E. Lumsden; Treasurer and Membership Secretary: E. Watt.
Formed by an amalgamation of the Scottish Society for Industrial Archaeology and the Scottish Society for the Preservation of Historical Machinery. Its main aim is to promote interest in Scottish industrial history and increase awareness of the importance of recording and, in some cases, preserving the physical remains of industrial processes. Regular meetings and site visits are organised. A quarterly newsletter is produced and, jointly with the Business Archives Council, the journal *Scottish Industrial History* is produced.

SCOTTISH INFORMATION OFFICE, New St Andrew's House, Edinburgh EH1 3TD; T.-031-556 8400.

Director: C.F. Corbett.
Information to the press, radio and television on the work of the Scottish Office departments; advice to ministers on information and publicity matters; publicity campaigns for Scottish Office departments; press arrangements for Royal and state visits to Scotland; agent in Scotland of the Central Office of Information; advice to UK departments on information/publicity matters affecting Scotland.

SCOTTISH INLAND WATERWAYS ASSOCIATION, (SIWA), 11 Arden Street, Edinburgh EH9 1BR; T.-031-229 7149.

Chairman: Donald Mackinnon; Treasurer: Colin Maclean; Secretary: Nancy M. Philp.
Aim is to promote the restoration and development of the Scottish waterways for commercial and leisure purposes. Has both

individual membership and group membership for anyone or any organisation supporting the aim of the association.

SCOTTISH INSTITUTE OF ADULT AND CONTINUING EDUCATION, (SIACE), 30 Rutland Square, Edinburgh EH1 2BW; T.-031-229 0331/0311.

Founded: 1949.
Director: Dr Elisabeth Gerver; President: Dr Ethel Gray, CBE; Convener: Alex Inglis, OBE.
Provides contact, co-operation and support for adult and continuing educators in Scotland. Serves as an information centre on the education of adults in Scotland and promotes discussion of policy and practice amongst providers of adult and continuing education. Provides a forum for dissemination of good practice and promotes publication of results of work in adult and continuing education. Ensures the discussion of adult and continuing education is part of education debates and keeps Scotland in touch with developments abroad. Membership is open to organisations and individuals concerned with the education of adults in Scotland. Has 25 corporate, 58 associate, and 57 individual members.

SCOTTISH INTERNATIONAL EDUCATION TRUST, 22 Manor Place, Edinburgh EH3 7DS; T.-031-225 1113.

Charitable trust.

SCOTTISH INTERNATIONAL GATHERING TRUST, 25 Dublin Street, Edinburgh; T.-031-557 4059.

Founded: 1975.
President: post vacant; Chairman: Lt Col H.C. Paterson, TD; Vice Chairman: Colin Deans.
Aims to strengthen links between Scots worldwide and promote increased commercial, cultural and educational activity through International Gatherings in various countries (every four years in Scotland itself). Non-political and non-profit-making.

SCOTTISH JOINT COMMITTEE ON RELIGIOUS EDUCATION, c/o 46 Moray Place, Edinburgh EH3 6BH; T.-031-225 6244.

Joint Conveners: Rev William Henney (Churches), Archibald Armour (Teachers); Joint Secretaries: Rev Alasdair J. Morton (Churches), Frederick L. Forrester (Teachers).
Joint committee of the Educational Institute of Scotland and the various interests concerned with religious education.

SCOTTISH JUDO FEDERATION, (SJF), 8 Frederick Street, Edinburgh EH2 2HB; T.-031-226 3566.

Founded: 1938.
Chairman: John Adams; Honorary Secretary/Treasurer: Owen Clarke; Vice Chairman: Eric Kane; Technical Director: Colin McIver; Office Administrator: Laura Fraser.
Amateur sporting body concerned primarily with developing the sport of judo. Main activities include issuing membership, organising national and international events and operating a junior certificate scheme. Membership: 4,000 junior, 2,000 senior, 150 clubs.

SCOTTISH JUNIOR GAS ASSOCIATION, c/o British Gas plc Scotland, 4 Marine Drive, Edinburgh.

Founded: 1904.
President, Council: W.W. McManus; Vice President: Miss A.N. Kilpatrick; Honorary Treasurer: S. Kane; Honorary Secretary: A.A. Meenaghan.
Professional body for members in the gas industry.

SCOTTISH KARATE BOARD OF CONTROL, c/o Secretary, 16 Royal Crescent, Glasgow G3 7SL.

Secretary: Mr D. Bryceland.

SCOTTISH KEEP FIT ASSOCIATION, 18 Ainslie Place, Edinburgh EH3 6AU; T.-031-226 4401.

Founded: 1952.
Chairman: Mrs M. Malcolm; Vice-chairman: Mrs A. Burrows; Honorary Treasurer: Mrs M. McMurtrie; Development Officer: Miss M. Clowe.
Founded to expand the work previously undertaken by the Scottish Women's Keep Fit Association. The association is the national body for keep fit and is recognised as such by education authorities and the Scottish Sports Association. Responsible for the training of leaders to teach all age groups and teaching certificates are awarded at both basic and national level in fitness and exercise, and movement and recreative dance.

SCOTTISH KENNEL CLUB, (SKC), 6B Forres Street, Edinburgh EH3 6BJ;

T.-031-226 6808.
Founded: 1881.
Convener: Mr P. Mann; Vice-convener: Major J.G. Logan; Secretary General: Mr I.A. Sim.
Principal objective is the promotion and encouragement of the improvement and well-being of dogs. The three main functions are: to run an open club for members; to act as the delegated authority of The Kennel Club in Scotland; to provide an information source on all matters relating to dogs in Scotland. Members total 1,500 and, along with the public, they are served by a full-time office, which also administers licences for over 400 dog shows each year in Scotland. Two major championship shows are run each year at Ingliston, and there are obedience, agility, working trial and field trial events.

SCOTTISH KNITWEAR ASSOCIATION, 55 John Finnie Street, Kilmarnock KA1 1HQ; T.-0563 23568.
Founded: 1970.
Chairman: Ian S.T. Watson; Vice Chairman: D.W.H. Jebb; Secretary and Treasurer: T.H. Smith.
Formed by the amalgamation of the Scottish Hosiery and Knitwear Manufacturers' Association and the Scottish Hosiery Manufacturers' Federation. Acts as an employers' association and provides the employers' representation on the joint negotiating committee responsible for the Scottish Knitwear Trade Wages Agreement. The association is also a trade association which represents the views of the industry in Scotland to Government and statutory bodies on all matters affecting the industry, both independently and via membership of the Scottish Knitwear Council.

SCOTTISH LACROSSE ASSOCIATION, c/o Secretary, Humbie Farm, Kirkliston, West Lothian; T.-031-333 3466.
Secretary: Mrs Jennifer Dudgeon.

SCOTTISH LADIES' GOLFING ASSOCIATION, (SLGA), 5 Brownhills House, St Andrews KY16 8PL; T.-0334 76849.
Founded: 1904.
President: Mrs P.M. Hay; Chairman: Miss Joyce Cooper; Secretary: Mrs Judy Cox; Honorary Treasurer: Miss J.B. Lawrence; Honorary Secretary and Treasurer, County Golf: Miss M.J. Greig; Vice-chairman: Mrs W.L. Connon.

Exists to further the interests of women's amateur golf in Scotland.

SCOTTISH LAND COURT, 1 Grosvenor Crescent, Edinburgh EH12 5ER; T.-031-225 3595.
Founded: 1911.
Chairman: The Hon Lord Elliott; Principal Clerk: K.H.R. Graham; Senior Legal Assessors: J.G. Riddoch, J.F. Rankin.
Considers applications by landlords and/or tenants of any agricultural subjects in Scotland whether these be farms, crofts or smallholdings, where there is a dispute.

THE SCOTTISH LANDOWNERS' FEDERATION, (SLF), 18 Abercromby Place, Edinburgh EH3 6TY; T.-031-556 4466.
Founded: 1906.
President: The Duke of Atholl; Convener: P.C. Macdonald; Director: D.J. Hughes Hallett.
The officially recognised lobbying organisation for owners of rural land in Scotland. Work is carried out by: representing members at all Government levels; helping members solve problems connected with land ownership and use; encouraging beneficial legislation in the development of rural land; briefing MPs thus providing a Parliamentary lobby; monitoring all taxation matters affecting land including capital gains tax, capital transfer tax, development land tax and a possible wealth tax; providing an interchange of ideas on land ownership; promoting recognition of the responsibilities of owning land; communicating the work and experience of SLF committees through its journal *Landowning in Scotland* and through local meetings. Membership: 4,200.

SCOTTISH LAW AGENTS SOCIETY, (SLAS), 33-34 Charlotte Square, Edinburgh EH2 4HF; T.-031-225 1516.
Founded: 1884.
President: Alan M. Stewart; Vice-president: James S. McDonald; Secretary: George F. Davidson; Editor, *Scottish Law Gazette*: Dr Enid Marshall.
Since its inauguration by Royal Charter in 1884, the society has been a respected channel through which all matters affecting the legal profession are discussed. The society is complementary to the Law Society of Scotland and is independent of it. Produces a memorandum book (revised and issued annually) and *Scottish Law Gazette* (issued quarterly). Both publications are

issued free to members. Membership is open to all enrolled solicitors in Scotland.

SCOTTISH LAW COMMISSION, 140 Causewayside, Edinburgh EH9 1PR; T.-031-668 2131.

Founded: 1965.
Chairman: The Hon Lord Maxwell; Full-time Commissioners: Dr E.M. Clive, Sheriff C.G.B. Nicholson, QC; Full-time Parliamentary Draftsman: J.F. Wallace, QC.
The commission has general responsibility for recommending reform of the law of Scotland with a view to its simplification and modernisation. It receives and considers proposals for law reform, and provides information and advice to Government departments and other authorities concerned with proposals for law reform. It also recommends the repeal of obsolete legislation. Liaison is maintained with the Law Commission for England and Wales, and with relevant professional and academic bodies.

THE SCOTTISH LAWN TENNIS ASSOCIATION, (SLTA), 12 Melville Crescent, Edinburgh EH3 7LU; T.-031-225 1284.

Secretary: Douglas Lynd, MBE.
The governing body for tennis in Scotland. Has 200 affiliated clubs with some 21,000 playing members.

SCOTTISH LEGAL ACTION GROUP, 40 Perth Road, Dundee; T.-Dundee 28572.

Founded: 1975.
Chairman: Prof Alan Paterson; Secretary: Hilary Patrick; Editor, SCOLAG: Prof Ian Willock.
Responds to law reform proposals, publishes SCOLAG (monthly journal of law reform and information) and holds conferences. Membership: around 450.

SCOTTISH LEGAL AID BOARD, 3-11 Melville Street, Edinburgh EH3 7PE; T.-031-226 4061.

Founded: 1986.
Chairman: Mr D.B. Grant, TD.
Independent, non-departmental public body uniting most aspects of legal aid administration. Under the Legal Aid (Scotland) Act 1986, the board has responsibility for all types of legal aid, including the determination of applications for criminal legal aid for summary proceedings.

SCOTTISH LIBERAL PARTY, 4 Clifton Terrace, Edinburgh EH12 5DR; T.-031-337 2314.

President: Lord Mackie of Benshie; Leader: Sir Russell Johnston, MP; Chairman: John Lawrie; Vice Chairs: Iain Macfarlane, Anne Singh, Robert Aldridge; Political Director: Ron Waddell; Party Secretary: Mrs Rae Grant.
Political organisation.

SCOTTISH LIBRARY ASSOCIATION, (SLA), Motherwell Business Centre, Coursington Road, Motherwell ML1 1PW; T.-0698 52526.

Founded: 1908.
Executive Secretary: Robert Craig; Treasurer: Gavin Drummond.
Exists to promote libraries and librarianship. Has a membership of 2,500 representing all areas of library and information work.

THE SCOTTISH LICENSED TRADE ASSOCIATION, 10 Walker Street, Edinburgh EH3 7LA; T.-031-225 5169/7287.

Founded: 1880.
President: E.P. Watson; Senior Vice President: J.N. Manson; Junior Vice President: P.R. McCrudden; Secretary: E.W. Ridehalgh.
The only national association representing all sections of the licensed trade in Scotland. The association is the recognised body for the licensed trade in Scotland and is consulted by Government departments, national boards, press, radio and television and other authorities when the interests of the trade are under consideration.

SCOTTISH LOCAL AUTHORITIES SPECIAL HOUSING GROUP, 53 Melville Street, Edinburgh EH3 7HL; T.-031-226 3376.

Founded: 1963.
Director: P.H. Stringer.
Encourages better housing through common development of all matters relating to housing plans: provision, management and maintenance of housing stock and the continuing welfare of the tenant.

SCOTTISH MARINE BIOLOGICAL ASSOCIATION, (SMBA), Dunstaffnage Marine Research Laboratory, PO Box 3, Oban PA34 4AD; T.-Oban 62244.

Founded: 1884.
Director: Ronald I. Currie, CBE.

Research is mainly concerned with understanding the processes which control the marine ecosystem, particularly in Scottish coastal waters but also in the adjacent part of the North Atlantic. The emphasis is on an experimental approach, but a certain amount of survey work is also conducted and some projects are concerned with studying the effects of industrial developments on the coast on the marine environment, and with fish farming in Scottish waters. Research workers from universities make an important contribution to the programme.

SCOTTISH MARITIME MUSEUM, 132 Harbour Street, Irvine, Ayrshire; T.-0294 78283.
Director: Campbell McMurray; Curator: Robert Forsythe.

SCOTTISH MARRIAGE GUIDANCE COUNCIL, (SMGC), 26 Frederick Street, Edinburgh EH2 2JR; T.-031-225 5006.
Founded: 1948.
Chairman: Dr J.D. Haldane; Director: David Clark.
Responsible for the development of an effective marriage guidance service throughout Scotland. Selects and trains counsellors for work in local marriage guidance councils and supervises their work. Provides a service of information, education and research on matters relating to marriage and family life. Provides a consultative service and training to other organisations.

SCOTTISH MICROELECTRONICS DEVELOPMENT PROGRAMME, (SMDP), 74 Victoria Crescent Road, Dowanhill, Glasgow G12 9JN; T.-041-357 0340.
Founded: 1979.
Director: Mr D. Walker; Depute Directors: Mr A. Thomson, Mr A. Fyfe.
A Government funded agency which is promoting the use of microcomputers in Scottish education. Following an initial four year project, SMDP is now a division of the Scottish Council for Educational Technology and is developing a software library, an information service and a research and development function. SMDP and the Scottish local authorities are now working closely to co-ordinate these developments within the framework of an agreed national plan.

SCOTTISH MILK MARKETING BOARD, Underwood Road, Paisley PA3 1TJ; T.-041-887 1234.
Chairman: Andrew L. Howie; Managing Director: J.R. Laidlaw; Deputy Managing Director: Dr J.D.W. McQueen; Director of Creameries: A.S. McCartney; Finance Director: J.M.S. Pirie; Secretary: W. Davidson.
Responsible for the administration of the Scottish Milk Marketing Scheme, under which all milk to be marketed by dairy farmers in the board's area from Montrose to the Solway must be sold to the board, apart from around 2% which the board licences for direct sale. The board sells 1,100 million litres of milk per annum, with a value of £186 million. The commercial division operates six transport depots and six creameries which purchase around 25% of all milk to manufacture into a wide range of milk products with a turnover of £63 million per annum. The board also provides a range of producer services either on a commercial basis or in a free advising capacity.

THE SCOTTISH MILK PUBLICITY COUNCIL LTD, 266 Clyde Street, Glasgow G1 4JH; T.-041-221 4838.
Founded: 1957.
Chairman: James A. Brown; Vice-chairman: Alan Wiseman; Secretary: John Russell.
Exists to advertise and promote the value, benefits and sale of milk and milk products. Members are from: the Scottish Milk Marketing Board; the Scottish Dairy Trade Federation; the Scottish Association of Milk Product Manufacturers.

THE SCOTTISH MILK RECORDS ASSOCIATION, (SMRA), Underwood Road, Paisley PA3 1TJ; T.-041-887 1234.
Founded: 1903.
Director of Milk Recording Services: B.R. Speight; Chairman: J.A. Brown; Vice-chairman: W. Kilpatrick.
Provides a range of individual cow milk production recording services to dairy farmers. About 1,200 farmers (about 40% of dairy producers) use the association's services. These services include official milk recording, (the internationally recognised standard system), simplified milk recording (a cheaper alternative), and CowPak, concentrating on health, breeding and fertility.

SCOTTISH MINING MUSEUM TRUST, Lady Victoria Colliery, Newtongrange, Midlothian EH22

4QN; T.-031-663 7519.
Founded: 1984.
Director: Dr Eamon Hyde; Depute Director: Colin McLean; Chairman: William Johnston. Has two sites, one at Lady Victoria Colliery and one at Prestongrange. Aims to tell the story of mining in Scotland throughout 800 years of history. Registered as a charity, with financial support from Lothian Regional Council, East Lothian District Council, Midlothian District Council and the Manpower Services Commission Community Programme.

SCOTTISH MOTOR RACING CLUB, (SMRC), 25 Market Square, Duns, Berwickshire TD11 3EQ; T.-0361 82370.
Founded: 1946.
Honorary President: Jackie Stewart; Chairman: Walter Robertson; Vice Chairman: Hugh McCaig; Secretary: Robin Traill; Treasurer: Peter Poole.
Organises motor car race meetings at the Ingliston and Knockhill race circuits from March to October each year.

SCOTTISH MOTOR TRADE ASSOCIATION LTD., (SMTA), 3 Palmerston Place, Edinburgh EH12 5AF; T.-031-225 3643.
Founded: 1903.
President: Mr J.J.H. Livingstone; Vice-president: Mr D. McLintock; Treasurer: Mr A.D. Campbell; Director: Mr W.M. Bryson.
Exists to 'encourage, promote and protect the motor trade in Scotland'. Organises the biennial Scottish Motor Show. Has almost 1,500 retailing members, ranging from the largest distributors and main dealers to the smallest back street workshops. Also has a section of some 250 non-retailing members, mostly based outside Scotland, such as vehicle and component manufacturers and finance companies, whose membership allows them to exhibit in the Scottish Motor Show. Members have to meet certain conditions and standards and only those motor traders who have passed an inspection test are allowed to join.

SCOTTISH MUSEUMS COUNCIL, County House, 20-22 Torphichen Street, Edinburgh EH3 8JB; T.-031-229 7465.
Chairman: Colin Thompson.
The principal channel for central Government funding for almost 400 local museums and galleries in Scotland. Aims to improve the quality of local museum and gallery pro-

vision. Services to members include grants for projects, conservation work, and advice and consultancy services. Through its training courses, publications and other activities, it provides a forum for those involved in museums. Limited company, with charitable status, controlled by an independent board of directors.

SCOTTISH MUSIC INFORMATION CENTRE, (SMIC), 7 Lilybank Gardens, Glasgow G12 8RZ; T.-041-334 6393.
Founded: 1969.
Chairman: Prof Hugh Macdonald; Manager: John Purser: Librarian/Secretary: Jane Livingston.
Exists for the promotion of Scottish music from the basis of a unique and growing collection of Scottish classical music of all periods, including an audio collection, scores, parts etc for sale or hire. Free catalogue and brochures are available. There is a folk music library and reference library and services include information on all aspects of Scottish music, exhibitions, lectures, radio programmes, photocopying and binding etc. A new publishing venture includes *Stretto* magazine and contemporary Scottish music for solo instruments.

SCOTTISH NATIONAL BLOOD TRANSFUSION SERVICE, Headquarters Unit, Ellens Glen Road, Edinburgh EH17 7QT; T.-031-664 2317.
National Medical Director: Dr J.D. Cash.
NHS supplier of blood and blood products to Scotland. Regional transfusion centres in Inverness, Aberdeen, Dundee, Glasgow and Edinburgh, which is also the home of the service's Protein Fractionation Centre, a pharmaceutical factory manufacturing therapeutic products from human plasma. The service also provides laboratory and clinical support to the Scottish health boards. Total staff: 1,100.

SCOTTISH NATIONAL CAMPS ASSOCIATION, (SNCA), 57 Melville Street, Edinburgh EH3 7HL; T.-031-226 6391.
Founded: 1947.
Chairman: William McDonald; Secretary: Raymond Thomson.
Administers four outdoor centres in central Scotland: one near Edinburgh, one in the upper Clyde Valley, one beside the Queen Elizabeth Forest Park in the Trossachs, and one in Strathmore. All centres are open

between March and October each year. There is sports equipment for hire and help can be given with programming. Open to organised groups only.

SCOTTISH NATIONAL COUNCIL OF YMCAs, 11 Rutland Street, Edinburgh EH1 2AE; T.-031-228 1464.
Founded: 1875.
President: Robert B. Jack; Chairman: Keith McIntosh; General Secretary: Robert King; Deputy General Secretary: Brian Gorham; Director of Sport and Recreation: George Ross; Secretary for Christian Education and Programming: Colin McAulay.
Works for the equal development of body, mind and spirit, particularly of young people. Based in 40 towns and cities in Scotland and works with the unemployed of all ages. Provides apartments for young homeless people. Has hostels and conference centres and provides life and social skills training for YTS trainees, who are engaged by various client companies.

SCOTTISH NATIONAL DICTIONARY ASSOCIATION LTD, (SNDA), 27 George Square, Edinburgh EH8 9LD; T.-031-667 1011, Ext. 6681.
Founded: 1929.
Chairman: Sir Kenneth Alexander; Secretary and Treasurer: John S. Gordon.
Founded with the aim of preserving and encouraging the Scots language. The publication of the 10 volumes of the *Scottish National Dictionary* was completed in 1976 and in 1985 the association published the *Concise Scots Dictionary.* Its research and publishing programmes are being continued.

SCOTTISH NATIONAL FEDERATION FOR THE WELFARE OF THE BLIND, 8 St Leonard's Bank, Perth PH2 8EB; T.-0738 26969.
Founded: 1917.
Honorary Secretary and Treasurer: J.N. Innes.
Promotes the well-being and protects the interests of the blind in Scotland by the co-operation and mutual assistance of various affiliated bodies.

SCOTTISH NATIONAL GALLERY OF MODERN ART. See National Galleries of Scotland.

SCOTTISH NATIONAL INSTITUTION FOR THE WAR BLINDED, PO

Box 500, Gillespie Crescent, Edinburgh EH10 4HZ; T.-031-229 1456.
Secretary and Treasurer: J.B.M. Munro.
Provides rehabilitation, training, settlement, and after care for men and women blinded on service with the armed forces.

SCOTTISH NATIONAL ORCHESTRA SOCIETY LTD, (SNO), 3 La Belle Place, Glasgow G3 7LH; T.-041-332 7244.
Founded: 1950.
Chairman: Raymond M. Williamson; General Administrator: Stephen Carpenter; Deputy General Administrator: Erik Knussen; Musical Director: Neeme Jarvi; Secretary: G.L.K. Murray, WS.
The orchestra, whose patron is The Queen, is the direct successor of the Scottish Orchestra which was established in 1891. Gives concerts throughout Scotland and the United Kingdom, has undertaken several European tours, and is the only British orchestra outside London to have toured in the USA. Gives over 100 public concerts annually, plus concerts for schools and has a heavy recording schedule. Has 92 permanent musicians, plus ancillary and administrative staff. Administers its own rehearsal hall which is also used for public concerts by many musical organisations. Has over 4,000 season ticket holders, about 1,500 members of its supporters club (Friends of the SNO), and its average annual audience numbers between 175,000 and 200,000.

SCOTTISH NATIONAL PARTY, (SNP), 6 North Charlotte Street, Edinburgh EH2 4JH; T.-031-226 3661.
Founded: 1928.
President: Rt Hon Donald Stewart, PC, MP; Chairman: Gordon Wilson, MP; Senior Vice Chairman: Mrs Margaret Ewing; National Secretary: John Swinney; National Treasurer: Alasdair Morgan.
A moderate, left-of-centre party with members and branches throughout the country. Has had continuous Parliamentary representation since Winnie Ewing's victory in the 1967 Hamilton by-election. Independence means, to the SNP, the establishment of a Scottish Parliament, elected by proportional representation, with sovereign control over all Scottish affairs. The party would wish Scotland to remain a member of the Commonwealth, under the Crown.

SCOTTISH NATIONAL POOL COUNCIL, c/o Honorary General

Secretary, 3 Strath Gardens, Dores, Inverness IV1 2TT.
Honorary General Secretary: Mr N.A. Donald.

SCOTTISH NATIONAL PORTRAIT GALLERY. See National Galleries of Scotland.

SCOTTISH NATIONAL SKI COUNCIL, 110A Maxwell Avenue, Bearsden, Glasgow G61 1HU; T.-041-934 0760.
Secretary: Catherine Legget.

SCOTTISH NATIONAL WAR MEMORIAL, (SNWM), The Castle, Edinburgh EH1 2YT; T.-031-226 7393.
Founded: 1927.
Chairman of Trustees: Major The Rt Hon The Earl Haig, OBE; Secretary and Treasurer: Major J.D.M. Watson; Curator: T.C. Barker.
Scotland's national shrine commemorating the 1914-18 War dead. Rolls of honour of all Scottish regiments and of Scots men and women who died in all other branches of the British and Commonwealth armed services. Those who died in the 1939-45 War, and in medal areas since 1945 have since been added. Designed by Sir Robert Lorimer. Sculpture, carving, bronze reliefs, trophies and regimental colours on display. An annual service of commemoration is held in May. Admission is free on application (there is a charge for the castle).

SCOTTISH NEIGHBOURHOOD ENERGY ACTION, (SNEA), Unit 1/1, 8 Elliot Place, Finnieston, Glasgow G3 8EP; T.-041-226 3064.
Founded: 1983.
Convener: Alan Sinclair; Vice-convener: Robert Barnham; Treasurer: Allan Paterson; Secretary: Tony Nec.
Promotes and supports energy and employment projects throughout Scotland. A comprehensive advice, information and training service is provided to over 60 projects in both rural and urban parts of Scotland. Membership is open to all community, voluntary, commercial and statutory organisations.

SCOTTISH NETBALL ASSOCIATION, 16 Royal Crescent, Glasgow G3 7SL; T.-041-332 5144.
Administrator: Miss A. Murray.

SCOTTISH AND NEWCASTLE BREWERIES plc, Abbey Brewery, Holyrood Road, Edinburgh EH8 8YS; T.-031-556 2591.
Founded: 1960.
Chairman: David Nickson; Chief Executive: Alick Rankin.
Brewers, public house owners and hoteliers. Turnover (1985): £707.2 million.

SCOTTISH NEWSPAPER PROPRIETORS' ASSOCIATION, (SNPA), Edinburgh House, 3-11 North St Andrew Street, Edinburgh EH2 1JU; T.-031-557 3600.
President: Mr D.J.R. Smail; Senior Vice President: Mr R.C.M. Frost; Director: Mr J.B. Raeburn.
The employers' organisation and trade association for the weekly newspaper in Scotland. Its 34 member firms publish some 120 weekly newspapers, all but 15 of which are paid-for titles. The association's main areas of involvement are industrial relations, education and training and advertising. It plays an active part in the Press Council and maintains close liaison with, and is consulted by, Government departments.

SCOTTISH AND NORTHERN IRELAND PLUMBING EMPLOYERS' FEDERATION, (SNIPEF), 2 Walker Street, Edinburgh EH3 7LB; T.-031-225 2255.
Founded: 1923.
Director: W. Todd Soutar; Secretary: Robert D. Burgon.
The national trade association for plumbing and domestic heating. Has 1,100 member firms throughout Scotland and Northern Ireland. Operates a code of fair trading which provides for conciliation and arbitration of any complaints against member firms. Provides advice to members on industrial relations, education and training, and commercial and legal matters. Lists of local members are available on request.

SCOTTISH NURSERY NURSES' EXAMINATION BOARD, 38 Queen Street, Glasgow G1 3DY; T.-041-248 7900.
Founded: 1967.
Chairman: Dr W.W. Easton; Secretary: D. Hemingway.
Provides courses of education and training for nursery nurses in Scotland, assesses students' attainments, and makes awards.

SCOTTISH OFFICE, New St Andrew's House, Edinburgh EH1 3SK; T.-031-556 8400.

Secretary of State: Rt Hon Malcolm Rifkind, MP, QC; Minister of State for Health and Social Work, Highlands and Islands and Tourism: Lord Glenarthur; Minister for Education, Agriculture and Fisheries: John MacKay, MP; Minister for Local Government and the Environment: Michael Ancram, MP; Minister for Industry and Home Affairs: Ian Lang, MP; Permanent Under Secretary of State: Sir William Fraser, GCB.

The Secretary of State for Scotland is responsible in Scotland for a wide range of statutory functions which in England and Wales are the responsibility of a number of departmental ministers. He also works closely with ministers in charge of Great Britain departments on topics of special significance to Scotland within their fields of responsibility. His statutory functions are administered by five main departments: Department of Agriculture and Fisheries for Scotland; Scottish Development Department; Scottish Education Department; Scottish Home and Health Department; and Industry Department for Scotland. These departments (plus Central Services embracing the Solicitor's Office, the Scottish Information Office, Establishment, Liaison and Finance Divisions) are collectively known as the Scottish Office. In addition there are a number of other Scottish departments for which the Secretary of State has some degree of responsibility; these include the Scottish Courts Administration, the Department of the Registrar General for Scotland (the General Register Office), the Scottish Record Office and the Department of the Registers of Scotland. The Secretary of State also bears ministerial responsibility for the activities in Scotland of several statutory bodies whose functions extend throughout Great Britain, such as the Manpower Services Commission and the Forestry Commission.

SCOTTISH OFFICIAL BOARD OF HIGHLAND DANCING, Saltire House, 13 Atholl Crescent, Edinburgh EH3 8HA; T.-031-228 2731.

Secretary: Miss M. Rowan.

SCOTTISH OFFSHORE TRAINING ASSOCIATION LTD, (SCOTA), Blackness Avenue, Altens, Aberdeen AB1 4PG; T.-0224 899707.

Founded: 1973.

Director: N.G. Duggan; Training Officer: Mrs A.P. Alexander.

SCOTA is an association of companies, engaged in offshore production, drilling and service activities, and was set up to cater for the training of personnel employed in the offshore oil industry. It is non profit making and is funded through the income derived from its course activity. It is controlled by a board of directors composed of up to 16 representatives of member companies, and has its own purpose-built training centre. Membership: 149 companies.

SCOTTISH OPERA, 39 Elmbank Crescent, Glasgow G2 4PT; T.-041-248 4567.

Founded: 1962.

Chairman, Board of Directors: Dr L.J. Paterson; Vice-chairman: W. Proudfoot; Managing Director: R. Mantle; Music Director: Sir Alexander Gibson, CBE; Opera Administrator and Deputy Managing Director: J.L. Graham.

International opera company based in Glasgow. Tours Scotland, the north of England and abroad. Has an extensive education programme.

SCOTTISH ORIENTEERING ASSOCIATION, (SOA), c/o The Secretary, 5 The Chanonry, Aberdeen AB2 1RP; T.-0224 484375.

Founded: 1962.

President: Dr Margaret Fraser; Vice-president: Dr Ian Hendrie; Secretary: Dr Brenda Nisbet; Treasurer: David Cooke; Membership Secretary: Dr Chris Aust; Fixtures Secretary: Michael Murray.

Orienteering is a competitive sport, a mixture of cross country running and map reading in which the competitor navigates round an ordered series of checkpoints. Races are normally held in forested terrain and vary in length according to age and sex. The sport is organised in Scotland by the association. There are 18 open and nine closed clubs with approximately 1,000 active members in all. All levels of competition from national championships to small club events are organised, and there are wayfaring courses for families.

THE SCOTTISH ORNITHOLOGISTS' CLUB, (SOC), 21 Regent Terrace, Edinburgh EH7 5BT; T.-031-556 6042.

Founded: 1936.

President: John M.S. Arnott; Vice-president: Dr Jeremy J.D. Greenwood; Secretary: John C. Davies; Honorary Treasurer: William G.

Harper.
Formed with the aim of encouraging ornithology in Scotland. Has nearly 3,000 members and 13 branches around Scotland. Organises an annual weekend conference in the autumn and a one-day birdwatchers' conference in the spring. Publishes a quarterly newsletter *Scottish Bird News*, a twice-yearly journal *Scottish Birds*, and the annual *Scottish Bird Report*. The club's Waterston Library is the best ornithological reference library in Scotland. The Bird Bookshop, run by the club for the benefit of ornithology in Scotland, is the world's leading ornithological bookseller.

SCOTTISH PARACHUTE CLUB, (SPC), Strathallan Airfield, Auchterarder, Perthshire; T.-Auchterarder 2572.
Founded: 1960.
Chief Instructor: Rob Noble-Nesbitt; Chairman: Ian Hunter; Secretary: Maggie Butler; Treasurer: Brian Conlon.
The major parachuting facility in Scotland. In 1985 it trained over 700 first jumpers and the membership carried out a total of some 5,000 parachute descents. Parachute training courses, which are run almost every week of the year by the club, are open to everyone over 16 years of age, provided they are in good health.

THE SCOTTISH PATRIOTS, 76 Constitution Street, Edinburgh EH6 6RP; T.-031-554 7951.
Founded: 1946.
Honorary President: Robert M. Robertson; Vice President and Secretary: Violet MacInnes; Treasurer: Robina Wood; Editor, *The Patriot*, Iain McGregor.
Independent independence movement founded by the late Wendy Wood, devoted to maintaining Scotland's identity in politics and culture.

SCOTTISH PHARMACEUTICAL FEDERATION, 135 Buchanan Street, Glasgow G1 2JQ; T.-041-221 1235.
Founded: 1919.
Chairman: Bernard Brown; Secretary and Treasurer: Robert H. Stewart.
Employers' association representing the commercial interests of retail pharmacists.

SCOTTISH PHYSICAL EDUCATION ASSOCIATION, c/o Secretary, Balcanquhal Cottage, Glenfarg, Perth PH2 9QD; T.-05773 269.

Secretary: Mrs J. Thompson.

SCOTTISH PISTOL ASSOCIATION, (SPA), c/o 15 Branscroft, Kilbarchan PA10 2LU; T.-Kilbarchan 4459.
Chairman: Mrs C.M. Johnston; Honorary Treasurer: Mrs M. MacDonald; Honorary Secretary: J. Curran.
The association is the governing body of pistol shooting in Scotland. It selects competitors to represent Scotland at national level at home and abroad and runs four main meetings a year. Individual and club membership is available.

SCOTTISH POETRY LIBRARY ASSOCIATION, (SPLA), Scottish Poetry Library, Tweeddale Court, 14 High Street, Edinburgh EH1 1TE; T.-031-557 2876.
Founded: 1982.
Honorary Convener: Angus Calder; Honorary Secretary: William Wolfe; Honorary Treasurer: Eric Wishart; Director: Tessa Ransford; Librarian: Dr Tom Hubbard.
The library houses a collection of work by 206 poets from within Scotland, in Gaelic, Scots and English, and work by poets from other countries. Books, cassettes and magazines may be borrowed, by post if necessary. Current magazines and poetry pamphlets are on sale. A regular display of poetry from a particular region, country, poet or group is arranged. A newsletter, *SPLASH*, keeps the 600 members, both individuals and organisations, informed of poets, books and events. The association researches, and provides information on, all aspects of contemporary poetry. Everyone is welcome.

SCOTTISH POLICE COLLEGE, Tulliallan Castle, Kincardine-on-Forth, by Alloa FK10 4BE; T.-0259 30333.
Founded: 1954.
Commandant: Major-General David Alexander, CB.
The college, the only such establishment in Scotland, provides residential training courses for recruits and traffic, detective and senior officers. The commandant, who is appointed by the Secretary of State, answers to a board of governors whose chairman is the Secretary of the Scottish Home and Health Department. Members are drawn from the Convention of Scottish Local Authorities, the police associations and selected independent members. Her Majesty's Chief Inspector of Constabulary is

an assessor to the board.

SCOTTISH POLICE FEDERATION, 5 Woodside Place, Glasgow G3 7PD; T.-041-332 5234.
Founded: 1919.
Chairman: Alistair W.A. Wallace; General Secretary: Alexander Gowl.
Staff association for members of the federated ranks of the Scottish police service.

SCOTTISH POLO ASSOCIATION, c/o The Secretary, The Grange, Cupar, Fife; T.-Gauldry 234.
Secretary: Capt M. Fox-Pitt.

THE SCOTTISH POST OFFICE BOARD, (SPOB), West Port House, 102 West Port, Edinburgh EH3 9HS; T.-031-228 7200.
Founded: 1986.
Chairman: Ian Barr; Board Member, Letters: John Mackay, TD; Board Member, Corporate Resources: James Furneaux; Board Member, Counters: John Haldane; Board Member, Parcels: Nigel Millar; Board Secretary and Public Relations Adviser: Martin Cummins.
The SPOB is the Post Office's corporate presence in Scotland. Postal operations are handled by three businesses: letters, counters and parcels. Each business is managed as a distinct entity within the corporation, providing services for each other on a commercial basis. The Scottish Post Office Board is responsible to the chairman of the Post Office for the northern letter territory of Scotland and the North of England, for four counter districts and a Scottish parcels district.

SCOTTISH PRISON SERVICE, St Margaret's House, 151 London Road, Edinburgh EH8 7TG; T.-031-556 8400.
Director: A.M. Thomson; Deputy Directors: T.J. Kelly, W. McVey, W.J. Fearnley, T. Collinson.
Administers prisons and other types of penal establishments in Scotland.

SCOTTISH PUBLISHERS ASSOCIATION, (SPA), 25A South West Thistle Street Lane, Edinburgh EH2 1EW; T.-031-225 5795.
Founded: 1974.
Chairman: Richard Drew; Vice Chairman: Stephanie Wolfe Murray; Treasurer: Christian Maclean; Honorary Secretary: Bill Campbell.

Has 55 members representing almost all book publishing activity in Scotland. Assists members in all aspects of publishing, particularly in the promotion and marketing of their books, both nationally and internationally.

THE SCOTTISH RAILWAY PRESERVATION SOCIETY, (SRPS), The Station, Bo'ness, West Lothian EH51 0AD; T.-0506 822298.
Founded: 1961.
Chairman: J. Hill; Secretary: P.R. Ovenstone; Treasurer: S.J. Leslie; Vice-chairman: W.S. Sellar.
Aims to preserve, display and interpret Scotland's railway heritage. Has amassed the largest and most comprehensive collection of Scottish rolling stock, some of which is used to operate a regular steam passenger service on the society's railway at Bo'ness. The railway and the society's museum are operated by a volunteer workforce drawn from a total membership of 950.

SCOTTISH RECORD OFFICE, (SRO), HM General Register House, Princes Street, Edinburgh EH1 3YY; T.-031-556 6585.
Keeper of the Records of Scotland: Dr Atholl L. Murray; Deputy Keeper and Curator of Historical Records: James D. Galbraith; Deputy Keeper, Records Liaison Division: Andrew M. Broom; Secretary, National Register of Archives (Scotland): Dr Barbara L.H. Horn; Conservation Officer: Dr Peter D. Anderson; Chairman, Scottish Records Advisory Council: Prof R.H. Campbell.
Has been responsible for preserving the public records of Scotland since the 13th century, and other records transmitted to the keeper, and for making them available to the public. Also responsible for the selection, disposal and transfer of non-current records of Government departments, public bodies and courts. Keeps a national register of archives and surveys records in private hands and advises and assists owners. The Scottish Records Advisory Council advises the Secretary of State, the Lord President of the Court of Session and the Lord Justice General on matters concerning Scottish public records.

SCOTTISH RECORDS ASSOCIATION, c/o Strathclyde Regional Archives, Mitchell Library, North Street, Glasgow G3 7DN; T.-041-227 2402.

Founded: 1977.
Chairman: Dr Grant G. Simpson; Secretary: Mr A.M. Jackson.

Objects are to arouse public interest in historical records and to create an enlightened public opinion on matters affecting their custody, preservation and use. Among other activities, the association holds two conferences each year on subjects relating to Scottish history. Has over 450 members, who include private owners, archivists and other custodians of records, and researchers, both amateur and professional.

SCOTTISH RECORD SOCIETY, c/o Dr James Kirk, Honorary Secretary, Scottish History Department, University of Glasgow, Glasgow G12 8QQ.

Founded: 1897.
President: Prof Gordon Donaldson; Honorary Treasurer: Rev Duncan Shaw; Chairman of Council: Dr Athol Murray.

Publishes volumes of calendars and indices of public records and private muniments relating to Scotland.

SCOTTISH RECREATIONAL LAND ASSOCIATION, (SRLA), 18 Abercromby Place, Edinburgh EH3 6TY; T.-031-556 4466.

Founded: 1972.
Convener: J.P. Grant, Younger of Rothiemurchus; Secretary: D.J. Hughes Hallett; President: The Duke of Atholl; Vice-president: Prof J.T. Coppock.

The association recognises the increased demand for leisure and recreation and the pressures that can mean on the countryside. Its aims are: to encourage public access to land in a controlled and responsible manner; to balance recreational demands with the conservation of the countryside and its wildlife; to protect the interests of those who live and work on the land; to pool and consolidate the experience and expertise of SRLA members; to provide specialist advice on the practical, legal and commercial aspects of recreational land use. Membership: 105.

SCOTTISH REFORMATION SOCIETY, (SRS), 17 George IV Bridge, Edinburgh EH1 1EE; T.-031-225 1836.

Founded: 1850.
Chairman: Rev James Crichton; Vice Chairman: Rev David L. Wright; Honorary Treasurer: Mr A. Fraser MacLennan; Secretary: Rev A. Sinclair Horne.

Founded to spread scriptural teaching on the distinctive tenets of Protestantism, with particular emphasis on adherence to the consensus of the Reformed Confessions. Work is carried out through lectures, visual aid programmes and video presentations. The society is a charity maintained entirely by public subscriptions.

THE SCOTTISH RETIREMENT COUNCIL, 212 Bath Street, Glasgow G2 4HW; T.-041-332 9427.

Founded: 1958.
Chairman: Prof Sir Ferguson Anderson, OBE; Vice Chairmen: Dr O. Taylor Brown, OBE, Dr A.J. Weir; Treasurer: A. Brown Wilson; Director: S. Graham Hoey; Secretary: Mrs M. Davies.

The council is the national consultative organisation for preparation for retirement throughout Scotland. In Strathclyde Region it organises pre-retirement courses, runs three day-workshop centres and a part-time employment bureau for the retired. Has five associated regional groups in Strathclyde, Lothian, Tayside, Dumfries and Galloway and Fife. Acts as a resource centre for Scotland and can advise on the availability of courses throughout the country.

SCOTTISH RIFLE ASSOCIATION, c/o Honorary Secretary and Treasurer, 63 Beechlands Drive, Clarkston, Glasgow G76 7UX; T.-041-639 1209.

Honorary Secretary and Treasurer: Hamish L. Hunter.

SCOTTISH RIGHTS OF WAY SOCIETY LTD, (SROWS), 1 Lutton Place, Edinburgh EH8 9OD; T.-031-447 9242.

Founded: 1845.
Chairman: I.S. Fraser; Vice-chairman: L.B. Watson; Honorary Secretary: R.A. Dickson; Honorary Treasurer: D.A. Whitaker.

Exists to preserve, defend and acquire public rights of way in Scotland and to do whatever necessary to preserve or restore rights of way which may be in danger of being lost. Erects, restores and repairs bridges, guide-posts and signs, fences, stiles, gates and resting places in connection with rights of way, and repairs the roads or pathways themselves. Defends and prosecutes, directly or indirectly, suits or actions for the preservation or recovery of rights of way.

SCOTTISH RIVER PURIFICATION BOARDS' ASSOCIATION, City Chambers, Glasgow G2 1DU; T.-041-221 9600.
Founded: 1957.
Secretary: I.G. Fraser.
Protects the interests, rights, and privileges of river purification authorities, and facilitates the exchange of ideas and discussion of common problems.

SCOTTISH ROAD SAFETY CAMPAIGN, Slateford House, 53 Lanark Road, Edinburgh EH14 1TL; T.-031-444 1155.
Founded: 1985.
Chairman: David Palmer; Secretary: A. Fraser Dryburgh.
Set up by the Secretary of State for Scotland to organise a publicity programme in an attempt to combat Scotland's road accident problems. Over 26,000 people are killed or injured on Scottish roads each year, proportionally more than in England or Wales, and whilst the campaign was launched initially in support of European Road Safety Year 1986, it has continued. The committee appointed to develop material has representation from local authorities, the police, motoring and road safety organisations.

SCOTTISH ROCK GARDEN CLUB, (SRGC), c/o The Secretary, The Linns, Sheriffmuir, Dunblane FK15 0LP; T.-Dunblane 822295.
Founded: 1933.
President: Mr E.G. Watson; Secretary: Dr E. Stevens; Treasurer: Mr L.N. Bilton; Subscription Secretary: Miss K.M. Gibb; Editor: Mr A.D. McKelvie; Seed Exchange Manager: Mrs J. Wyllie.
Has a present worldwide membership of over 4,000, with a Scottish membership of around 1,900. Formed to create an interest in, and encourage the cultivation of, rock garden (alpine) and peat garden plants. In Scotland, there are groups in 13 centres, with regular programmes of lectures during the winter months and garden visits in summer. Competitive plant shows, to which non-members are welcome, are organised in the spring by five of these local groups. Two issues of the club's journal, *The Rock Garden* are published annually. Other activities include an annual discussion weekend and a seed exchange programme.

SCOTTISH RUGBY UNION, (SRU),
Murrayfield, Edinburgh EH12 5PJ; T.-031-337 2346.
Founded: 1873.
President: Dr D.W.C. Smith; Vice Presidents: W.L. Connon, T. Pearson; Secretary: I.A.L. Hogg; Treasurer: I.A. Forbes; Administrative Secretary: H.H. Penman; Technical Administrator: J.H. Roxburgh.
National sporting organisation. There are 112 clubs and five district unions in membership of the SRU and 145 clubs in membership of the district unions.

SCOTTISH SCHOOLBOYS' CLUB, (SSC), 39A Lansdowne Crescent, Glasgow G20 6NH; T.-041-334 5649.
Founded: 1912.
Chairman: David Williamson, CBE; Secretary: Prof John Cowan; Treasurer: William Gemmill, MBE; National Organiser: Iain M. Gillespie.
Formed for pupils attending secondary schools. Has branches in Edinburgh, Glasgow, Dundee, and Greenock and one covering the rest of Scotland. School games nights, Sunday meetings, weekend camps and other activities are organised along with the summer and Easter camps which promote the club's aim which is to 'help its members to discover the full meaning of the Christian faith'. Membership: around 1,000.

SCOTTISH SCHOOLS ATHLETIC ASSOCIATION, (SSAA), c/o The Secretary, 11 Muirfield Street, Kirkcaldy KY2 6SY; T.-0592 260168.
Founded: 1934.
President: John McGhie; Treasurer: David Downie; Secretary: Alex Jack.
Responsible for athletics in all Scottish schools. Organises six national events each year and two international events with England, Ireland and Wales, at school level (up to 19 years old). Affiliated to the Scottish Amateur Athletic Association and the British Amateur Athletic Board. Also a constituent member of the British Schools International Athletic Board. Has 450 secondary schools in direct membership, and 13 district schools' athletics associations and all primary schools as affiliate members.

SCOTTISH SCHOOLS BASKETBALL ASSOCIATION, (SSBA), 8 Frederick Street, Edinburgh EH2 2HB; T.-031-225 7143.
Founded: 1960.
Chairman: Malcolm Renny; Secretary: Gordon Blair; Treasurer: James Morrow.
Objects are to develop and promote basket-

ball and to control the playing of basketball in competitions organised by the association in Scottish schools.

THE SCOTTISH SCHOOLS' FOOT-BALL ASSOCIATION, (SSFA), 5 Forth Park Gardens, Kirkcaldy KY2 5TD; T.-0592 261811.

Founded: 1903.
President: William B. Harrower; General Secretary: Robert M. Docherty; Assistant General Secretary: Alex B. McMenemy; Treasurer: John C. Watson; Under-15s Secretary: Peter McAuley; Under-18s Secretary: David Morris.
Object is to foster the mental, moral and physical development and improvement of boys through the medium of association football, and to help charitable funds and purposes. Has 54 affiliated associations and approximately 350 secondary schools and 1,500 primary schools in membership. Organises trials leading to the selection of three international squads: under-15, under-16 and under-18.

SCOTTISH SCHOOLS GOLF ASSOCIATION, c/o Leith Academy, Duke Street, Leith, Edinburgh; T.-031-554 0606.

Secretary: Mr J.D. McLeod.

SCOTTISH SCHOOLS SCIENCE EQUIPMENT RESEARCH CENTRE, (SSSERC), 103 Broughton Street, Edinburgh EH1 3RZ; T.-031-556 2184/ 031-557 1037.

Founded: 1965.
Secretary to Governors: Mr A. McKay; Director: John Richardson; Depute Director: Allen Cochrane.
Largely funded and wholly controlled by regional and islands councils as education authorities, via the education committee of the Convention of Scottish Local Authorities. Provides central consultancy services on the purchase and use of school science and technology equipment. Provides education authorities and the Curriculum Development Service with a wide variety of services on a commissioned basis. These services include a central ad-hoc technical and safety advisory service for teachers. The centre's publications and activities include a regular *Bulletin*, technical and safety auditing of curricular and other materials and the running of courses for teachers and technicians.

SCOTTISH SCHOOLS SWIMMING ASSOCIATION, c/o Secretary, Almado, 18 Durward Drive, Glenrothes, Fife; T.-0592 752475.

Secretary: Mrs C.M. Smith.

SCOTTISH SCULPTURE WORKSHOP, 1 Main Street, Lumsden, Huntly, Aberdeenshire AB5 4JN; T.-04646 372.

Founded: 1979.
Chairman: Frank Pottinger; Secretary: Fredrick Bushe.
Offers facilities for making sculpture.

SCOTTISH SECONDARY TEACHERS' ASSOCIATION, (SSTA), 15 Dundas Street, Edinburgh EH3 6QG; T.-031-556 5919/0605.

Founded: 1946.
President: Donald C. Halliday; Vice-president: N.J. Boyle; General Secretary: Alex A. Stanley; General Treasurer: J.R. McKelvie; Minutes Secretary: A.B. Fulton; Immediate Past President: D. Campbell.
Trade union representing secondary teachers in Scotland. Recognised by the Scottish Education Department and by all local authorities and has three places on the Scottish Joint Negotiating Committee for Teaching Staff in School Education, the national negotiating body for Scottish teachers. Membership: 7,500.

THE SCOTTISH SEED AND NURSERY TRADE ASSOCIATION, (SSNTA), 12 Bruntsfield Crescent, Edinburgh EH10 4HA; T.-031-447 1035.

Founded: 1917.
President: Bruce T. Welch; Vice President: A.M. Beattie; Secretary: J.R.L. Cruickshank.
Protects and advances the interests of those engaged in (or doing business in Scotland in) the seed trade, whether agricultural, horticultural, wholesale or retail, and in the nursery trade.

SCOTTISH SEED POTATO DEVELOPMENT COUNCIL, 10 Rutland Square, Edinburgh EH1 2AS; T.-031-228 6768.

Founded: 1981.
Chairman: John Fotheringham, OBE; Chief Executive: John Bethell.
Established by the Secretary of State for Scotland with the aim of achieving the maximisation of profitability of the seed potato

industry.

SCOTTISH SHELLFISH GROWERS ASSOCIATION, Tigh Na Speir, Connel, Argyll PA37 1PH; T.-0631 71 505.

Founded: 1981.

Chairman: Andrew Lane; Treasurer: Peter Williams; Secretary: Janet Church; NFU Representative: Norrie Etherson; Orkney Islands Representative: Inge Dickie; Western Isles Representative: Iain MacLeod.

Has members throughout Scotland ranging from specialist shellfish farms to part-time crofter growers. Founded as a body to represent growers nationally, the association acts as a forum to air the views of members and to provide useful and profitable information for all.

SCOTTISH SHOOTING COUNCIL, c/o Secretary, 39 Pelstream Avenue, Stirling FK7 0BG; T.-0786 75769.

Secretary: Dr G. Webb.

SCOTTISH SKI CLUB, (SSC), Muircambus, Elie, Leven, Fife KY9 1HD; T.-033 334 200.

Founded: 1907.

President: Dr Mary Allison; Secretary: Mrs Jean Lindesay-Bethune; Treasurer: Brian Latto; Membership Secretary: Calum T.A. Cheyne.

Active in all areas of skiing: racing, race training, grass skiing, artificial slope skiing, free style skiing and touring. Local sections in Glasgow, Stirling and the Cairngorm area hold regular gatherings for members. Club races include giant slalom and slalom and a decathlon. Publishes a journal yearly. Membership: around 2,300.

SCOTTISH SMALL-BORE RIFLE ASSOCIATION, c/o Secretary, 18 Breck Terrace, Penicuik, Midlothian EH26 0RJ; T.-Penicuik 74155.

Secretary: Mrs Anne M. Hamilton.

SCOTTISH SOCIETY FOR AUTISTIC CHILDREN, Room 2, 2nd Floor, 12 Picardy Place, Edinburgh EH1 3JT; T.-031-557 0474.

Founded: 1968.

Chairman: Ruth Hampton; Vice Chairman: S.R. Lockley; General Secretary: Mrs I.M. Watson.

Educates and cares for children and adults diagnosed as autistic or with severe communication problems.

SCOTTISH SOCIETY OF COMPOSERS, (SSC), c/o Scottish Music Information Centre, 7 Lilybank Gardens, Glasgow G12 8RZ; T.-041-334 6393.

Founded: 1980.

President: William Wordsworth; Chairman: John Hearne; Secretary and Treasurer: William Sweeney.

Main aims are: the furtherance of Scottish contemporary music, the encouragement of young composers and the performance and recording of works by established composers. Membership is open to anyone. Has issued two recordings of Scottish contemporary music and publishes *Stretto* quarterly jointly with the Scottish Music Information Centre. Administers the SSC Performing Rights Society Award which is given annually for services to Scottish contemporary music and organises a schools' composition competition as well as one for Royal Scottish Academy of Music and Drama students.

SCOTTISH SOCIETY FOR THE EMPLOYMENT OF EX-REGULAR SAILORS, SOLDIERS AND AIRMEN, New Haig House, Logie Green Road, Edinburgh EH7 4HQ; T.-031-557 1747.

Founded: 1886.

Chairman: Col H.F.O. Bewsher, OBE; Secretary: Flt Lt F. Roberts.

Object is to assist men and women who have served with good character in the regular armed forces of the Crown (or with non-regular service between 3 September 1939 and 3 September 1945) to re-establish themselves in civilian life on completion of their service, or to transfer to the reserves and, in later years, to find suitable or alternative employment. No fee is charged and registration records are available for inspection.

SCOTTISH SOCIETY OF THE HISTORY OF MEDICINE, (SSHM), c/o Dr D. Dow, The Archives, University of Glasgow, Glasgow G12 8QQ.

President: Dr A.H.B. Masson; Treasurer: Dr M. Eastwood; Joint Honorary Secretaries: Dr D. Dow; Dr D. Wright.

Concerned with promoting interest in the history of medicine. Holds three or more meetings a year with at least one in Edinburgh and at least one in Glasgow. Membership is open to anyone with an interest in the history of medicine. Membership: over 200.

SCOTTISH SOCIETY FOR THE MEN-

TALLY HANDICAPPED, 13 Elmbank Street, Glasgow G3 4QA; T.-041-226 4541.
Founded: 1954.
Chairman, Scottish Council: P. Bruce, MBE; Treasurer: Dr M.J. Tomkinson; Director: Iain M. McMurray; Deputy Director: Hugh W.L. Stewart.
Concerned with all aspects of the welfare of mentally handicapped people and their families. Founded by parents, the society has 80 branches in all parts of Scotland and a membership of over 6,000, providing a range of services.

SCOTTISH SOCIETY FOR NORTHERN STUDIES, (SSNS), c/o School of Scottish Studies, 27 George Square, Edinburgh EH8 9LD; T.-031-667 1011.
President: David Sellar; Secretary: Morag MacLeod; Treasurer: Patrick Topping.
Objective is to foster closer friendship between Scandinavians, Scots and the northern English. Spring and summer day-long meetings are held, but the main base is in Edinburgh where the AGM is held November. Membership: around 200.

SCOTTISH SOCIETY OF PLAYWRIGHTS, 37 Otago Street, Glasgow G12 8JJ; T.-041-339 1787.
Founded: 1973.
Chairman: Ian Brown; Vice Chairman: Chris Hannan; Secretary: Charles Hart; Treasurer: A.J. Stewart.
Formed by a group of playwrights to promote the development and production of theatre writing in Scotland and to help playwrights in all matters affecting them.

SCOTTISH SOCIETY FOR PREVENTION OF CRUELTY TO ANIMALS, 19 Melville Street, Edinburgh EH3 7PL; T.-031-225 6418.
Founded: 1839.
Chairman: Neil McCall Smith, JP; Vice Chairman: Peter Simpson; Chief Executive: Sir Cameron Rusby, KCB, LVO; Treasurer: T.D. Straton, TD.
Represents animal welfare interests to Government, local authorities, and others. Maintains an inspectorate to patrol and investigate and to advise owners of their responsibility for the welfare of animals in their care. Educates young people to realise their responsibilities.

SCOTTISH SOCIETY FOR THE PRE-

VENTION OF VIVISECTION, (SSPV), 10 Queensferry Street, Edinburgh EH2 4PG; T.-031-225 6039.
Founded: 1912.
Director: Clive Hollands; Deputy Director: Leslie Ward.
An animal welfare society concerned with the protection of animals from cruelty, the prevention of the infliction of suffering, and the abolition of vivisection. **ST. ANDREW ANIMAL FUND:** Established to undertake the purely charitable activities of the SSPV. Seeks to promote humane attitudes towards animal life and the development of a proper understanding and appreciation of all living things. **COMMITTEE FOR THE REFORM OF ANIMAL EXPERIMENTATION:** The SSPV provides a secretariat for the committee, which is drawn from both Houses of Parliament and the fields of science and medicine, as well as animal welfare. Devoted to the reform of the law relating to the use of animals for research experiments and other laboratory purposes. **SCOTTISH GREY SEAL GROUP:** Chairman: Clive Hollands. Represents the Scottish viewpoint on the conservation and protection of the grey seal.

SCOTTISH SOCIETY OF WOMEN ARTISTS, (SSWA), 13 Braehead Loan, Edinburgh EH4 6BL; T.-031-339 6952.
Founded: 1924.
Acting Secretary/Treasurer: Valerie Fiddes; President: Helen Firth; Vice-president: Sheana Stephen.
Aims to give encouragement and opportunity to women artists. Admits to membership artists of every outlook, whether in painting, sculpture, design or applied art. Holds an annual exhibition in the Royal Scottish Academy Galleries.

SCOTTISH SOLAR ENERGY GROUP, (SSEG), c/o Physics Department, Heriot-Watt University, Riccarton, Edinburgh EH14 4AS; T.-031-449 5111.
Founded: 1980.
Chairman: A.W.K. MacGregor; Secretary: J.I.B. Wilson; Treasurer: W.E. Ferguson.
Object is to promote research, development and application of the direct usage of solar energy in Scotland. Several meetings are held each year, often associated with a visit to a solar energy application and an international conference was inaugurated in

1984. A newsletter is included with the cost of membership and the group has 30-40 members with a range of interests and qualifications.

SCOTTISH SOLICITORS DISCIPLINE TRIBUNAL, 5 Rutland Square, Edinburgh EH1 6PE.
Founded: 1933.
Judicial tribunal operating under the provisions of the Solicitors (Scotland) Act 1980 and empowered primarily to hear complaints of professional misconduct against solicitors enrolled in the register of solicitors in Scotland.

THE SCOTTISH SPECIAL HOUSING ASSOCIATION, (SSHA), 9-21 Palmerston Place, Edinburgh EH12 5AJ; T.-031-225 1281.
Founded: 1937.
Chairman: D.S. Mason, CBE, JP; General Manager: F.C. Marks, OBE.
A Government financed body which designs, provides and manages housing to rent throughout Scotland. Currently owns some 85,000 houses. Governed by a council of management consisting of a chairman and six members, appointed by the Secretary of State for Scotland. Provides special needs housing, new and rehabilitated housing in inner urban areas, especially Glasgow, and housing for incoming workers to areas of industrial growth, in addition to housing for general needs. Also has an important programme of modernisation of its older housing stock and designs and builds housing on an agency basis for many public bodies. Builds either by using contractors or its own building department.

SCOTTISH SPINA BIFIDA ASSOCIATION, (SSBA), 190 Queensferry Road, Edinburgh EH4 2BW; T.-031-332 0743.
Founded: 1965.
Chairman: T. Neil Graham; Vice-chairman: Mr D. MacRae; Honorary Treasurer: Mrs M.A. Ballantine; Executive Officer: Mrs A.D. Smith.
A registered charity established to improve the quality of life of those with spina bifida and/or hydrocephalus and allied disorders. Help is provided by means of a national information service, a national counselling service, group and family holidays, national sports training, independence training and leisure activities. Has nine branches covering the whole of Scotland, with a considerable degree of autonomy, their own office

bearers and their own programmes of activities, providing locally based services.

SCOTTISH SPINAL CORD INJURY ASSOCIATION, Princes House, 5 Shandwick Place, Edinburgh EH2 4RG; T.-031-228 3827.
Founded: 1960.
Executive Officer: Margaret Jones; Chairman: James Laird; Honorary Secretary: George Robertson, OBE; Treasurer: A.R. Mitchell.
Exists to help spinal cord injury victims with welfare, encouragement in sporting activities and research into resultant paralysis from such injuries. Membership is open to all spinal injured people with associate membership for interested parties. Provides specially adapted holiday accommodation for disabled people.

SCOTTISH SPORTS AID (SSA), 11 Market Street, Edinburgh EH1 1DE; T.-031-225 5484; 031-663 9239.
Founded: 1980.
Chairman: R.C. Miquel, CBE; Chairman of Advisers: G.A. Hunter, OBE; Administrator: D.J. O'Brien.
Offers grants to competitors, especially the young, who are deemed to have the talent to represent Scotland at any sport. Financial aid is given to cover costs of travel and accommodation away from the home town, for extra coaching and higher competition.

SCOTTISH SPORTS ASSOCIATION.
See The Scottish Sports Council.

SCOTTISH SPORTS ASSOCIATION FOR THE DISABLED, c/o Honorary Secretary, 14 Gordon Court, Dalclaverhouse, Dundee; T.-0382 40263.
Honorary Secretary: Bill Fenwick.

THE SCOTTISH SPORTS COUNCIL, (SSC), 1 St Colme Street, Edinburgh EH3 6AA; T.-031-225 8411.
Founded: 1972.
Chairman: Peter Heatly, CBE; Chief Executive: J.K. Hutchison; Deputy Chief Executive: R. McDonald; Director of Administrative Division: F.N. Brydon; Director of Facilities Planning Division: I.G. Davies; Director of Sports Development Division: D.G. Casey; Head of Information Services Department: G. Shepherd.
Established by Royal Charter with the objects of fostering the knowledge and

practice of sport and physical recreation among the public at large in Scotland, and the provision of facilities. Receives annual grant-in-aid from the Government from which it provides financial assistance to governing bodies of sport, for coaching, administration and international events and to local authorities and others for sports projects including national and demonstration facilities. Undertakes research and provides research grants, provides information and advisory services and operates three national sports training centres: *Glenmore Lodge, National Outdoor Training Centre,* Aviemore. T.-Aviemore 86256. Principal: F.W.J. Harper. *Inverclyde National Sports Training Centre,* Largs. T.-Largs 674666/7. *Cumbrae National Water Sports Training Centre,* Largs. T.-Largs 674666/7. Principal (Inverclyde and Cumbrae): M.R. Barratt. The SSC has established a Scottish Sports Association (formerly Scottish Standing Conference of Sport), membership of which is open to all the governing bodies of sport and physical recreation in Scotland and other appropriate organisations. Its functions include acting as a consultative body to the Scottish Sports Council.

SCOTTISH SQUASH RACKETS ASSOCIATION, (SSRA), 18 Ainslie Place, Edinburgh EH3 6AU; T.-031-225 2502.

Founded: 1936.
President: Mr R.McG. Young; Secretary: Miss B.M. Carmichael; Director of Squash: Mr R.C. Smeaton.
Aims to foster the playing of the game in Scotland at all levels.

SCOTTISH STANDING CONFERENCE OF VOLUNTARY YOUTH ORGANISATIONS, (SSCVYO), Atholl House, 2 Canning Street, Edinburgh EH3 8EG; T.-031-229 0339.

Founded: 1942.
Chairman: Cuthbert Douse, MBE; Vice Chairmen: Ian Brown, Sheila Moyes; Chief Officer: John Knox.
The co-ordinating body for all major youth organisations in Scotland. Its concerns are youth work policy, voluntary/statutory partnership, issues affecting young people, encouragement of the participation of young people in the decision making structures in youth work, relationships with the Scottish Education Department, training, public relations and marketing of youth work, and developmental and innovatory youth work.

SCOTTISH STOCK EXCHANGE, Stock Exchange House, PO Box 141, Glasgow; T.-041-221 7060.

Founded: 1973.
Chairman: W.B. Carmichael; Vice Chairman: C.M. Brown; General Manager: J.H.B. Adams.
Maintains the Scottish trading floor of the Stock Exchange.

SCOTTISH SUB AQUA CLUB, 16 Royal Crescent, Glasgow G3 7SL; T.-041-339 9291.

Honorary Secretary: Ian Whittaker; Administrator: Elisabeth Brown.

SCOTTISH TABLE TENNIS ASSOCIATION, (STTA), 18 Ainslie Place, Edinburgh EH3 6AU; T.-031-225 3020.

Founded: 1936.
Chairman: Brian W. Christie; Deputy Chairman: David B. Stewart; Treasurer: Ian A. Dunbar; Vice Chairman, Administration: Stanley H. Buchan; Vice Chairman International Affairs: B. Denis George.
Exists for the development of table tennis in Scotland.

SCOTTISH TARTANS MUSEUM, Comrie, Perthshire PH6 2DW; T.-0764 70779.

Founded: 1975.
Administrative Secretary: Mrs Pamela Masson.
Founded by the Scottish Tartans Society. Houses the most comprehensive collection of tartans and Highland dress in the world, and a unique archive of all known tartan setts. The museum includes a working weaver's cottage where the weaving of tartan is demonstrated, and a dye garden. In its first year, it won the Museum of the Year Award for the Best Small Museum in Scotland.

SCOTTISH TARTANS SOCIETY, Scottish Tartans Museum, Davidson House, Comrie, Perthshire PH6 2DW; T.-0764 70779.

Founded: 1963.
President: The Duke of Atholl; Vice President and Chairman: Dr D.G. Teall of Teallach; Vice Chairman: Angus Whitson; Honorary Treasurer: Ruairidh Halford-Macleod; Press and Publicity Officer: Rennie McOwen.
Exists to study the origins and development of tartans and Highland dress. Maintains a

register of all known tartans and has over 1,500 patterns on record.

SCOTTISH TELEVISION, (STV), Cowcaddens, Glasgow G2 3PR; T.-041-332 9999.
Founded: 1957.
Chairman: Sir Campbell Fraser; Managing Director: William Brown; Director of Facilities: Ferdinando Coia; Director of Programmes: Gus Macdonald; Finance Director: Alan L. Montgomery; Director of Sales and Marketing: Alan Chilton; Controller, Personnel and Industrial Relations: Colin Waters; Company Secretary: Don Kinloch; Controller Public Relations: John Loch; Press Relations Manager: Brian MacLaurin; Controller News and Current Affairs: David Scott; Controller of Sport: Russell Galbraith; Controller of Drama: Robert Love; Controller Entertainment: Sandy Ross; Controller Religion and Education: Robert McPherson.
Independent television contractor for Central Scotland.

SCOTTISH TERTIARY EDUCATION ADVISORY COUNCIL, (STEAC), Room 3/112 New St Andrew's House, Edinburgh EH1 3SY; T.-031-556 8400, Ext. 4473.
Founded: 1984.
Chairman: D.M. McCallum, CBE; Vice Chairman: Dr T.R. Bone; Secretary: N. MacLeod.
Established to report on future strategy for higher education in Scotland, including the arrangements for providing institutions with financial support and the general principles which should govern relationships between universities and other institutions; and to advise the Secretary of State for Scotland on any other matters he may refer to it. The council reported in December 1985 on the first part of its remit and then began a review of the Scottish Business School. In addition to the chairman and vice chairman, it comprises seven members from higher education, industry and commerce, all of whom serve on a personal basis.

SCOTTISH THEATRE COMPANY, 37 Otago Street, Glasgow G12 8JJ; T.-041-339 8777.
Founded: 1980.
Chairman, Board of Governors: Martin Reid-Foster; Artistic Director: Tom Fleming; Administrator: Ruari McNeill.
The company's policy is to present the best of Scots and international drama, using a growing ensemble of Scottish actors and directors, and a group of distinguished guest designers, to evolve a distinctive style. Its productions have toured large and small theatres throughout Scotland, been presented at the Edinburgh Festival in 1984 and 1985 and at Mayfest in 1986. In November 1986, STC opened the Warsaw International Theatre Festival with the first production of Ane Satyre of the Thrie Estaites to have been seen outside Scotland.

SCOTTISH TOURIST BOARD, (STB), 23 Ravelston Terrace, Edinburgh EH4 3EU; T.-031 332 2433.
Founded: 1969.
Chairman: A.R. Devereux, CBE; Chief Executive: G. Hare; Director of Development: Dr J.G. Adams; Director of Marketing: N.C. Chumley; Director of Area Operations: D.J. MacIntyre; Director of External Relations: J.A. Stuart; Director of Finance: J.M. Wallace.
Established under the Development of Tourism Act. Seeks to maximise the economic benefits of tourism to Scotland by attracting holidaymakers, encouraging the development of visitor facilities, and increasing employment through tourism. Promotes Scotland through innovative marketing campaigns, carries out joint marketing schemes with the tourist trade, and provides financial assistance to stimulate new developments in tourist facilities such as hotels, heritage attractions, self catering establishments, and sporting facilities. Co-ordinates a network of area tourist boards and is introducing a new national classification and grading scheme for holiday accommodation.

SCOTTISH TRADES UNION CONGRESS, (STUC), 16 Woodlands Terrace, Glasgow G3 6DF; T.-041-332 4946.
Founded: 1897.
Chairperson: Mr R. Curran; Vice-Chairperson: Mr R. Gillespie; Treasurer: Mr J. Morrell; General Secretary: Mr C. Christie; Deputy General Secretary: Mr J. Henry; Assistant Secretaries: Mr D. Harrison, Mr W. Speirs.
Association of trade unions which meets as an assembly of delegates at a five-day annual congress in April. More than 70 unions representing a million members, and 47 local trades councils, are directly affiliated to congress. The STUC plays an influential role in social, economic and industrial issues.

The following are among the unions affiliated to the STUC. In most cases, the unions are British based, but the names and addresses given are those of the Scottish officials, and the membership figures relate to Scotland only.

Amalgamated Union of Engineering Workers (Engineering, Foundry & Construction Section), 145-165 West Regent Street, Glasgow G2 4RZ; T.-041-248 7131. Regional Officers: Mr H. McLevy (Engineering Section); Mr J. Taylor (Foundry Section, T.-0324 24459); Mr J. Connelly (Construction Section, T.-041-889 8228). Membership: 95,000.

Amalgamated Union of Engineering Workers (Technical, Administrative Supervisory Section), 420 Sauchiehall Street, Glasgow G2 3JD; T.-041-332 0247. Divisional Secretaries: Mr N. McIntosh, Mr R. Corbitt. Membership: 16,700.

Banking, Insurance and Finance Union. See separate entry.

Associated Society of Locomotive Engineers and Firemen, 38 Cumbrae Terrace, Kirkcaldy KY2 6FQ; T.-0592 266117. Scottish Secretary: Mr G. Rodger. Membership: 2,200.

Association of Lecturers in Colleges of Education in Scotland. See separate entry.

Association of Scientific, Technical & Managerial Staffs, 1 Woodlands Terrace, Glasgow G3 6DD; T.-041-331 1216. National Officer: Bryan Fox. Membership: 25,000.

British Actors' Equity Association, 65 Bath Street, Glasgow G2 2BX; T.-041-332 1669. Scottish Secretary: Mr J. Service. Membership: 1,700.

Confederation of Health Service Employees 28 Leonard Street, Perth; T.-0738 31591. Scottish Secretary: Mr C. Binks. Membership: 24,600.

Educational Institute of Scotland. See separate entry.

Electrical, Electronic, Telecommunication and Plumbing Union, Stanley House, 71 Hamilton Road, Motherwell ML1 3DG; T.-Motherwell 69316. Scottish Officer: Mr A.B. McLuckie. Membership: 29,000.

Fire Brigades Union, 4th Floor, 52 St Enoch Square, Glasgow; T.-041-221 2309. Scottish Regional Secretary: Mr A. McGuire. Membership: 4,700.

Furniture, Timber and Allied Trades Union, 46 Carlton Place, Glasgow G5 9TQ; T.-041-429 5507. Scottish Secretary: Mr R. McCallum. Membership: 3,300.

General, Municipal, Boilermakers & Allied Trades Union, Fountain House, 1-3 Woodside Crescent, Glasgow G3 7UJ; T.-041-332 8641. Regional Secretary: Mr J. Morrell. Membership: 115,000.

Iron and Steel Trades Confederation, 8 Royal Crescent, Glasgow G3 7SL; T.-041-332 8435. Divisional Officer: Mr J.C. Lewis. Membership: 5,300.

Musicians' Union, 135 Wellington Street, Glasgow G2 2XD; T.-041-248 3723. Scottish District Organiser: Mr J. Fagan. Membership: 3,000.

National Association of Schoolmasters/ Union of Women Teachers. See separate entry.

National Communications Union, Room 205, Telephone House, 357 Gorgie Road, Edinburgh EH11 2RP; T.-031-337 1345. Scottish Secretary: Mr A. Hibberd. Membership: 12,500.

National Graphical Association, 75 York Street, Glasgow G2 8JX; T.-041-221 3668. Scottish Secretary: Mr N. Dennison. Membership: 2,600.

National and Local Government Officers Association, 87-97 Bath Street, Glasgow G2 2ER; T.-041-332 0006. District Secretary: Mr C. Gallacher. Membership: 78,600.

National Union of Hosiery and Knitwear Workers, 44 Kelvingrove Street, Glasgow G3 7RZ; T.-041-333 0990. Scottish Secretary: Mr J. Robertson. Membership 3,800.

National Union of Mineworkers: Scottish Area, 5 Hillside Crescent, Edinburgh EH7 5DZ; T.-031-556 2323. Scottish Secretary: Mr E. Clarke. Membership: 6,400.

National Union of Public Employees, Douglas House, Belford Road, Edinburgh EH4 3UQ; T.-031 226 2662. Secretary: Mr R. Curran. Membership: 71,000.

National Union of Railwaymen, 36 Avon Road, Edinburgh EH4 6RD; T.-031-336 8231. Divisional Officers: Mr A. Barr; Mr C. Wynd (T.-0786 823054). Membership: 12,300.

National Union of Seamen, 9-15 James Watt Street, Glasgow G2 8NF; T.-041-248 7534. Scottish Secretary: Mr L. Green. Membership: 3,000.

National Union of Tailors and Garment Workers, Albany Chambers, 534 Sauchiehall Street, Glasgow G2 3LX; T.-041-331 2747. Scottish Secretary: Mr F. Dickinson. Membership: 10,000.

Scottish Carpet Workers Union, 46 Carlton Place, Glasgow G5 9TD; T.-041-429 5199. Secretary: Mr J. Kerr. Membership: 1,000.

Scottish Prison Officers' Association, 21 Calder Road, Saughton, Edinburgh EH11 3PF; T.-031-443 8105. Secretary: Mr J.B. Renton. Membership: 3,000.

Scottish Secondary Teachers' Association. See separate entry.

Society of Civil and Public Servants, 7 Royal Terrace, Edinburgh EH7 5AB; T.-031-556 0407. Scottish Officer: Mr P.J. Kelly. Membership: 9,000.

Society of Graphical and Allied Trades '82, 25 Newton Place, Glasgow G3; T.-041-332 1501. Branch Secretary: Mr R. Gillespie. Membership: 19,000.

Tobacco Workers' Union, 180 West Regent Street, Glasgow G2 4RW; T.-041-248 3118. Scottish Secretary: Mr R.T. Brown. Membership: 1,100.

Transport and General Workers' Union, 290 Bath Street, Glasgow G2 4LD; T.-041-332 7321. Scottish Secretary: Mr H. Wyper. Membership: 133,000.

Transport Salaried Staffs' Association, 180 Hope Street, Glasgow G2 2WE; T.-041-332 4698. Scottish Secretary: Mr R.S. King. Membership: 3,800.

Union of Communication Workers, 28 Kirkhill Road, Edinburgh EH6 5DD; T.-031-667 7083. Scottish Secretary: Mr R. Devine. Membership: 15,400.

Union of Construction, Allied Trades and Technicians, 6 Fitzroy Place, Glasgow G3 7RL; T.-041-221 4893. Scottish Secretary: Mr J. McBride. Membership: 30,300.

Union of Shop Distributive and Allied Workers, Muirfield, 342 Albert Drive, Glasgow G41 5PG; T.-041-427 6561. Scottish Divisional Officer: Mr P. McCormick. Membership: 48,000.

SCOTTISH TRAFFIC AREA, (STA), 83 Princes Street, Edinburgh EH2 2ER; T.-031-225 5494.
Founded: 1930.
Traffic Commissioner and Licensing Authority: H. McNamara; Clerk to Traffic Commissioner: D.W. McDiarmid.
Responsible for licensing of buses and heavy goods vehicles and their drivers and appeals on taxi fare scales.

SCOTTISH TRAMPOLINE ASSOCIATION, c/o Secretary, 18 Ainslie Place, Edinburgh EH3 6AU; T.-031-226 4401.
Secretary: Major John D. Beeton.

SCOTTISH TRAMWAY & TRANSPORT SOCIETY, PO Box 78, Glasgow G3 6ER.
Founded: 1952.
Chairman: Graham Ewing; Past Chairman: Stuart Little; General Secretary: John G. Fender; Treasurer: Alan Ramsay; Editor, Scottish Transport: Brian Deans; Committee Member: Ian Fraser.
Exists for research into tramway and transport history and the preservation of both tramway and other transport equipment. Publishes books on the subjects. Actively supports the National Tramway Museum at Crich, as well as supporting other projects. The society is often consulted on a wide range of transport questions.

SCOTTISH TRANSPORT GROUP, Carron House, 114-116 George Street, Edinburgh EH2 4LX; T.-031-226 7491.
Founded: 1969.
Chairman: W.T. Stevenson; Managing Director: I.S. Irwin, CBE; Secretary: John Stark.
Public authority under The Transport Act 1968. Operates the principal bus network in Scotland through the companies of the Scottish Bus Group, the main sea ferry services in the Clyde and the Western Isles under the flag of Caledonian MacBrayne Ltd, and has associated interests in travel, insurance, and in transport marketing, advertising, and public relations.

SCOTTISH TREKKING AND RIDING ASSOCIATION, c/o Secretary, Tom-na-Gairn, Trochry, by Dunkeld, Perthshire; T.-035-03 220.
Secretary: Mrs Y. Learmonth.

SCOTTISH TUG OF WAR ASSOCIATION, c/o Honorary Secretary, Strathendrick, 54 Majors Loan, Falkirk FK1 5QG; T.-0324 20768.
Honorary Secretary: Mr W. Paterson.

SCOTTISH UNITED SERVICES MUSEUM, (SUSM), The Castle, Edinburgh EH1 2NG; T.-031-225 7534.
Founded: 1930.
Keeper: S.C. Wood; Curators: W.G.F. Boag, C.J. Burnett, A.L. Carswell.
Scotland's national museum of the armed forces in their Scottish context and a component part of the National Museums of Scotland. Collections and displays feature all forms of military antiquities from the 17th to the 20th centuries and a library of 10,000 volumes is open to the public by prior arrangement.

SCOTTISH UNIVERSITIES RESEARCH AND REACTOR CENTRE, (SURRC), East Kilbride, Glasgow G75 0QU; T.-03552 20222.
Founded: 1963.
Director: Prof M.S. Baxter; Deputy-Director: Mr J.A. Izatt; Chairman of Management Committee: Prof J.S. Gillespie; Chairman of Scientific Advisory Committee: J.H. Burnett. Has a staff of 66 and is funded primarily by a

consortium of five Scottish universities to provide research and training facilities in applied nuclear and isotopic sciences. Principal activities include nuclear reactor physics and engineering, radiochemistry and trace element measurements, nuclear medicine, radioisotope manufacture, environmental radioactivity studies, nuclear waste disposal research, archaeological science and isotope geology involving dating of rocks and minerals and assessment of their origins by measuring their isotopic compositions. The institute is heavily funded by outside bodies and industry and is Scotland's prime centre of applied nuclear science expertise.

SCOTTISH URBAN ARCHAEOLOGICAL TRUST LTD, (SUAT), 55 South Methven Street, Perth PH1 5NX; T.-0738 22393.
Founded: 1982.
Chairman: Charles Murray; Company Secretary: Philip Holdsworth.
Established to understand the origins and functions of Scottish medieval towns through archaeological excavation and research. The only towns for which it is not responsible in this way are Aberdeen and Edinburgh. Work is funded by grants from the Scottish Development Department, local and regional Government, the Manpower Services Commission and commerce and industry.

THE SCOTTISH VETERANS' GARDEN CITY ASSOCIATION, (SVGCA), New Haig House, Logie Green Road, Edinburgh EH7 4HQ; T.-031-557 1188.
Founded: 1915.
Chairman: Lt Col W.B.Swan, CBE, TD, JP; Honorary Treasurer: James Grier; General Secretary: Sqn Ldr P.H. Baker, RAF (Ret).
Maintains 600 cottages throughout Scotland for the benefit of disabled ex-service and merchant navy people. Former members of police and fire services may also apply. The association is managed by voluntary local committees.

SCOTTISH VOCATIONAL EDUCATION COUNCIL (SCOTVEC), 38 Queen Street, Glasgow G1 3DY; T.-041-248 7900.
Founded: 1985.
Chairman: Dr P. Clarke; Vice Chairman: W. Hughes; Chief Executive: T.J. McCool; Depute Directors: D. Hemingway, A.F. Moore, Dr I.H. Anderson.

Set up by the Secretary of State for Scotland to replace the Scottish Technical Education Council and the Scottish Business Education Council. The council has taken over from SCOTEC and SCOTBEC responsibilities for the development of courses, the assessment of standards and the certification of students at Higher National Certificate, Higher National Diploma, postgraduate and post experience levels. In addition, SCOTVEC has been charged with the duty of administering the new National Certificate which is designed to replace all non-advanced further education and vocational education courses in Scotland. The SCOTVEC National Certificate has already replaced the SCOTBEC non-advanced awards up to the level of SNC and SND, and is now replacing the majority of SCOTEC non-advanced awards up to ONC and OND level and will gradually replace all the City and Guilds craft courses in Scottish colleges.

SCOTTISH VOLLEYBALL ASSOCIATION, Castlecliff Workshops, 25 Johnston Terrace, Edinburgh EH1 2NH.
General Secretary: Ian McGowan; Technical Director: N. Moody; Executive Officer: Liz Fowler.

SCOTTISH WAR ON WANT, (SWOW), 266 Clyde Street, Glasgow G1 4JH; T.-041-204 1315.
Founded: 1951.
Scottish Organiser: Laurie Gardner; Scottish Administrator: Linda Gray; Chairperson: Mark Lazarowicz; Treasurer: Christine Hamilton.
SWOW is a campaign against world poverty, combining development projects with research, education and campaigns to shape a better future. It is associated to War on Want and raises funds and supports development projects throughout the world.

SCOTTISH WATER SKI ASSOCIATION, (SWSA), 18 Ainslie Place, Edinburgh EH3 6AU; T.-031-226 4401.
Chairman: John Holden; Secretary: Mary Smee; Treasurer: June Holden.
Aims to promote and expand water skiing in Scotland and improve safety for everyone. Has 21 affiliated clubs with around 500 members in total. Has a racing section, a tournament section and a barefooting section. Coaching is available at all levels.

SCOTTISH WHOLESALE DRUGGISTS ASSOCIATION, (SWDA), Smiths Place House, Leith Walk, Edinburgh EH6 8NU; T.-031-554 1551.
Chairman: G. Haselden; Secretary: C.C. Cumming.
Exists for the discussion amongst members of matters of common interest to those engaged in the wholesale drug trade in Scotland. Aims to furnish its members with advice, information and assistance on technical, legal and other matters. Promotes social activities amongst its members.

SCOTTISH WILD LAND GROUP, (SWLG), 93 Queen Street, Alva, Clackmannanshire FK12 5AH; T.-0259 60102.
Founded: 1982.
Co-ordinator: Terry Smith.
Pressure group concerned with the promotion of the conservation of Scotland's wild land by increasing public awareness of the problems and by pressing for the adoption of planning policies which recognise conservation as a relevant part of the economy, compatible with appropriate development, provision of long-term employment and thriving rural communities. Membership is open to all individuals. A quarterly magazine *Wild Land News* is free to members.

SCOTTISH WILDLIFE TRUST, (SWT), 25 Johnston Terrace, Edinburgh EH1 2NH; T.-031-226 4602.
Founded: 1964.
Chief Executive: John R. Baldwin.
The national voluntary body involved in the conservation of all forms of wildlife and their habitats in Scotland. Establishes and manages wildlife reserves, carries out surveys of wildlife and their distribution, and advises public and private landowners on wildlife conservation. Has local branches and representatives throughout Scotland. Members can attend lectures and films in winter, outings in the summer, and can join in practical conservation work at all times. Produces a magazine *Scottish Wildlife* which is published three times a year and is issued to SWT members. Membership: over 8,000.

SCOTTISH WIREWORK MANUFACTURERS ASSOCIATION, (SWMA), 36 Renfield Street, Glasgow G2 1BD; T.-041-248 6161.
Secretary: A. Ferrie.

SCOTTISH WOMEN'S AID, 11 St Colme Street, Edinburgh; T.-031-225 8011.
Founded: 1975.
Voluntary organisation which works with 32 local women's aid groups in Scotland providing advide, support, and refuge for battered women and their children. The national office concentrates on children, training, education and information, the law and housing with regard to battered women.

SCOTTISH WOMEN'S AMATEUR ATHLETIC ASSOCIATION, (SWAAA), 18 Ainslie Place, Edinburgh EH3 6AU; T.-031-226 4401.
Founded: 1930.
President: Mrs Isabel Robertson; Vice-president: Mrs Hilda Everett; Honorary Secretary: Mrs Isabell Docherty; Honorary Treasurer: Mrs Chris Gisbey; Honorary Championship Secretary: Mrs Ruth Booth; Honorary Coaching Secretary: Mrs Aileen Samuels.
Object is to foster, encourage and control women's amateur athletics in Scotland. Affiliated club membership: 79.

SCOTTISH WOMEN'S BOWLING ASSOCIATION, c/o Secretary, 55A Esplanade, Greenock PA16 7SD; T.-0475 24140.
Secretary: Mrs Eleanor Allan.

SCOTTISH WOMEN'S CROSS COUNTRY AND ROAD RUNNING ASSOCIATION, 18 Ainslie Place, Edinburgh EH3 6AU; T.-031-226 4401.
Secretary: Mrs J. Ward.

SCOTTISH WOMEN'S FOOTBALL ASSOCIATION, c/o Honorary Secretary, 26 Oak Grove, Craigshill, Livingston, West Lothian EH54 5JD; T.-0506 37613.
Honorary Secretary: Miss Elizabeth Creamer.

SCOTTISH WOMEN'S HOCKEY ASSOCIATION, (SWHA), 18 Ainslie Place, Edinburgh EH3 6AU; T.-031-226 4401.
Founded: 1900.
President: Mrs Wendy McLean; Vice-presidents: Miss Ann Ferguson, Mrs Gina Logan; Honorary Treasurer: Miss Jenny Lorimer; Honorary Match Secretary: Mrs Doreen

Barclay; Honorary Indoor Hockey Match Secretary: Miss Davina Crawford.
The governing body for all aspects of women's hockey in Scotland. Objects are to foster and to encourage the game of hockey in Scotland and to do all other things necessary and desirable for the promotion of the interests of the game. There are 120 clubs in membership, with 172 teams and a total registration of over 3,000 members. Clubs are grouped into seven district associations and these districts have a fair degree of autonomy in the running of their own affairs and send representatives to the association's domestic committee.

SCOTTISH WOMEN'S INDOOR BOWLING ASSOCIATION, c/o Secretary, 1 Underwood Road, Burnside, Rutherglen, Glasgow G73 3TE.

Secretary: Mrs R. Thompson.

SCOTTISH WOMEN'S RURAL INSTITUTES, (SWRI), 42 Heriot Row, Edinburgh EH3 6ES; T.-031-225 1724.

Founded: 1917.
Chairman: Mrs I.D. MacKenzie; Vice-chairmen: Mrs B. Kelly, Mrs M. Mackie; Honorary Treasurer: Mrs N. Whamond.
Objects are: to provide social, educational and recreational opportunities for those who live and work in the country or are interested in country life; to study home economics and improve the amenities of the home; to encourage the production of home grown foods and use them to the best advantage; to encourage home and local industries, both individual and co-operative, and uphold high standards of craftsmanship; to consider family welfare and any matters which affect the home; to consider citizenship and any matters which affect the community; to help to preserve the beauties and traditions of rural Scotland and to work for peace and international understanding and goodwill.

SCOTTISH WOOLLEN INDUSTRY, (SWI), 45 Moray Place, Edinburgh EH3 6EQ; T.-031-229 3149.

Founded: 1984.
Chairman: R.F. Gray; Vice-chairman: J.D. Birchall; Director: Fergus M. Wood; Training and Industrial Relations Officer: W.J.R. Ritchie; Promotions Manager: Anne Ritchie.
Formed from five organisations. Represents the weaving, spinning and associated companies in Scotland, and has as its principal role the corporate promotion of the indus-

try. Has two main arms: the Training and Industrial Relations Council and a publicity council. In addition, a technical committee looks after the research and technical needs of the industry. Has 48 members with a total workforce of around 4,500.

SCOTTISH YOUTH HOSTELS ASSOCIATION, (SYHA), 7 Glebe Crescent, Stirling FK8 2JA; T.-0786 72821.

Founded: 1931.
Honorary Presidents: W.R. Ballantyne, OBE, JP, The Rt Hon Lord Fraser of Tullybelton, PC; Chairman: J.P. Lawson; Vice-chairman: J.L. Taylor; Honorary Treasurer: J.S. Dickson; General Secretary: J. Martin.
Maintains 80 youth hostels throughout Scotland varying from cottages to castles and providing inexpensive accommodation for the young and 'young at heart'. In summer, the association's Breakaway Holiday programme offers a wide range of activity holidays including sailing, windsurfing and pony trekking. In winter, the association offers downhill and cross-country ski courses on the Cairngorm and Glenshee slopes. Offers conference facilities, a rent-a-hostel scheme for groups and family rooms at certain hostels.

SCOTTISH YOUTH THEATRE, (SYT), 48 Albany Street, Edinburgh EH1 3QR; T.-031-557 2224/0962.

Founded: 1977.
Chairman: Dr Tom Kinninmont; Vice Chairman: Andrew McCallum; Artistic Director: Robin Peoples; Administrator: Carolyn Lappin.
Exists to provide and assist with the provision of drama activities for young people all over Scotland, aged between 12 and 21. Courses run throughout the year include a five week summer festival, stage management and acting courses, a young playwrights' scheme, and television and radio courses. Workshop tutors are available to conduct classes in all aspects of theatre, dance, mime, drama, clowning, stage fighting etc at any time of the year in all parts of the country.

THE SCOUT ASSOCIATION, THE SCOTTISH COUNCIL OF, 18 Hanover Street, Edinburgh EH2 2QN; T.-031-226 7375.

Founded: 1908.
President: The Lord Forbes, KBE, JP; Chief Commissioner of Scotland: W. Garth Morrison; Chairman of the Scottish Committee:

G.J. Wilson; Honorary Treasurer: F.A. Ainslie; Secretary: R. Hendy Procter.

The association is registered as an educational charity and its aim is to help young people to develop in mind, body and spirit so that wherever they are, they will act as responsible, caring members of the community. This is achieved through a progressive training programme which combines adventure, challenge and enjoyment and which is based on the scout promise and law, guided by adult leaders.

SCRIPTURE UNION - SCOTLAND, 9 Canal Street, Glasgow G4 OAB; T.-041-332 1162.
Founded: 1867.
Chairman: C.P. Kimber; Honorary Treasurer: J.N. Gibson; General Secretary: Rev J.M.F. Butler.
Organisation of Christian groups in schools, camps and missions for study, fellowship and witness. Provides training for Sunday school teachers and youth leaders. Publishes and distributes materials for personal Bible study and church use. Total staff (full and part-time): 46.

SEA FISH INDUSTRY AUTHORITY, Sea Fisheries House, 10 Young Street, Edinburgh EH2 4JQ; T.-031-225 2515.
Founded: 1981.
Chairman: J. Philip Rettie, TD; Deputy Chairman: B. Davies; Chief Executive: J.C.H. Richman; Secretary: R. Alastair Davie.
A statutory body concerned with everything in the industry from catchers to consumers.

SENSE-IN-SCOTLAND. See National Deaf Blind and Rubella Association.

7:84 THEATRE COMPANY SCOTLAND, 31 Albany Street, Edinburgh EH1 3QN; T.-031-557 2442.
Founded: 1973.
Artistic Director: John McGrath.
The company's first production was *The Cheviot, The Stag and The Black, Black Oil.* Since then, it has performed more than 20 productions throughout Scotland. 7:84 has established a theatre in Scotland which aims to present the realities of working class life and history directly to working class audiences. It has its roots in the popular tradition of entertainment.

THE 1745 ASSOCIATION, c/o The Secretary, Ferry Cottage, Corran, Ardgour, Fort William PH33 7AA; **T.-085 55 306.**
Founded: 1947.
Chairman: Baron Alastair Livingstone of Lismore; Secretary: Miss Christian W.H. Aikman; Treasurer: Rev Kenneth E. Wigston; Editor: Miss Barbara Fairweather; Vice-chairman: Major S.F. MacDonald Lockhart of Lee.
Marks the sites of Jacobite history. Preserves and disseminates articles and notes dealing with Jacobite history. Furthers the study of the history of the House of Stuart and the Jacobite period. Arranges an annual gathering within Scotland at a different venue each year. Issues quarterly notes to members. The association is non-political and non-sectarian.

SHELTER-SCOTTISH CAMPAIGN FOR THE HOMELESS, 65 Cockburn Street, Edinburgh EH1 1BU; T.-031-226 6347.
Founded: 1968.
Chairman, Scottish Advisory Council: Dr Peter Robson; Director: Noel Dolan; Depute Director: Martyn Evans.
Campaigns on behalf of Scotland's homeless and badly housed. Uses the casework experience of Shelter's three housing aid centres, develops local projects and conducts research and educational work.

SHETLAND CHAMBER OF COMMERCE, 122 Commercial Street, Lerwick ZE1 0EX; T.-Lerwick 4739.
Founded: 1974.
Chairman: Mr J. Boxwell; Secretary: Mrs V.J. Cousins.

SHETLAND FISHERMEN'S ASSOCIATION, (SFA), 14 Alexandra Buildings, Lerwick, Shetland ZE1 0LL; T.-0595 3197.
Secretary: J.H. Goodlad; Chairman: R.B. Laurenson; Vice-chairman: J. Anderson.
A long established organisation which represents all full-time fishermen in Shetland. Has around 100 member vessels. Acts as a pressure group representing the views of its members on fisheries matters to Government bodies at all levels. Policy is determined by an executive committee of 17 fishermen who are elected annually on a geographical basis throughout the islands.

SHETLAND FISH PRODUCERS ORGANISATION LTD, (SFPO), 14 Alexandra Buildings, Lerwick, Shetland ZE1 0LL; T.-0595 3197.

Founded: 1982.
Chief Executive: John H. Goodlad; Chairman: David Anderson; Vice Chairmen: James Fullerton (White Fish), David Hutchison (Pelagic).
In common with other producers' organisations, the primary concern is with administering the EEC market support system which provides financial compensation in respect of fish which fail to reach a minimum price. Responsible for the orderly management of the Shetland fishing fleet, of which all the larger Shetland vessels are members. Policy is determined by 12 directors who are representative of, and elected by, the member vessels.

SHETLAND HEALTH BOARD, 28 Burgh Road, Lerwick, Shetland ZE1 0QP.
Founded: 1974.
Chairman: Mrs F. Grains; General Manager: Mr D.C. March; Treasurer: Mr D.P.P. Eva; Chief Administrative Medical Officer: Dr Jill Macdonald; Chief Administrative Nursing Officer: Mrs M. Henderson; Chief Administrative Dental Officer: Mr J. Allan.
Provides health services in Shetland.

SHETLAND ISLANDS COUNCIL, Town Hall, Lerwick, Shetland; T.-Lerwick 3535.
Founded: 1974.
Convener: E. Thomason; Director of Administration: Patrick B. Regan; Director of Construction: William E. Smith; Director of Design and Technical Services: Bryan Davison; Director of Education: Robin A. Barnes; Director of Environmental Health and Trading Standards: Douglas C. Smith; Director of Finance: Malcolm E. Green; Director of Housing: James McConville; Director of Leisure and Recreation: John P. Nicolson; Director of Planning: Gordon L. Mann; Director of Ports and Harbours: Albert M. Flett; Director of Research and Development: John M. Burgess; Director of Social Work: Peter Malcolmson.
Political composition of council: Independent 21, Labour 4. Population of area: 23,440.

THE SHETLAND PONY STUD-BOOK SOCIETY, 8 Whinfield Road, Montrose, Angus DD10 8SA; T.-0674 73148.
Founded: 1890.
President: Major N.H. Hambro; Vice-president: I.G. Thomson; Secretary and Treasurer: D.M. Patterson.
Collects, verifies and publishes the pedigrees of Shetland ponies. Maintains the unimpaired purity of the breed and promotes the breeding of Shetland ponies. A volume of the stud-book is published each year and the society produces an annual journal and two newsletters per annum.
Membership: 1,500 in the United Kingdom and overseas.

SHETLAND TOURIST ORGANISATION, Information Centre, Lerwick ZE1 0LU; T.-0595 3434.
Founded: 1969.
Chairman: A.R. Inkster; Director of Tourism: M.S. Mullay.
Promotes tourism in Shetland.

SKYE AND LOCHALSH DISTRICT COUNCIL, Park Road, Portree, Isle of Skye IV51 9EP; T.-0478 2341.
Founded: 1974.
Chairman: John F. Munro; Chief Executive: David H. Noble; Director of Finance and Depute Chief Executive: Kenneth Goddard; Director of Environmental Health: Norman Gillies.
Political composition of council: Independent 10, SDP 1. Population of district: 11,300.

SOCIAL DEMOCRATIC PARTY, COUNCIL FOR SCOTLAND, 5 Royal Exchange Square, Glasgow G1 3AH; T.-041-221 8871.
Founded: 1981.
Chairman: Charles Kennedy, MP; Vice-chairman: Moira Craig; Secretary: Sheila Wells; Treasurer: Hilary Campbell; Scottish Organiser: Arthur Adair.
Branch of the United Kingdom political party.

SOCIETY OF ANTIQUARIES OF SCOTLAND, The Royal Museum of Scotland, Queen Street, Edinburgh EH2 1JD; T.-031-225 7534, Ext. 327.
Founded: 1780.
President: Prof L. Alcock; Secretary: Dr T.F. Watkins; Treasurer: R.J. Mercer.
Exists for the study of the antiquities and history of Scotland. Has published a substantial volume of proceedings almost annually since 1855, and has recently initiated a monograph series, the purpose of both of these being to present the results of current research. Sponsorship of research is a major concern and grants are made each year for a variety of projects. The society meets in Edinburgh and Aberdeen to hear papers on a wide range of topics.

Each year, six Rhind lectures are given by an eminent authority and normally there is at least one day conference. Membership: around 2,400.

SOCIETY OF MASTER PRINTERS OF SCOTLAND, (SMPS), Edinburgh House, 3-11 North St Andrew Street, Edinburgh EH2 1JU; T.-031-557 3600.

Founded: 1910.
President: Mr C.I. McAulay; Vice President: Mr D.C. McCormick; Director: Mr J.B. Raeburn.
The employers' organisation and trade association for the printing industry in Scotland. Through its representative role, it seeks to promote and protect the interests of the industry and its 240 member firms and it liaises with, and is consulted by, central and local Government, the CBI and related employer organisations, the relevant trade unions, educational bodies and others. Services to members include industrial relations, education and training, management accounting, commercial and advisory services.

SOCIETY OF SOLICITORS IN THE SUPREME COURTS OF SCOTLAND, SSC Library, Parliament House, Edinburgh EH1; T.-031-556 4070.

Founded: 1784.
President: Mark Sischy; Vice-president: Alistair J. Robertson; Secretary: Alistair R. Brownlie; Treasurer: David A. Lamb; Fiscal: J.I. Wilson; Librarian: J. Haldane Tait.
Consists of some 250 solicitors mostly, but not all, in the vicinity of Edinburgh, whose work lies principally in the supreme courts of Scotland - the Court of Session and the High Court of Justiciary. As part of the College of Justice in Scotland, the society encourages the development of Scots law, the practice of law and the contribution of solicitors to law and public life.

SOCIETY OF WRITERS TO HM SIGNET, Signet Library, Parliament Square, Edinburgh EH1 1RF; T.-031 225 4923.

Founded: 1594.
Keeper of the Signet: The Earl of Wemyss and March, KT; Deputy Keeper: Peter C. Millar; Treasurer: Ian T. Johnstone; Clerk: Andrew M. Kerr.
Originally, the Signet was the private seal of the early Stuart kings, and the Writers to the Signet were those authorised to supervise its use and, later, to act as clerks to the courts. The earliest recorded use of the Signet was in 1369, but the society did not take definite shape until 1594, when the King's secretary, as Keeper of the Signet, granted commissions to a deputy keeper and 18 other writers. The function of the society has changed much since then, but every summons initiating an action in the Court of Session still 'passes the Signet', meaning that it is stamped with the Royal seal. The society is consulted on many legal matters and is represented on the governing bodies of many organisations. Has around 850 members, most being solicitors in private practice in Edinburgh. The society is particularly noted for its ownership of the Signet Library, one of the finest Georgian buildings in the country.

SOLWAY RIVER PURIFICATION BOARD, Rivers House, Irongray Road, Dumfries DG2 0JE; T.-0387 720502.

Founded: 1954.
Director: Mr C.P. James; Clerk and Treasurer: Mr W.W. Japp.
A pollution prevention authority and also the hydrological authority for its area. Responsible for promoting the cleanliness of rivers and tidal waters.

SOUTH FIFE ENTERPRISE TRUST LTD, 4 Bridge Street, Dunfermline, Fife KY12 8DA; T.-0383 739279.

Director: Mr D. Blues.

SOUTH OF SCOTLAND CHAMBER OF COMMERCE, 19 Buccleuch Street, Hawick, Roxburghshire; T.-0450 72267/8.

Founded: 1861.
Secretary: A.L. Rintoul.

SOUTH OF SCOTLAND ELECTRICITY BOARD, (SSEB), Cathcart House, Spean Street, Glasgow G44 4BE; T.-041-637 7177.

Founded: 1955.
Chairman: Donald Miller; Deputy Chairman: Dr Ian M.H. Preston; Director of Engineering: Dr A.F. Pexton; Director of Finance and Commercial Development: G.H. Reid.
The board's remit is to provide a secure, safe and economical supply of electricity to over 1.6 million domestic, commercial and industrial customers in the South of Scotland. The major functional areas are power generation, transmission and distribution of electricity, and commercial and accounting activities. The board has 16 power stations,

over 80,000 kilometres of lines and cables, 36,800 substations, and 11,800 employees. Turnover exceeds £887 million.

SPRINGBURN COLLEGE, 110 Flemington Street, Glasgow G21 4BX; T.-041-558 9001.
Founded: 1962.
Principal: A.J. Ironside; Depute Principal: N. MacNicol; Registrar: R.S. Masson.
College of further education with 2,500 students.

STEVENSON COLLEGE OF FURTHER EDUCATION, Bankhead Avenue, Edinburgh EH11 4DE; T.-031-453 6161.
Founded: 1970.
Principal: David Dick, OBE; Depute Principal: Ian Miller.
College of further education.

STEWARTRY DISTRICT COUNCIL, Council Offices, Kirkcudbright DG6 4JG; T.-0557 30291.
Founded: 1974.
Convener: John Nelson; Chief Executive and Director of Administration: W.L. Dick-Smith, OBE; Director of Finance and Housing: John C. Howie; Director of Technical Services: Alexander Strachan; Director of Environmental Health: W.P. Davidson.
Non-political authority, 12 members. Population of district: 23,058.

STIRLING DISTRICT COUNCIL, Municipal Buildings, Stirling FK8 2HU; T.-0786 79000.
Founded: 1974.
Convener: John Wyles; Chief Executive: Robert Black; Director of Development: Maurice Dobson; Director of Environmental Health: Charles Gibson; Director of Financial Services: Ronald Bryson; Director of Housing: David Forsyth; Director of Leisure and Recreation: Stuart Mackenzie.
Political composition of council: Labour 10, Conservative 9, Independent 1. Population of district: 81,147.

STIRLING ENTERPRISE PARK, John Player Building, Stirling FK7 7RP; T.-0786 63416.
Director: Derek Gavin.
Local enterprise trust.

STIRLING, UNIVERSITY OF, Stirling FK9 4LA; T.-0786 73171.
Founded: 1967.

Chancellor: Sir Montague Finniston; Principal and Vice-chancellor: Dr A.J. Forty; Deputy Principal: Prof J. Trainer; University Secretary: R.G. Bomont; Chairman of the Board of Studies for Arts: Prof S.I.J. Lockerbie; Chairman of the Board of Studies for Education: Prof J.H. Duthie; Chairman of the Board of Studies for Management and Social Sciences: Prof D.H. Allen; Chairman of the Board of Studies for Science: Prof L.B. Wilson.
Degrees granted are either BA or BSc. The teaching year is divided into two semesters of about 15 weeks each, with two intervening vacation periods. The units of study which make up the courses last one semester instead of the year-long courses used in most other universities. The use of this shorter unit of study means that it is much easier for a student to change the direction of his or her studies if so desired. Has 2,324 undergraduates.

STOW COLLEGE, 43 Shamrock Street, Glasgow G4 9LD; T.-041-332 1786.
Founded: 1934.
Chairman of College Council: J. Stephen; Principal: Dr D.W. Snaith; Depute Principal: I. McKenzie Smith; Registrar: S. Stevenson.
College of further education serving the central and eastern districts of Glasgow with community and further general education. The college is a principal centre of technical education for Strathclyde and neighbouring regions. Full-time, part-time and evening courses are offered. Has 3,425 students.

STRATHCLYDE PASSENGER TRANSPORT EXECUTIVE, Consort House, 12 West George Street, Glasgow G2 4PF; T.-041-332 6811.
Founded: 1973.
Director General: Stephen R. Lockley; Director (Technical Services and Development): Hamish R. Taylor; Director (Finance and Personnel): John McNamee; Secretary and Legal Adviser: Gavin J.F. Mason.
Exists for the co-ordination of public transport in Strathclyde and the operation of the Glasgow underground system.

STRATHCLYDE RAPE CRISIS CENTRE, (SRCC), PO Box 53, Glasgow G2; T.-041-221 8448.
Founded: 1976.
A collective of 20 women who, on a voluntary basis, take equal responsibility for the running of the centre. Offers free and confi-

dential advice for women and girls who have been raped or sexually assaulted, no matter when or how. Can be contacted by telephone or letter and further help can be given via personal contact if necessary.

STRATHCLYDE REGIONAL COUNCIL, Strathclyde House, 20 India Street, Charing Cross, Glasgow G2 4PF; T.-041-204 2900.

Founded: 1974.
Convener: James Jennings; Vice Convener: David M. Sanderson; Leader of the Council: Charles Gray; Chief Executive: Robert Calderwood; Senior Depute: Ian S. McFarlane; Director of Architectural and Related Services: Jack C. McDougall; Head of Consumer and Trading Standards: Clive A. Howard-Luck; Chief Constable: Alexander K. Sloan; Head of Direct Works: Campbell J. McKelvie; Director of Education: Edward Miller; Head of Estates: Neil G. MacFarlane; Director of Finance: Archibald Gillespie; Firemaster: Clive B. Halliday; Director of Personnel and Management Services: James M. Weir; Director General, Passenger Transport Executive: Stephen R. Lockly; Director of Physical Planning: Robert G. Maund; Head of Public Relations: Henry D.M. Dutch; Reporter to Children's Panel: F.J. Kennedy; Director of Roads: William S. McAlonan; Director of Sewerage: William T. Greer; Director of Social Work: Frederick E. Edwards; Director of Water: William T. Devenay.
Responsible for providing major local authority services to 2.383 million people, just under half the population in Scotland. With 103 elected members and a staff of 110,000, it is the largest regional council in the country. Its 1986-87 budget is £1,854 million more than half of which is spent on education. Other major responsibilities include highways and transportation, social work, and police and fire. Political composition: Labour 87, Conservative 6, Alliance 5, SNP 3, Independent 2.

STRATHCLYDE, UNIVERSITY OF, 16 Richmond Street, Glasgow G1 1XQ; T.-041-552 4400.

Founded: 1964.
Chancellor: Rt Hon The Lord Todd of Trumpington, OM; Principal and Vice-chancellor: Dr Graham Hills; Vice-principal: Prof David J. Tedford; Deputy Principals: Prof Michael J. Baker, TD, Prof William C. Bowman; Dean of the Faculty of Engineering: Prof J.T. Webster; Dean of the Faculty of Science: Prof J.N. Sherwood; Dean of the Faculty of

Arts and Social Studies: Dr G. Gordon; Dean of Strathclyde Business School: Prof N. Hood; Registrar and Secretary: David W.J. Morrell.
The university, with a full-time student population of 7,500, is a leading centre of teaching and research in engineering, the sciences, business studies, the arts and social studies. In the belief that Britain's industrial recovery depends on a skilled, educated workforce, Strathclyde is committed to providing professional and vocational education and to developing and maintaining contact with industry and commerce.

STRATHKELVIN DISTRICT COUNCIL, PO Box 4, Tom Johnston House, Civic Way, Kirkintilloch, Glasgow G66 4TJ; T.-041-776 7171.

Founded: 1974.
Provost: Robert M. Coyle, JP; Chief Executive Officer/Director of Environmental Services: C. Mallon; Director of Administration: W.B. Kilgour; Director of Finance: D. Brant; Director of Housing Services: C. Rowbury; Director of Personnel: J.M. Rennie; Director of Leisure and Recreation: W.H. Barrow; Director of Planning and Development: R.G. Dent.
Political composition of council: Labour 11, Conservative 3, SDP/Liberal Alliance: 1. Population of district: 89,357.

STRATHKELVIN ENTERPRISE TRUST, Rochdale Place, Kirkintilloch; T.-041-777 7171.

Director: Donald MacInnes.

STRATHSPEY RAILWAY ASSOCIATION, The Station, Boat of Garten, Inverness-shire PH24 3BH; T.-Boat of Garten 692.

Founded: 1972.
Chairman: L.D.M. Grant; Secretary: D.M. Norris.
Supports the Strathspey Railway Company in the operation of trains between Aviemore and Boat of Garten. Raises funds to operate a railway operated primarily by steam traction.

SUNDAY MAIL, 40 Anderston Quay, Glasgow G3 8DA; T.-041-248 7000.

Founded: 1919.
Editor: Endell Laird.
Sunday newspaper circulating throughout Scotland.

SUNDAY POST, Courier Buildings,

Dundee DD1 9QJ; T.-0382 23131.
Founded: 1920.
Editor: William Anderson.
Sunday newspaper circulating throughout
Scotland.

**SUSTRANS (Scottish Railway Path
Project), 53 Cochrane Street,
Glasgow G1 1HL; T.-041-552 8241.**
Charitable company advising on and pro-
moting the construction of shared
pedestrian/cycle facilities. Current pro-
jects: Lochwinnoch loop line and Callander-
Killin route.

**SUTHERLAND DISTRICT COUNCIL,
District Offices, Golspie, Sutherland;
T.-Golspie 3192.**
Founded: 1974.
Chairman: Mrs L. Mackenzie; Chief Execu-
tive and Director of Administration: D.W.
Martin; Director of Finance: W. Sutherland;
Director of Technical and Housing Services:
G. Durrand; Director of Environmental
Health: F. Hayward.
Non-political authority, 14 members.
Population of district: 13,000.

T

**TALBOT RICE GALLERY, Old Col-
lege, South Bridge, Edinburgh EH8
9YL; T.-031-667 1011, Ext. 4308.**
Founded: 1970.
Curator: Dr J.D. Macmillan; Gallery Assistant: Bill Hare; Gallery Attendant: Mr J.
Archibald; Gallery Secretary: Mrs M.I.
Macnamara.
Contains the University of Edinburgh's art
gallery, consisting of two rooms: the
Georgian Playfair gallery and the modern
exhibition gallery. The gallery also provides
a reading room for art magazines and some
studio space for students. The Playfair gallery contains the Torrie collection of old
master paintings and bronzes including the
bronze horse made around the late 16th
century by Florentine sculptor Giam-
bologna which is the finest Renaissance
bronze in Scotland. The exhibition gallery is
designed to take changing exhibitions
which range in character from the historical
to the contemporary.

**TAY RIVER PURIFICATION
BOARD, 1 South Street, Perth PH2
8NJ; T.-Perth 27989.**
Founded: 1975.
Chairman: R.A. Pullar, JP; Director: J.A.
Rangeley; Depute Director: D.F. Miller;

Clerk: J.A. Wallace; Treasurer: I.B. McIver.
River pollution prevention and hydrometric
authority for an area consisting of the catch-
ment areas of the Rivers Earn, Eden, Lunan,
North Esk, South Esk, Tay and Dighty
Water.

**TAYSIDE COMMUNITY RELA-
TIONS COUNCIL, 6 North Isla Street,
Dundee; T.-0382 25802.**
Founded: 1973.
Chairman: Dr S. Sarkar; Secretary: Mrs M.K.
Faulkner.
Exists to promote good community relations
and equality of opportunity, especially in
education, employment and housing.

**TAYSIDE HEALTH BOARD, 'Ver-
nonholme', Riverside Drive, Dundee
DD1 9NL; T.-0382 645151.**
Founded: 1974.
Chairman: Mr D.B. Grant; General Manager:
Dr R.C. Graham; Chief Administrator and
Secretary: Mr T.G. Clark; Treasurer: Mr J.R.
Hudson; Chief Area Nursing Officer: Miss
M.M. Shand; Chief Administrative Medical
Officer: Dr R.G. Small.
Responsible for administration and
management of the health services within
the area of Tayside Region. Certain acute
services are provided for some adjacent
parts of neighbouring areas, giving a total
population to be served of over 430,000.
There are 28 hospitals in Tayside, with a
total of around 5,400 beds, and a total staff,
including the community services, of 13,500.

**TAYSIDE REGIONAL COUNCIL,
Tayside House, 28 Crichton Street,
Dundee; T.-0382 23281.**
Founded: 1974.
Convener: John McAllion; Vice-convener:
Mrs Margo H. Lennie; Leader of Administra-
tion: Ronald Tosh; Chief Executive: J.
Wallace; Depute Chief Executive: A.G.
Mitchell; Director of Education: D. Robert-
son; Director of Finance: I. McIver; Firemas-
ter: A. Winton; Director of Information
Processing Services: A. Allan; Director of
Manpower Services: P. Toal; Director of
Planning: H. Ramsay; Chief Constable: J.
Bowman; Director of Property Services: R.
Leslie; Director of Roads and Transport: J.F.
White; Director of Social Work: S. Moxley;
Director of Trading Standards: A. Mitchell;
Director of Water Services: A. Cockburn.
Political composition of council: Labour 20,
Conservative 14, SNP 9, Independent 2,
Liberal/Alliance 1. Population of region
394,322.

TELFORD COLLEGE OF FURTHER EDUCATION, Crewe Toll, Edinburgh EH4 2NZ; T.-031-332 2491.
Founded: 1968.
Principal: Dr Michael A. Taylor; Depute Principal: Terry Davies; Assistant Principals: George B. Wann, John M. Thomson.
Contains 13 departments. More than 11,000 students enrolled in the session 1986-87, 8,000 of whom attend day classes. While more advanced work is done in specialist fields of most departments, the major part of the college work is concerned with easing the transition from school into employment and helping the young entrant in his or her chosen career in a wide range of jobs in industry and commerce.

TENANT PARTICIPATION ADVISORY SERVICE, (TPAS), 20-24 St Andrew's Street, Glasgow G1 5PD; T.-041-552 3633.
Founded: 1980.
Director: Sheila Adamson; Development Officer: Sandra Wilson; Information Worker: Moira Harte; Administrative Secretary: Karen MacLeod.
A membership organisation which is the only housing agency in Scotland which works for both landlords and tenants. Negotiates between council and tenant over issues of joint concern, provides training and information for tenants' associations and tenants' federations and training sessions for councillors and housing officials. Produces notes and information packs, and provides videos, a library service and meeting areas for members' use.

THIRD EYE CENTRE, 350 Sauchiehall Street, Glasgow G2 3JD; T.-041-332 7521.
Chairman: Richard Clark; Director: Chris Carrell; Administrator: Erika King.
Arts centre specialising in contemporary art. Studio theatre, bookshop, vegetarian cafe, and bar, as well as two main galleries.

THISTLE AWARD SCHEME, 18 Ainslie Place, Edinburgh EH3 6AU; T.-031-226 4401.
Founded: 1971.
Administrator: Mrs Edna Turner.
Athletic award scheme based on 'personal best' system incorporating combined results for track and field events. A target is set for each age group (ranging from 9 to over 50). An average of 12,000 awards (gold, silver, bronze, blue) are made throughout Scotland each year. Operated in schools, clubs, youth organisations, sports centres. The Thistle Award Committee comprises members of three parent bodies (Scottish Women's Amateur Athletic Association, Scottish Amateur Athletic Association, Scottish Schools' Athletics Association).

THE THISTLE FOUNDATION, 27A Walker Street, Edinburgh EH3 7HX; T.-031-225 7282.
Director: Philip Croft.
A major Scottish charity providing accommodation and care for physically disabled people, with over 100 purpose-built houses for families and a hostel for the single disabled where full care is provided. A respite care unit offers short stay accommodation to physically disabled people on a regular basis, thereby giving relatives a break from continuous caring. Twenty-four hour medical and nursing care, physiotherapy, occupational therapy and extensive recreational facilities are available to all residents.

THURSO TECHNICAL COLLEGE, Ormlie Road, Thurso, Caithness KW14 7EE; T.-0847 66161.
Founded: 1959.
Principal: Colin M. MacLean; Depute Principal: William J. Donald.
Built primarily to provide education and training for personnel at Dounreay Experimental Reactor Establishment nearby. Now provides a wider range of courses, including agriculture, business and secretarial studies, carpentry and joinery, catering, computing, electrical installation, health studies, modern languages, and motor vehicle work.

TRANSPORT USERS CONSULTATIVE COMMITTEE FOR SCOTLAND, 249 West George Street, Glasgow G2 4QE; T.-041-221 7760.
Founded: 1947.
Secretary: Mr K. Cairns.
Statutory body which represents users of British Rail (Scottish Region) and ferry services operated by Caledonian MacBrayne Ltd. Required to report to Department of Transport and Secretary of State for Scotland when objections are received to proposed withdrawals of rail and ferry services respectively.

TRAVELLING PEOPLE, SECRETARY OF STATE'S ADVISORY COMMITTEE ON SCOTLAND'S, St

Andrew's House, Edinburgh EH1 3DD; T.-031-556 8400.
Founded: 1971.
Chairman: Rev N.J. Shanks; Deputy Chairman: Mr M.H. Garland; Secretary: Mr G.T. Musselbrook.
Advises the Secretary of State for Scotland on issues relating to travelling people and, in particular, encourages progress towards the achievement of the Secretary of State's pitch targets by 1988, with the aim of securing full site provision by December of that year. The committee will review and update these targets in 1987-88. It also advises particular local authorities on appropriate ways to secure adequate provision of traveller sites and resolve disputes that may arise over details of such provision.

TRAVERSE THEATRE, 112 West Bow, Grassmarket, Edinburgh EH1 2PD; T.-031-226 2633.
Founded: 1963.
Chairman: Angela Wrapson; Vice Chairman: John Gray; Administrator: Anne Bonnar; Artistic Director: Jenny Killick.
Consistently performs new plays by new playwrights, particularly young Scottish playwrights. Specialises in innovative work.

TRON THEATRE CLUB, 63 Trongate, Glasgow G1 5HB; T.-041-552 4267.
Founded: 1981.
Chairman: Mrs L. H. Sullivan; Administrator: Linda Haase; Artistic Director: Michael Boyd.
Professional organisation staging contemporary theatre, music, dance and exhibitions.

TSB SCOTLAND plc, Henry Duncan House, 120 George Street, Edinburgh EH2 4TS; T.-031-225 4555.
Chairman: Richard T. Ellis, OBE, DL; Deputy Chairman: J.H. Forbes MacPherson, CBE; Executive Directors: Anthony B. Davidson, Alastair C. Dempster, Ian H. Macdonald, OBE (Chief General Manager), David A. McLean, Eric Wilson.
TSB Scotland, through its 276 branches, offers a wide range of personal and commercial services designed to meet the changing needs of the Scottish market place.

TWEEDDALE DISTRICT COUNCIL, District Offices, Rosetta Road, Peebles EH45 8HG; T.-0721 20153.
Founded: 1974.

Chairman: John P. Campbell; Chief Executive: G.H.T. Garvie; Director of Finance: V. Cree; Director of Technical Services: J.B. Forrest.
Political composition of council: Independent 10. Population of district: 14,373.

TWEED RIVER PURIFICATION BOARD, Burnbrae, Mossilee Road, Galashiels TD1 1NF; T.-2425/4797.
Founded: 1975.
Chairman: Major D.J. Anderson, MBE, MC; Director and River Inspector: J.C. Currie; Clerk: Charles M. Anderson; Treasurer: Duncan M. Brown.
Comprises 15 members: five from the regional council, five from the district councils, and five appointed by the Secretary of State to represent particular interests in the area. The board's area is 1,750 square miles and includes the catchment of the Tweed and all the tidal streams from Cove to Burnmouth but excludes the estuary and that part of the main river which lies within the English boundary. Some 4,200 samples are taken annually for analysis, involving about 42,000 tests for pollution control purposes. River and rainfall measurement is also routinely determined throughout the area from 25 river gauging stations and an appropriate number of rainfall stations.

U

UNITED FREE CHURCH OF SCOTLAND, 11 Newton Place, Glasgow G3 7PR; T.-041-332 3435.
Founded: 1929.
Senior Principal Clerk: Rev Alexander Innes; Junior Principal Clerk: Rev Joseph G. McPhee; General Treasurer: John Gray; Convener, Executive Council: Andrew K.M. Rankin; General Secretary: Mrs Isabel D. Baird.
Presbyterian church with a membership of 10,000 in 83 congregations. Has 31 ministers, excluding those who are retired, and eight missionaries (seven working at home and one abroad).

V

VOLUNTARY SERVICES ORKNEY, (VSO), Quest Buildings, Albert Street, Kirkwall, Orkney; T.-0856

2897.
Chairman: Kathleen Ireland; Vice-chairman: John Simmons; Treasurer: Joe Malloch; Joint Co-ordinators: Ross Andrew, Norma Campbell.
An independent, voluntary organisation with charitable status. Remit: to assess the needs of the local community, aid new organisations and help existing organisations to adapt to new situations, encourage voluntary work, collaborate with statutory authorities over concerns of common interest and encourage the statutory agencies to support groups in the voluntary sector.

VOLUNTARY SERVICE ABERDEEN, 38 Castle Street, Aberdeen AB9 1AU; T.-0224 586395.
Founded: 1870.
Chairman: Gordon Hardie; Vice Chairman: Michael Archibald; Honorary Treasurer: Philip Dawson; Secretary: William Howie.
Provides a range of residential and day care facilities and fieldwork services to people in need within the city, particularly the elderly and disabled, single parent families and children at risk. Annual expenditure is in the region of £2 million. Has 250 paid staff, including professional social workers and voluntary service co-ordinators, and over 800 volunteers are actively involved in its caring work. Fosters voluntary effort through servicing co-ordinating committees, and through its charities aid scheme, volunteer bureau and its role as a Community Programme managing agency.

W

THE WEIR GROUP PLC, 149 Newlands Road, Glasgow G44 4EX; T.-041-637 7111.Q Founded: 1871.
Chairman: Viscount Weir; Managing Director: Ronald Garrick.
Engineering group. Turnover (1985): £140 million.

WESTERN ISLES HEALTH BOARD, 37 South Beach, Stornoway, Isle of Lewis PA87 2BN; T.-0851 2997.
Founded: 1974.
Chairman: Mrs M.A. MacMillan; General Manager: Mr J.J. Glover; Chief Administrative Medical Officer: Dr P.A. Birt; Chief Area Nursing Officer: Miss C. MacLean; Treasurer: Mr J.B. Dick; Chief Administrative Dental Officer: Mr I.M. Matheson.

Health authority for the Western Isles area. Serves population of 31,000.

WEST HIGHLAND MUSEUM, Cameron Square, Fort William PH33 6AJ; T.-0397 2169.
Founded: 1922.
Curator/Secretary: Fiona C. Marwick.
An independent, self-financing museum with displays of geology, natural history, archaeology, social history, local history and Jacobite memorabilia. Open all year round except Sundays.

WEST LOTHIAN COLLEGE OF FURTHER EDUCATION, Marjoribanks Street, Bathgate; T.-0506 634300.
Principal: H. Ferrie; Depute Principal: G. Bonnar; Assistant Principal: L. Hutchinson; Registrar: A. Smith.
College of further education with 5,200 students.

WEST LOTHIAN DISTRICT COUNCIL, St David House, South Bridge Street, Bathgate, West Lothian EH48 1TT; T.-Bathgate 53631.
Founded: 1974.
Convener: D. McCauley; Chief Executive: W.N. Fordyce; Director of Administration: G.R.B. Blair; Director of Finance: S.H. Stirton; Director of Physical Planning: G. McNeill; Director of Architectural Services: G.A. Stenhouse; Director of Environmental Health: J.B. McIntyre; Director of Housing Services: J.T. Spraggon; Director of Leisure and Recreation: R.B. Taylor.
Political composition of council: Labour 18, Independent 3, SNP 3. Population of district: 141,532.

THE WEST OF SCOTLAND AGRICULTURAL COLLEGE, Auchincruive, Ayr KA6 5HW; T.-0292 520331.
Founded: 1899.
Principal: Prof J.M.M. Cunningham; Deputy Principals: Dr D.J. Martin, Mr H.A. Waterson; Secretary and Treasurer: Mr E. Innes.
Founded in Glasgow to combine the work of the Scottish Dairy Institute at Kilmarnock with that of the Agricultural Department of the Glasgow and West of Scotland Technical College. In 1927, the estate of Auchincruive was presented to the college and work was carried out both in Glasgow and Auchincruive until 1974, when the Glasgow centre was closed. Since 1974, the

estate of Auchincruive has been developed as a centre for education, to provide a general and specialist advisory service for farmers and growers, and to carry out applied research and development work. Areas of special interest include the science, husbandry, and economics of milk, beef, and sheep production, milk utilisation, the treatment and use of farm waste, grass production and utilisation, and protected crop production.

WEST OF SCOTLAND SCIENCE PARK, (WSSP), Garscube Estate, Glasgow G20 0SP; T.-041-946 7161.
Founded: 1983.
Area Manager, Property: Helen Hood; Science Park Manager: Alasdair McNicoll. Registered science park and founder member of the United Kingdom Science Park Association. The project is a joint initiative of the Scottish Development Agency and the universities of Strathclyde and Glasgow. The objectives are to encourage and support appropriate enterprises engaged in the research, development and initial stages of the commercial exploitation of products and services based on scientific knowledge and ideas. Appropriate enterprises will be encouraged to emerge as centres of excellence from within the universities and colleges, as well as from the wider population of established businesses.

WEST SOUND, Radio House, Holmston Road, Ayr KA7 3BE.
Founded: 1981.
Managing Director: Joseph Campbell.
Independent local radio station for Ayrshire.

WIGTOWN DISTRICT COUNCIL, District Offices, Sun Street, Stranraer DG9 7JJ; T.-0776 2151.
Founded: 1974.
Chairman: D.R. Robinson; Chief Executive and Director of Administration: A. Geddes; Depute Chief Executive and Director of Finance: B.W. Ward; Director of Architectural Services: J.G. Sowerby; Director of Technical Services: S. Atkinson; Director of Environmental Health: J.H. McMillan.
Political composition of council: Independent/Non-political 13, SNP 1. Population of district: 30,410.

WIGTOWN RURAL DEVELOPMENT COMPANY LTD, Royal Bank Building, 44 Victoria Street, Newton Stewart, Wigtownshire DG8 6BT;

T.-0671 3434.
Founded: 1983.
Managing Director: W. Phillips.
Offers assistance to all sectors of the business community, including grants and loans, training, advice, premises, marketing and financial guidance.

WILLIAM COLLINS PLC, Westerhill Road, Bishopbriggs, Glasgow G64 2QT; T.-041-772 3200.
Founded: 1819.
Chairman and Chief Executive: F.I. Chapman; Deputy Chairman: Sir Charles Troughton; Vice Chairman and Group Managing Director: G. Craig; Vice Chairman: R.C. Smith; Group Managing Director - Glasgow Operations: H.C. Paton.
Holding company for the Collins group of companies engaged in book publishing, printing, wholesaling and retailing. Publishes educational and reference books, paperbacks (imprints include Fontana, Pan, Granada, and Armada), Bibles, fiction, natural history, children's books, atlases and diaries.

WILLIAM LOW & COMPANY PLC, PO Box 73, Baird Avenue, Dryburgh Industrial Estate, Dundee; T.-0382 814022.
Founded: 1868.
Chairman: C. Blake; Deputy Chairman: I.W. Stewart; Managing Director: J.L. Millar; Marketing Director: C.C.R. Mitchell; Finance Director: H.L. Findlay; Retail Director: A.L. Leslie.
Supermarket retailers operating 68 supermarkets and 14 freezer centres throughout Scotland and England. Turnover (1086): £233 million.

WOMEN'S ROYAL VOLUNTARY SERVICE, (WRVS), Scottish Headquarters, 19 Grosvenor Crescent, Edinburgh EH12 5EL; T.-031-337 2261.
Founded: 1938.
Chairman, Scotland: The Hon Mrs Mary Corsar; Vice-chairmen, Scotland: Mrs S.G. Ballantine, Mrs E. Ross.
Assists Government departments, local authorities and voluntary bodies in organising and carrying out welfare and emergency work for the community on a nationwide network operated through local authority regions and districts and working from 74 offices.

WORKERS' EDUCATIONAL ASSOCIATION, (WEA).
North of Scotland District: 163 King Street, Aberdeen AB2 3AE; T.-0224 642725. District Secretary: Adrian Jones; Chairman: Tim Mustard.
South East Scotland District: Riddle's Court, 322 Lawnmarket, Edinburgh EH1 2PG; T.-031-226 3456. District Secretary: Colin Kirkwood; Chairman: Alan Swan.
West of Scotland District: 212 Bath Street, Glasgow G2 4HW; T.-041-332 0176. Secretary: Jean Barr; Chairman: Alasdair Nicolson.
Aims to interest men and women in their own continued education. More specifically, it encourages those who are most disadvantaged educationally to come back into education, whether for vocational reasons, or for their own personal development. The association is a voluntary organisation, registered as a charity.

YWCA SCOTTISH NATIONAL COUNCIL, 7 Randolph Crescent, Edinburgh EH3 7TH; T.-031-225 7592.
Founded: 1855.
President: Mrs R.A. Dingwall-Smith; Convener of Scottish Executive: Mrs H. Birrell; Honorary Treasurer: Mrs P. McCabe; General Secretary: Miss S.A. Moyes.
Part of the YWCA of Great Britain which is now the oldest and largest international women's Christian movement in the world (existing in 80 countries). Membership is open to girls and boys over the age of 7, and to women and men regardless of religion, race or creed. Provision for leisure activities is offered to all ages and services and facilities are offered to the community, particularly to unemployed youth, ethnic minorities, families etc. Issues of concern include the environment, human rights, peace education, migrant women and girls, and health and women's concerns.

Y

YOUNG ENTERPRISE SCOTLAND, 123 Dysart Road, Kirkcaldy KY1 2BB; T.-0592 51597.
Founded: 1986.
Regional Director: Ronald J. Wylie.
Part of the educational charity established in 1963 to provide practical business experience for young people aged 15-19 by helping them to form and run their own companies in miniature. During 1986-87, over 100 companies will be operated in Scotland with practical advice being given by 300 voluntary business advisers. The young people gain in self-confidence and ability to communicate and develop skills needed for the transition into the world of business.

Z

ZOOLOGICAL SOCIETY OF GLASGOW AND THE WEST OF SCOTLAND, Glasgow Zoo, Calderpark, Uddingston, Glasgow G71 7RZ; T.-041-771 1185.
Founded: 1936.
President of Council: W.R.S. MacKenzie; Vice-presidents: Dr A. Young, TD, J.B. MacWilliam; Director/Secretary: R.J.P. O'Grady; Curator: Lutz Kuschinski; Education Officer: Stephen Bostock.
Develops and maintains zoological gardens for the West of Scotland. The zoo was opened to the public in 1947 and attracts 150,000 visitors every year.

INDEX

CHAMBERS OF COMMERCE

CHURCHES AND RELIGIOUS ORGANISATIONS

COLLEGES

CONSERVATION AND HERITAGE

CONSUMER ORGANISATIONS

COUNTRYSIDE INTERESTS

DEVELOPMENT CORPORATIONS

EDUCATIONAL BODIES
See also COLLEGES, UNIVERSITIES

ENTERPRISE TRUSTS

GOVERNMENT DEPARTMENTS AND PUBLIC BODIES

HEALTH BOARDS

HEALTH AND MEDICINE
See also HEALTH BOARDS

INDUSTRY AND COMMERCE
See also CHAMBERS OF COMMERCE, DEVELOPMENT CORPORATIONS, ENTERPRISE TRUSTS, MAJOR COMPANIES

INTERNATIONAL INTERESTS

LEGAL AND JUDICIAL BODIES

LEARNED SOCIETIES

LOCAL AUTHORITIES

MAJOR COMPANIES

NEWSPAPERS AND BROADCASTING ORGANISATIONS

POLITICAL PARTIES

PRESSURE GROUPS

PROFESSIONAL ORGANISATIONS

RESEARCH ORGANISATIONS

RIVER AND PORT AUTHORITIES

SPORTS/LEISURE ORGANISATIONS

TOURIST ORGANISATIONS

TRADE ASSOCIATIONS

TRADES UNIONS

UNIVERSITIES

VOLUNTARY & CHARITABLE

WOMEN'S ORGANISATIONS

YOUTH ORGANISATIONS